PEARSON   ALWAYS LEARNING

Wellness
A Guide for Achieving a Healthy Lifestyle

Paul F. Granello, PhD

With Contributions by:

Christopher Christmas, Adam Clevenger, Stephen C. Davis, Maria Elliot, Brian C. Focht, Todd Gibbs, Samuel T. Gladding, Catherine Griffith, Daniel Guterriez, Karen Michelle Hunnicutt-Hollenbaugh, Gerald A. Juhnke, Michael Lewis, Patrick Mullen, Melvin J. Witmer

Excerpts taken from:

Wellness Counseling
by Paul F. Granello

D1295270

Pearson Learning Solutions, 501 Boylston Street, Suite 900,
Boston, MA 02116
A Pearson Education Company
www.pearsoned.com

Printed in the United States of America

14   18

000200010271784275

EEB/LC

ISBN 10: 1-269-37372-2
ISBN 13: 978-1-269-37372-2

This book is dedicated to

Darcy, the most-well person I know.

Mel Witmer, a wellness pioneer.

My colleagues at the Wellness Institute.

CONTENTS

CHAPTER 1 WELLNESS: HEALTHCARE FOR THE 21ST CENTURY   1

CHAPTER 2 EVOLUTION OF WELLNESS   10

CHAPTER 3 A MODEL OF WELLNESS   27

CHAPTER 4 CREATING GOOD GOALS AND SUSTAINING MOTIVATION: TOOLS FOR LASTING BEHAVIOR CHANGE   36

CHAPTER 5 COGNITION: RULES FOR REALITY   50

CHAPTER 6 EMOTIONAL REGULATION   61

CHAPTER 7 PHYSICAL ACTIVITY AND PSYCHOLOGICAL WELL-BEING   73

CHAPTER 8 FINANCIAL WELLNESS   87

CHAPTER 9 PREVENTATIVE SELF-CARE: BENEFITS OF MODERN MEDICINE   100

CHAPTER 10 SPIRITUALITY AND MEANING   110

CHAPTER 11 CULTURAL AND ENVIRONMENTAL ASPECTS OF WELLNESS   130

CHAPTER 12 SOCIAL RELATIONSHIPS: HOW TO INCREASE YOUR SOCIAL CAPITAL AND SUCCESS   150

CHAPTER 13 CREATIVITY: SPARK OF WELLNESS   166

INDEX   173

1 WELLNESS: HEALTHCARE FOR THE 21ST CENTURY

Paul F. Granello & Melvin J. Witmer

*Health is a state of complete physical, mental
and social well-being, and not merely
the absence of disease or infirmity.*

WORLD HEALTH ORGANIZATION, 1948

Healthcare in the United States is an extremely hot topic. Daily, the news contains information on issues related to the "healthcare crisis" in our country. Healthcare issues impact almost all individuals in our society in one way or another because they encompass almost all social spheres: economic (rising costs), legal (medical malpractice lawsuits, privacy in use of electronic medical records), business (managed care, pharmaceutical company profits), scientific (stem cell research), technological (telemedicine, online counseling), religious (abortion and contraception), and of course political (equity of access for the uninsured; mental health insurance parity). Although it certainly could be argued that all of these issues are significantly important in their own right and deserve attention, this chapter posits that they are just the symptoms of a much more fundamental and entrenched problem with the healthcare system in the United States today.

HEALTHCARE: A FUNDAMENTAL MISMATCH

The problem is that our traditional biomedical model of healthcare is grossly mismatched for our American society's 21st century healthcare needs. It is this basic mismatch between our present-day needs and the dominant biomedical paradigm that is either directly causing or significantly contributing to our problems with healthcare in the United States today. To illustrate the mismatch between our modern healthcare needs and our traditional healthcare approach, let us look at how the causes of death have changed from a century ago to the present day (summarized in Table 1.1). In 1900, the traditional biomedical model of healthcare, with a focus on finding the underlying causes of infectious diseases, worked very well. The average lifespan was 49 years, and most people died of infectious diseases such as influenza and tuberculosis. Treatment was focused on helping sick people manage the symptoms of disease. Today, things are very different, and the average lifespan is now 77.7 years. Most people in the United States are not dying of infectious disease. Instead, they

1

TABLE 1.1 Leading Causes of Death

Causes of Death 1900*	Causes of Death 2010**
Pneumonia (all forms) and influenza	Heart disease
Tuberculosis (all forms)	Cancer
Diarrhea, enteritis, and ulceration of the intestines	Chronic lower respiratory diseases
Diseases of the heart	Stroke (cerebrovascular diseases)
Intracranial lesions of vascular origin	Accidents (unintentional injuries)
Nephritis (all forms)	Alzheimer's disease
All accidents	Diabetes
Cancer and other malignant tumors	Influenza and pneumonia
Senility	Nephritis
Diphtheria	Intentional self-harm (suicide)

*Source: *1900–1940 tables ranked in National Office of Vital Statistics, December 1947.*
    ***Centers for Disease Control and Prevention (CDC)/National Center for Health Statistics.*

are dying of **chronic, lifestyle-related diseases**. In our modern society, cardiovascular diseases, cancer, and diabetes are the leading causes of death.

In fact, in 2004, the Centers for Disease Control and Prevention (CDC), an agency within U.S. Department of Health and Human Services, reported that at least half of the premature deaths in the United States are caused by **lifestyle and behavioral factors.** Examples of conditions influenced by lifestyle and health behaviors are heart disease, cancer, stroke, accidental injuries, diabetes, alcoholism, drug abuse, low birth weight, and diseases preventable by immunization. A report in the *American Medical Association Journal* for the actual causes of death in 2000 noted that obesity would soon surpass smoking as the leading preventable cause of premature death (Mokdad, Marks, Stroup, & Gerberding, 2004). The reality is that most of what Americans are dying from today is either caused directly or exacerbated by our lifestyles. The shame is that many illnesses could be ameliorated if people knew how to live in a more balanced, healthful way.

Despite the knowledge that what we really need is help with avoiding and managing chronic illnesses, our healthcare system's primary attention is still focused on treatment of "sickness" and "dysfunction." Little attention is given to prevention of disease through the enhancement of health and well-being. As a society, we have committed ourselves and our resources almost exclusively to remediating problems rather than attempting to prevent them from occurring.

Consider the following facts related to healthcare in the United States today:

- Forty-five percent of Americans suffer from at least one chronic disease, a rate higher than that of any other country.
- Chronic diseases, such as heart disease, diabetes, pulmonary disease, and cancer, are among the most costly and most preventable diseases in the United States.
- Three out of every four healthcare dollars are spent treating chronic disease, and 7 out of 10 deaths are caused by chronic disease.

American Health Habits

Smoking, poor nutrition, and lack of physical activity are directly responsible for one-third of U.S. deaths. Nearly two-thirds of Americans are overweight or obese.

Source: CDC (2009a, 2009b).

Our current philosophy of healthcare in the United States appears to be something like the following: "Let's wait until people get really sick. Then we will treat them with high-tech procedures delivered by highly specialized medical doctors and technicians, and this will definitely cost everyone a lot of money." This philosophy is certainly reflected in the fact that of government funds spent on healthcare, 75 percent is used for the treatment of chronic diseases, with a total of only one percent of federal and two percent of state funds allocated to prevent these diseases. Noted physician Dr. Andrew Weil, M.D., summed up the current situation quite well when he stated, "We do not have a healthcare system; we have a disease management system." There truly appears to be a fundamental mismatch between our present-day population's need for prevention of chronic disease and the focus of our traditional healthcare system on treating the already sick.

RESULTS OF THE HEALTHCARE MISMATCH

If no problems resulted from the mismatch between our present-day healthcare system and the rest of our social context, then perhaps it would be of little consequence. At present, however, our traditional approach to healthcare has produced two significant problems. The first problem has to do with **quality**. A basic question that may help us understand the problem of the quality of care concerns a central function of any healthcare system, namely: "Is the healthcare system effectively reducing human suffering?" Reducing human suffering by keeping people from getting severely sick (prevention) would seem to be a logical primary goal of any healthcare system. Yet, the U.S. healthcare system at present is doing a poor job at reducing suffering through the prevention of illness.

A case in point is that in 1996, the five most costly (in terms of expenditures) medical conditions were:

- Heart disease
- Trauma-related disorders
- Cancer
- Asthma
- Mental disorders

A decade later in 2006, another ranking was done of the five most costly medical conditions—they were the exact same ones! Further, there was an increase in the expenditures for each of these conditions and also an increase in the number of people associated with these conditions, except in the case of trauma-related disorders. In fact, a study in 2008 ranked the United States last out of 14 industrialized countries in amendable deaths, which are deaths that could have been prevented with timely and effective care (Commonwealth Fund, 2008).

These facts seem to point out that our current model for the delivery of healthcare in the United States is not providing the quality that we need. However, the definition of what constitutes "quality" healthcare may be different depending on the healthcare paradigm that is being used. In the current biomedical paradigm, *quality* has evolved to mean that we focus on treating the chronically or severely ill with cutting-edge technologies delivered by specialist doctors at very great expense. The U.S. healthcare system has had many impressive accomplishments using this approach. For example, American survival rates for many diseases such as cancer and heart disease are some of the best in the world. Hospitals in the United States are the best equipped in the world, and we have highly trained physicians and nurses. The United States is the world leader in medical research, such as in the development of many "wonder drugs" and technologies such as imaging and hip replacements (Reid, 2009). Despite all of its problems, the fact is that for a very sick individual with the capacity to pay for care, our healthcare system can truly offer life-saving treatment.

Given that our healthcare system does provide good care for people who are acutely ill, perhaps the real question concerning quality is not about the provision of medical care to individuals, but is instead a broader public health question: What would our healthcare system be like if it was not focused on treating very sick individuals, but instead focused on preventing illness in the population as a whole? Such an approach is employing a much different paradigm for defining the quality of care. Quality of care in this paradigm is not defined as the healthcare outcome of a particular individual but rather as the overall health of the total population. Employing a prevention paradigm for healthcare might actually help to reduce human suffering and realize significant cost savings. For example, recent research indicates that if the United States can make modest improvements in prevention and management of disease by 2023, as many as 40 million cases of chronic disease could be avoided, for a potential savings of $218 billion annually in treatment costs. Further, improved productivity due to a decrease in chronic disease could contribute to an increase in the U.S. gross domestic product of $905 billion (DeVol et al., 2007).

The quality debate is very important, and it is related to the paradigm used to define what constitutes a successful outcome. Americans need to recognize what we do well in healthcare provision, but also acknowledge that we can do better, especially in the area of preventing illness. Unfortunately, due to economic pressures, we may not have as much time as we would like to gradually evolve our healthcare system. Soon, gradual change will not be an option, as large-scale, rapid change will be necessary to address issues of healthcare implementation. We can start making small changes now, or plan to make extensive changes in the future.

This brings us to the second problem with healthcare in the United States. The second problem is much less a matter of philosophic approach as an economic reality. It is simply that healthcare has become prohibitively expensive. Today, many individuals and employers are finding it impossible to purchase adequate healthcare at affordable rates. Since 1999, health insurance premiums have increased 119 percent for employers. Employers, especially small or midsized companies, cannot afford to offer healthcare benefits to employees. Further, employees' spending for health insurance coverage (employees' share of family coverage) increased 117 percent between 1999 and 2008 (Henry J. Kaiser Family Foundation, 2008). As a result of these dramatic increases in cost, more Americans simply have to do without healthcare insurance. In 2007, nearly 46 million Americans, or 18 percent of the population under the age of 65, were without health insurance (DeNavas-Walt, Proctor, & Smith, 2008). This is, of course, not only an economic issue, but also a humanitarian issue. Increasingly, the uninsured receive less preventive care, are diagnosed at more advanced disease stages, and, once diagnosed, tend to receive less therapeutic care and have higher mortality rates than insured individuals (National Center for Health Statistics, 2009). Further, millions more Americans, although insured, actually have coverage that will not provide them with sufficient reimbursement to cover the costs of treating a serious illness. This is why the number of U.S. bankruptcies due to medical debt is approximately 700,000 families each year. Many of these people had insurance that simply would not adequately cover the costs of required healthcare. At the same time, the number of bankruptcies due to medical debt in great Britain, Germany, the Netherlands, France, Japan, and Canada is zero (Reid, 2009).

Overall, healthcare costs have become a significant drain on our economy. Gross domestic product (GDP) is the value of all the goods and services that a country produces. In a review of the nature of our healthcare costs, Myers and Sweeney (2005) observed that the costs of illness increased from 5 percent to almost 16 percent of U.S. GDP in the period from 1960 to 2000. Currently, the health share of GDP is projected to reach 20.3 percent by 2018. In dollars and cents, this means that by 2018 Americans will be spending 20 percent of our entire economic output, or an estimated $4.3 trillion, on healthcare. Individually, of course, the more money we have to spend on healthcare, the less money we have to spend on anything else we may need or desire, such as food, housing, clothing, or education.

Information published by the World Health Organization (WHO) may best sum up both problems that currently characterize the U.S. healthcare system—paradigm mismatch and prohibitive cost: WHO data indicate that the United States spends more money than any other country in the world per capita on healthcare, while ranking 37th in the world on healthcare quality. Americans know they are not getting their money's worth from our healthcare system. According to a CBS News poll, 90 percent of Americans believe the U.S. healthcare system needs fundamental changes or needs to be completely rebuilt. Two-thirds of Americans believe the federal government should guarantee universal healthcare for all citizens (CBS News, 2007). It is interesting to note that at present, the United States is the only industrialized country in the world that does not provide a universal healthcare program.

Only one conclusion can be drawn from the data: **The U.S. healthcare system as it is now functioning and the biomedical paradigm upon which it is founded are no longer meeting our 21st century health needs for prevention of chronic illness, and the system is no longer economically sustainable.** We are approaching a crisis during which our healthcare system will move beyond inadequate; it will be totally broken and unserviceable.

Leaders in healthcare, government, business, and academia have long known this crisis was coming. Many leaders knew we needed to make substantial changes in our approach to healthcare and that continuing "business as usual" in our healthcare system would lead us down a path of poor quality and high cost. In fact, almost two decades ago, the U.S. government established health-promotion and disease-prevention goals. In 1990, Health and Human Services Secretary Dr. Louis Sullivan released the *Healthy People 2000* report, which challenged all Americans to healthier living. The purpose of the report was to bring us to our full potential. This meant: (1) increasing the span of healthy life for Americans, (2) reducing health disparities among Americans, and (3) establishing access to preventive services for all Americans. Health-promotion categories included physical activities and fitness; nutrition; tobacco use; use of alcohol and other drugs; family planning; mental health and mental disorders; violent and abusive behavior; and educational and community-based programs.

These goals, if they had been acted upon, may have taken us on a route that would have prevented a great deal of human suffering and economic burden. Why, then, did our government and healthcare system fail to embrace prevention and wellness in the 1990s?

There are potentially many reasons that could be given for why our healthcare system has been so slow to change from an illness-treatment system to a prevention and health-enhancement system. These reasons are both political and economic in nature and are deeply tied to the core of how our democratic and capitalistic society functions. Healthcare is, of course, big business in the United States. Many large companies that employ significant numbers of people have interests in maintaining the healthcare status quo. In 2009 alone, the healthcare industry spent almost $280 million lobbying Congress (Figure 1.1). This amount does not include additional direct contributions to congressional campaign funds by healthcare companies, healthcare associations, political action committees, or individuals working for healthcare companies.

The American Medical Association (AMA) has consistently fought the adoption of a universal healthcare system in the United States. The AMA has funded public relations firms to promote the idea that "socialized medicine" (a term coined by the AMA) would lead to poor healthcare for Americans.

It is interesting to note that American physicians earn two to three times more than their European counterparts. The United States is also the only developed country that relies on private companies to provide health insurance to its citizens. Private insurance companies generally have a 20 percent margin for administrative costs and profit. These companies generally oppose any government regulation of their businesses. In addition, American pharmaceutical companies oppose a national healthcare plan, fearing regulation of prices for drugs and a loss of profits. The pharmaceutical industry is the single largest lobbying group and has spent over $1.6 billion since 1998 lobbying Congress.

Incredibly, against this backdrop of enormous sums of money spent to inform Congress of the healthcare industries' viewpoints, businesses and institutions sought methods to control the ever-increasing costs of healthcare. In fact, numerous approaches have been implemented with greater or lesser degrees of success to cope with both the quality and cost issues. Chief among these approaches was the development of managed healthcare, and approach to insurance-cost containment that boomed in the 1990s.

Currently, approximately 241 million Americans receive their insurance coverage under the watchful eye of a managed care corporation. Managed care companies hired by employers attempt to hold down costs by negotiating fees with healthcare providers and controlling access to specialized care. The level of success managed care has had in controlling healthcare expenditures is debatable. However, at present, the cost savings associated with this approach have probably

INDUSTRY	AMOUNT SPENT
Makers of drugs and health products	$134,458,183
Hospitals and nursing homes	$50,330,605
Doctors and health professionals	$39,408,563
Health services and HMOs	$34,646,637
Miscellaneous health	$4,582,251
Health insurers	$16,315,247
TOTAL	$279,741,486

FIGURE 1.1 Lobbying for Healthcare in 2009
Source: Center for Responsive Politics, http://opensecrets
.org/lobby/issuesum.php?id=HCR&year=2013.

already been maximized. So, faced with real quality-of-care issues and the current economic realities, the question persists: Where can we go now with our approach to healthcare that will bring about positive changes?

WELLNESS: HEALTHCARE PARADIGM OF THE FUTURE

A study by the Trust for America's Health organization recently projected that an annual investment of $10 per person in evidence-based community prevention programs can yield significant cost savings. In five years, Medicare and Medicaid alone could yield net savings of $7 billion annually, and total U.S. medical spending could be reduced by $16 billion annually (Levi et al., 2008).

As early as 1947, WHO described health as something more than the absence of disease. In 1964, WHO emphasized this "something more" when it defined optimal health as "a state of complete physical, mental, and social well-being and not merely the absence of disease or infirmity" (WHO, 1964, p. 1). Wellness, as presented in this book, is a term used to represent an emerging treatment paradigm for healthcare (Granello, 1996) and an approach to total-health living. The wellness paradigm represents a reevaluation of the biomedical model of healthcare and the Western philosophical tradition of Cartesian dualism upon which it is based (Gordon, 1981; Gross, 1980; Still, 1986; Wulf, Pedersen, & Bloomberg 1990). The traditional medical model has a pathogenic, reductionist, and disease focus, whereas in contrast, the wellness model has a salutogenic (health-enhancing) focus that is related to constant striving for optimal functioning (Granello,1996). These models are summarized in Figure 1.2.

Despite the progressive WHO definition of health, physical and mental health continue to be limitedly defined in terms of the absence of disease and infirmity. Our standard for human development and adjustment has been the norm as a statistical average, instead of looking toward what is exceptional. The healthy person has been defined in terms of averages rather than what is genetically possible. Wellness looks beyond the absence of disease, however. The wellness continuum progresses from the treatment of illness to prevention and maintenance to growth, with a major emphasis on the latter—enhancement of life.

The wellness paradigm proposes that quality of life and longevity are the results of intentional behaviors occurring across multiple domains. More about these domains will be said in Chapter 3. For now, it is important to know that wellness is not the result of one instance of treatment. Wellness is not about taking the antidote after a snake bite; wellness is about avoiding the snake. Wellness also provides a way to manage the stressors of the snake bite if you can't avoid it. Wellness is the result of everyday choices that contribute to the health of the body and the mind.

The goal of wellness goes beyond health alone, however. An assumption made by the wellness model is that when people practice wellness, they experience more than just health benefits (the middle of the continuum just described). Practicing wellness enriches life when daily wellness

FIGURE 1.2   Divergent Models of Healthcare

behaviors lead to meaningful experiences. Many people derive meaning from their daily spiritual routines. Others find the experience of doing something creative or solving a problem to be meaningful. A wellness-oriented lifestyle is a tool by which people can cope with the stress of life, prevent or manage chronic illness, and add meaning and quality across the lifespan.

The question now is, will we accept the wellness challenge and focus on maximizing our own potential? Individuals should be asking questions like these: What are the outer limits of human possibilities? Of what are human beings capable? What is high-level wellness? *Human potential* refers to the possibilities inherent in being human. Our potential is limited to a large extent by our image of what we are and our vision of what we can become. The wellness model challenges traditional notions of what we are and supposes greater parameters for what we can become. Will we as individuals take up the wellness challenge?

THE WELLNESS CHALLENGE

The previous discussion detailed the reality of a healthcare system that is being outpaced by the demands of a population experiencing more and more chronic illness. It is likely that anyone who reads this book is living with or knows someone living with chronic illness. A family member may be diabetic, or the reader him- or herself may be living with depression. Hopefully, this experience can add personal perspective to the facts and figures cited, which may seem impersonal and distant. It is hard to see the ebb and flow of a culture-wide system; it is harder to refute your personal experiences.

Similarly, it may be difficult to see yourself playing a part in the system-level changes necessary to alter the healthcare system. No doubt, some readers may take up the legislative and administrative challenges involved in changing healthcare in America. However, many readers may be looking for a smaller way to make change. This book is about the smaller changes readers can make in their everyday lives that will impact their personal wellness and consequently the healthcare system as a whole. In making these small changes, readers can do more than change the healthcare system; they can impact cultural notions of health and well-being in the United States.

This book is intended to make readers aware of the nuts and bolts of wellness. After reading this book and working through the reflection exercises, readers will be able to define wellness, explain the need for a wellness perspective, understand the historical and cultural background of wellness, and describe a model of wellness. Additionally, readers will be able to define multiple domains of wellness and list methods for increasing balance across each domain.

The wellness journey is one that never ends. It is not so much a point of destination but the continuous traveling that brings its own satisfaction. This book is intended to give readers the tools to become a part of the wellness process. Lack of knowledge is no longer a reason for not being a part of the journey. There is no greater challenge than to take the road that leads us to the furthest reaches of human nature—happiness, life satisfaction, and fulfillment over the lifespan.

In the next chapter, we will take a journey through history to see how the wellness paradigm for healthcare has evolved over time to bring us to our present level of knowledge.

REFLECTION ACTIVITIES

1. Review the health section of your local newspaper. How many articles relate to lifestyle and/or chronic illness? How does this reflect the current state of wellness in your community?
2. Think about a healthy activity you enjoy doing regularly. Describe the important things it adds to your life, or how it positively affects you.

3. Identify some of your skills—these can be people skills, organizational skills, or anything else you are good at. Brainstorm how you could use these skills to increase your health and well-being.

References

CBS News. (2007). Polls. Retrieved from http://www .cbsnews.com/htdocs/ CBSNews_polls/health_care.pdf

Centers for Disease Control. (2004). Behavioral Risk Factor Surveillance System. Nationwide tobacco use [data set].

Centers for Disease Control. (2008, March). Chronic disease overview [fact sheet]. http://www.cdc.gov/obesity/ resources/factsheets.html

Centers for Disease Control. (2009a, May). Overweight and obesity: Health consequences [fact sheet]. http://www .cdc.gov/obesity/resources/factsheets.html

Centers for Disease Control. (2009b, May). Overweight and obesity: Childhood overweight and obesity.

Commonwealth Fund Commission on a High Performance Health System. (2008, July). Why not the best? Results from the National Scorecard on U.S. Health System Performance, 2008. Retrieved from http://www .commonwealthfund.org

DeNavas-Walt, C., Proctor, B., & Smith, J. (2008, August). *Income, poverty, and health insurance coverage in the United States: 2007.* Washington, DC: U.S. Census Bureau.

DeVol, R., Bedroussian, A., et al. (2007). *An unhealthy America: The economic burden of chronic disease.* Santa Monica, CA: The Milken Institute. Retrieved from http:// www.milkeninstitute.org/pdf/ES_ResearchFindings.pdf

Druss, B. G., Rosenheck R. A., Desai M. M., & Perlin J. B. (2002). Quality of preventive medical care for patients with mental disorders. *Medical Care, 4,* 129–136.

Gordon, J. S. (1981). Holistic medicine: Toward a new medical model. *Journal of Clinical Psychiatry, 42*(3), 114–119.

Granello, P. F. (1996). *Wellness as a function of perceived social support network and ability to empathize.* ProQuest Information & Learning, US). *Dissertation Abstracts International: Section B: The Sciences and Engineering, 57*(2), 1985.

Gross, S. J. (1980). The holistic health movement. *The Personnel and Guidance Journal, 59*(2), 96–100.

Henry J. Kaiser Family Foundation. (2008, September). Employee health benefits: 2008 annual survey. Retrieved from http://www.kff.org/insurance/7672/index.cfm

Kott, A., Fruh, D., Cameron, L., Greger, C., Klein, K., Lethert C., et al. (2009). Impact of chronic disease on U.S. health and prosperity: A collection of statistics and commentary. *2009 Almanac of chronic disease.* Retrieved from http://www.fightchronicdisease.org/

Levi, J., Segal, L. M., Juliane, C., et al. (2008). *Prevention for a healthier America.* Washington, DC: Trust for America's Health.

Mokdad, A. H., Marks, J. S., Stroup D. F., & Gerberding, J. L. (2004). Actual causes of death in the United States, 2000. *JAMA, 291,* 1238–1245.

Myers, J.E., & Sweeney, T.J. (2005). *Counseling for wellness: Theory, research, and practice.* Alexandria, VA: American Counseling Association.

National Center for Health Statistics. (2009, February). Health, United States, 2007: With chartbook on trends in the health of Americans. Retrieved from http://www .cdc.gov/nchs/data/hus/hus07.pdf

National Center for Health Statistics. Health, United States, 2009: With chartbook on health trends in the health of Americans. Center for American Progress. The Case for Health Reform. Hyattsville, Maryland. 2009.

Nolte, E., & McKee, M. C. (2008). Measuring the health of nations: Updating an earlier analysis. *Health Affairs, 27*(1), 58–71.

Parks, S., & Singer, F. (2006, October). Morbidity and mortality in people with serious mental illness. National Association of State Mental Health Program Directors, Medical Directors Council. Retrieved from http://www .nasmhpd.org

Preamble to the Constitution of the World Health Organization as adopted by the International Health Conference, New York, 19–22 June, 1946; signed on 22 July 1946 by the representatives of 61 States (Official Records of the World Health Organization, no. 2, p. 100) and entered into force on 7 April 1948.

Reid, T. R. (2009). *The healing of America: A global quest for better, cheaper, and fairer health care.* The Penguin Press HC.

Soni, Anita. (2009, July). *The five most costly conditions, 1996 and 2006: Estimates for the U.S. civilian noninstitutionalized population.* Statistical Brief #248. Rockville, MD: Agency for Healthcare Research and Quality. Retrieved from http://www.meps.ahrq.gov/mepsweb/ data_files/publications/st248/stat248.pdf

Still, A. (1986). The biology of science: An essay on the evolution of representational cognitivism. *Journal for the Theory of Social Behavior, 16*(3), 251–267.

Woolf, S. H. (2006, Fall). The big answer: Rediscovering prevention at a time of crisis in health care. *Harvard Health Policy Review, 7*(2), 5–20.

Wulff, H. R., Pederson, S. A., & Rosenberg, R. (1990). *Philosophy of medicine: An introduction.* Oxford: Blackwell Scientific Publications.

2 ▌EVOLUTION OF WELLNESS

Mel Witmer

Human life will never be understood unless its highest aspirations are taken into account. Growth, self-actualization, the striving toward health, the quest for identity and autonomy, the yearning for excellence (and other ways of phrasing the striving "upward") must now be accepted beyond question as a widespread and perhaps universal human tendency.

MASLOW, 1970, PP. XII, XIII

STRIVING FOR HEALTH AND WELLNESS

We who are living at the beginning of the 21st century are the first in human history to know what the characteristics of the well person are. Scientific research over the last 35 years has identified the factors that enhance the quality of our lives and extend longevity. Confirmation of the effects on health of self-defeating beliefs and destructive lifestyle behaviors has enabled us to understand the cause–effect relationships that contribute to disease, dysfunctional living, and premature death. In our knowledge, we have progressed from treatment and prevention of disease to the health and wellness of living. Spiritual, mental, emotional, physical, and social factors that enhance our well-being have been validated. More specifically, a meaningful life, realistic and rational thinking, a positive attitude, regular exercise, nutritional eating, satisfying work, leisure time, and satisfying interpersonal relationships are dimensions for improving the quality of living and extending the length of life. The key to adding life to our years and years to our life is self-responsibility—taking responsibility for self-care and lifestyle choices.

The inner desire for a life of health and wholeness is not a late-20th-century phenomenon. Our language reveals the presence of a holistic philosophy when Middle English terms were created to describe a state of well-being. As a Middle English word, *health* shares a root meaning with the words *hale, hearty, holy, heal,* and *whole*. Health, even then, was viewed as more than the absence of disease but rather a soundness of mind, body, and spirit. Although holistic health includes the prevention of illness and the management of disease, its focus is on enhancing one's well-being. The term *wellness* extends this meaning to include a person's physical, mental, and emotional states, social relationships, spiritual growth, and lifestyle.

The human brain operates as a health maintenance organization (Ornstein & Sobel, 1990). Each of the three major sections of the brain—the brainstem, limbic system, and cortex—and its subsystems has minding the health of the body as its primary function. Two of the systems, the brainstem and the limbic system, function automatically to manage the safety and maintenance of the body through the monitoring and regulation of breathing, heart rate, body temperature, blood pressure, and blood sugar level. Besides maintaining the internal stability of these physiological processes, the limbic system also is involved in emotional reactions that have to do with survival and self-protection. The third system, the cortex, is the seat for the rational abilities we develop as we grow and learn. It is responsible for processing information, making decisions, and carrying out actions, while the other two systems function automatically to assist the individual in maintaining optimal health.

This phenomenon was observed by Maslow (1970) from a psychological perspective when he noted that there appears to be a universal human striving toward health. This tendency to actualize the self is driven by an innate process. However, the development of the rational part of the brain, the cortex, introduces a conscious, free-thinking self. The individual can think and act in ways that affect the inner process, either to enhance health and well-being or impede it. Modern research can add knowledge to the collective wisdom of past generations to prevent disease and maximize health.

First, this chapter will provide a brief review of the history of health and medicine, with examples of this human tendency toward wholeness, an innate and inner striving toward what is humanly possible for high-level wellness. Next, we will finish the chapter by noting more recent contributions from academic disciplines and individuals related to the modern U.S. wellness movement.

GREEK HEALTH AND MEDICINE

Hippocrates

Western medicine begins with Hippocrates, a Greek physician of the 4th century BCE. His injunctions, "First do no harm," and "Physician—heal thyself," are well known. Lesser known is his breadth of vision on health and healing. He and his followers developed a scientific approach to medicine by respecting observation of natural events and disease and through experimentation. Hippocrates appreciated the social and ecological context in which illness occurs and the way physical manifestations of disease are shaped by psychological and spiritual forces (Gordon, 1996). He also taught that food was useful as medicine, and that dreams often held prophetic, diagnostic, and psychologically important messages.

Aristotle

A student of Plato and a Greek philosopher who wrote of the "good life," Aristotle taught long ago that what all people seek is happiness. He believed that those who were happy were people who identified with living well and doing well. He also advocated the "golden mean"—doing all things in moderation and avoiding extremes.

Aristotle distinguished happiness from pleasure: Happiness is not merely a subjective state of pleasure or contentment, but the kind of life we would all want to live if we understood our essential nature. When we fulfill the ideal of the virtuous life, we are happy. This view became known as *virtue ethics* and defines the importance of character development in pursuing the good life (Warburton, 1999). It is only by cultivating the virtues that one can flourish as a human being.

According to Aristotle, everyone wants to flourish, which is sometimes translated as "happiness." The original Greek word applies to a whole life, not just to particular emotional states you might find yourself in from day to day. Achieving true happiness is living your life successfully.

It is interesting to note that, currently, one of the most popular courses at Harvard University is Positive Psychology, which emphasizes psychological development and was pioneered by Martin Seligman, a professor at the University of Pennsylvania (Seligman, 2002). Underlying the academic study of the positive aspects of human development is the theme of happiness and creating a fulfilling and flourishing life. A similar course is being taught on more than 100 campuses around the country.

Asclepius

The Greeks attributed certain ideals and values to their gods and goddesses. The god of healing, Asclepius, had two daughters, each one symbolizing different approaches to health—one being treatment and the other prevention. His daughter Panacea was knowledgeable in the use of medication to *treat* diseases, embodying the principles of today's ongoing search for panaceas—drugs and other treatments to cure disease. Hygieia, his other daughter, was an expert on teaching ways of living in harmony with nature in order to *prevent* disease, today's equivalent of hygiene or health and the forerunner of wellness, a word that has its origin in the mid-17th century.

An Ancient Greek Wellness Center

Epidaurus was home to the ancient Greek sanctuaries for several Greek gods. Asclepius held first place in the religious life of Epidaurus from the 5th century BCE to the 4th century CE. It began as a religious center, then developed into a hospital sanctuary where people sought treatment for physical and mental illnesses (Charitonidou, 1978). It also became a social center with a serene and pleasant environment, hot and cold baths, guest houses, gymnasia, stadiums, and an amphitheater for theatrical performances. Its spring waters were thought to have special pharmaceutical qualities.

Persons arriving in Epidaurus for healing had an unquestionable faith in its curative powers. Prayers, sacrifices, and purifications were required. Upon arriving, they were met by a priest who told them to expect a dream in which a god would appear and assure them of a miracle and the treatment. For example, the god might order the patient to take daily physical exercise under the supervision of a special trainer. Certain foods or drinks might be prescribed. In certain respects, Epidaurus, more than 2,000 years ago, was even more comprehensive in treating the whole person than our modern-day so-called wellness centers and health spas. Even today, the Greeks greet one another with a wellness expression that means, "health to you."

JEWISH AND CHRISTIAN EMPHASES

Hebrew Health and Healing

In the Old Testament, God revealed himself as a healer and was sometimes referred to as "The Lord who heals." Throughout the Old Testament, healing prayers were addressed to God. The Lord was also seen as giving prescribed laws of health, which were observed as antidotes to sickness and disease. These laws can be summarized under six main headings: (a) the law of sanitation, (b) the law of cleansing, (c) the law of isolation, (d) the law of dietetics, (e) the law of personal disciplines, and (f) the law of rest (Stanger, 1978). There was growing awareness among the Hebrews that wholeness related to the total person. They believed that such wholeness began by being in harmony with God. *Shalom* in Hebrew is an expression for well-being, wholeness, individual health, and communal harmony.

The Early Christian Church

The notion of caring for the sick has religious roots. Certainly this is true for Christianity. New Testament writers often related the health of the body to the spiritual life of the individual. A wholesome spiritual life was believed to contribute to the health of the mind and body. In the first century after the death of Jesus, the Romans and non-Christian groups noted how the Christians cared for one another in their communities. The care was holistic in that they showed concern for their economic, social, and spiritual well-being, including health.

By the 4th century CE, Christians began to build hospitals and healing centers. In 379 CE, St. Basil built a 300-bed hospital in Caesarea, a city in Asia Minor, now Turkey. Similar healing centers were built in the growing cities of the Eastern and Western Christian empires. Religiously affiliated hospitals, foundling homes, and hospices spread with the establishment of cathedrals and monasteries. Although the healing ministry of the church waned for several centuries, each century throughout the Middle Ages had Christian leaders who kept it alive. Priests, monks, and nuns cared for the ill in sanctuaries throughout western Europe. The ministry of sacramental healing continued in the life of the church until the spirit of secular materialism invaded most institutions, even the church, in the 18th century (Kelsey, 1985). Science and medicine began to take over the treatment of disease and restoration to health.

Later Christian Emphases

Religiously affiliated colleges and universities trained large numbers of physicians in the Victorian age. The early 20th century saw dozens of hospitals built throughout the United States by religious groups. Although they may no longer be directly affiliated with a religious organization, many of these institutions still bear a reference to their Baptist, Catholic, Methodist, or Presbyterian roots in name if not in organization.

The rapid growth of medicine and medical research in the early 20th century replaced the traditional dependence upon religion for healing. Although the churches placed less emphasis on individual healing, they aligned themselves with medical science and the creation of institutions to heal the sick. By the 1970s, there was a revival of interest on the part of the older, Protestant denominations in the healing ministry. Prayer for individual healing and health continues to be a central part of Christian communities. Churches have also been adding congregational nurses in their total ministry, with an emphasis on education and prevention along with supportive and supplemental health services. The healing ministry of the Christian church has never been entirely lost in its 2,000 years of existence. The world's major religions continue with practices for healing the sick. Today, nearly two-thirds of U.S. medical schools teach required or elective courses on the relationship between religion and spirituality and medicine.

NATIVE AMERICAN HEALING

Akin to the Eastern philosophy is a belief of Native Americans in a holistic understanding of disease. They believe that disease is due to disharmony with nature, which includes family, friends, and the environment. Although healing practices among Native Americans have varied widely, some commonalities are present in philosophy and practice (Krippner, 1995). At the time of the North American conquest, at least 500 tribes lived in the territory that now comprises the United

States; thus global statements can be misleading. This review is intended to be more historic than current in its perspective.

As part of the holism that characterizes Native American medicine, the patient's spiritual condition is assessed and considered during diagnosis and treatment. Furthermore, many Native American treatments are considered spiritual in nature. Tribes make no arbitrary division between body and mind. In treatment, however, they may differentiate between those afflictions that are "natural disorders" and others that are believed to be "supernatural disorders." The natural disorders may be treated by herbs, diet, massage, and sweat baths, and the supernatural by rituals and magic, such as medicine wheels and sand paintings. Upholding the traditions of the family and the culture are important for maintaining health and overcoming disease.

Many Native American treatments were remarkably effective. Practitioners lanced boils, removed tumors, treated fractures and dislocations, and cleaned wounds in ways that were hygienic. Of the herbs used by the Rappachannock tribe, 60 percent have been found to have unquestionable medicinal value (Krippner, 1995). Any diagnosis and treatment in Native American healing considers patient behavior beyond the reporting of symptoms.

EASTERN AND CHINESE MEDICINE

The Eastern mind has viewed health as an integral part of one's total being, with no separation between the mind and body. Lifestyle is always in a dynamic relationship with the well-being of the person. In the Chinese language, *mind* and *body* are not separate terms. One word exists for describing the organism as a whole. The Chinese do, however, have many words to describe different types of energy in the body. Similarities exist between the Chinese and Indian view of energy and human life (Chin, 1992). The Eastern belief is that all energy comes from one universal source. The energy that exists within the universe is the same energy that exists within us. Movement of this energy is the basis of all life, and thus this energy must have something or somewhere to move to.

Eastern medicine has viewed the body not according to how each part functions on its own, but rather how it functions in relationship to the whole system (Chin, 1992). By looking at the body/mind in a holistic way, Eastern practitioners discovered a highly organized system of energy channels or pathways in addition to other body systems. It is distinct from the cardiovascular and nervous systems, yet intimately connected. Good health requires a healthy lifestyle and self-responsibility for maintaining balance in this energy system. If illness occurs, the balance in energy needs to be restored, thus calling for holistic methods to redistribute the energy to reach the balance for which it is constantly striving.

As an example of an Eastern discipline for holistic health, yoga combines the spiritual, mental, and physical. Self-effort, self-examination, and self-awareness are integral to disciplining one's mind, developing a philosophy of life, and exercising the body. Yoga practices include breathing properly, eating a balanced and nutritious diet, exercising with yoga postures, and engaging in some form of meditation that stills the mind. Qi gong and t'ai chi are other energy-balancing exercises that bring into harmony the flow of energy throughout and within the body and all of its organs. The Eastern integrated approach also uses massage, herbal therapy, dietary changes, and acupuncture (Gordon, 1996). The goal of the Eastern model of healing is the dual purpose of relieving and preventing pain and tension, and to promote harmony within the body and between the person and the environment.

MODERN WESTERN MEDICINE

With the rise of the scientific revolution and rationalistic thinking, body and mind were separated. Religion and science were also separated between the 15th and 17th centuries. Conflict highlighted by the split between Copernicus and the church over a sun-centered universe was eventually resolved, with religion taking the soul and science the mind and body. The dominant view has been that the physical and mental aspects of health are separate and subject to only limited interaction. The traditional model of illness became known as *dualistic,* with a newer biopsychosocial model emerging in the latter 20th century known as *holistic* (Bernard & Krupat, 1994). Four characteristics of the traditional model are *dualistic, mechanistic, reductionist,* and *disease oriented.* Health was defined as the absence of disease.

Reductionism in science led to the mind being separated from the body, with each being further separated into systems, organs, tissues, and cells. The natural environment was treated as if it consisted of separate parts. Individual, social, and cultural environments were treated separately. The individual and the ecological environment were also treated separately. Lifestyle was separated from health and disease.

Medicine led the way in this dualistic thinking with its preoccupation with disease and treatment of the symptoms of illness in a mechanistic way. The interrelationships of body, mind, and one's lifestyle were largely ignored as progress was made in treating and curing certain diseases. Research and treatment in much of Western medicine has been based upon studying cadavers, the germ theory of disease, and the pathology of illness. Eastern medicine, on the other hand, has obtained much of its knowledge from the systematic study of living, healthy human beings and the harmony and balance of life forces sustaining health.

MULTIDISCIPLINARY AND INTERDISCIPLINARY WELLNESS

Historical aspects in the development of healing, health, and wellness have been sketched out in the previous discussion in the form of concepts and practices. What follows is a summary of selected academic areas that are contributing to the scientific understanding of the "good life" as seen by Aristotle and contemporary efforts to improve the quality of life and longevity. The daughters of Asclepius, Panacea and Hyieia, are the two interacting concepts for wellness research, with the primary emphasis on the latter.

Jung, Adler, and the Drive Toward Wholeness

The mind does not like to be divided. Psychologist C. G. Jung (Storr, 1983) called this a drive toward wholeness and integration, in which all elements of the person come together to form a larger entity, the *self.* The mind strives to make sense of the conscious and unconscious aspects of thoughts, feelings, and experiences. Major world religions, in a spiritual sense, are the striving of the individual in response to a god-like image that is part of the collective unconscious. The divine nature of the unique human personality combines this uniqueness of *self* with eternity and the individual with the universe.

Alfred Adler (1927/1954), a psychologist and contemporary of Jung, wrote that the human organism strives to fulfill its purpose. Human behavior can be understood on the basis of what the individual perceives as being meaningful and goal achieving. Inherent in this goal is the desire to protect the self while striving to fulfill one's potential, thereby achieving a sense of wholeness.

Any part of the person could be understood by understanding the unified, indivisible whole (Adler, 1927/1954; Sweeney, 1998). With today's knowledge, Adler would be inclined to consider health and wellness as the ultimate goal and striving of humankind (Sweeney & Witmer, 1991).

Humanistic Psychology

Maslow, Rogers, and other humanistic psychologists created a "third force" in the development of psychology. The clinical and behavioral approaches they developed in the 1940s and early 1950s focused predominantly on the disease model of human behavior. Psychoanalysis was the dominant clinical theory for the first half of the 20th century. Its focus was primarily on the influence of unconscious forces—such as repressed impulses, internal conflicts, and childhood traumas—on the mental life and adjustment of the individual. Assessing and treating mental illness was the main focus of empirical research. Maslow (1968, 1971) noted psychology's preoccupation with the unhealthy and the average. His research attempted to define human beings in terms of what they can become. In his study of exceptional individuals, the individual's beliefs, emotions, values, healthy characteristics, and possibilities became eminent. Growth, autonomy, and the characteristics of the healthy personality reached fulfillment in what he called *self-realization*, or the *fully functioning person*.

Rogers (1951, 1961, 1983) pioneered the development of psychological and educational methods that facilitated personal growth. Positive regard, genuineness, and empathy were considered core conditions that facilitated growth as well as therapeutic change. Rogers's study of therapeutic change and Maslow's study of self-actualizing persons give us a glimpse of the "growing tip" of humankind, a stage of development described as "fully human."

Health and Social Psychology

Health psychology was officially recognized as a new field when the American Psychological Association (APA) approved its recognition as Division 38 of the APA in 1978 (Stone, Cox, Valdimarsdottir, Jandorf, & Neal, 1987). The discipline recognizes the physical, psychological, and social as three broad categories of factors involved in illness and health (Bernard & Krupat, 1994). While not as much a separate area for professional identity, the academic area of social psychology emerged as the application of social dimensions to how lifestyle events and certain behaviors influence one's health—for example, the connection between unsatisfactory social relationships and cardiovascular diseases. Friendship, marriage, divorce, loneliness, volunteer work, and involvement in community groups are legitimate areas for research and clinical application in exploring their relationship to health and disease.

Behavioral Medicine and Medical Research

At about the same time, another group of psychologists and physicians met to organize the Society of Behavioral Medicine. Behavioral medicine, or mind–body approaches, address not only physical symptoms, but also the framework of attitudes and behavior that surround an illness condition. It unites modern scientific medicine, psychology, nursing, nutrition, and exercise physiology to enhance the natural healing capacity of the body and mind (Benson & Stuart, 1992).

Publications on wellness, health, and fitness appearing in the early 1990s are indicative of how far medical research had advanced within two decades of the mind–body and wellness movement. The researchers of this era are multidisciplinary, with backgrounds in medical, biomedical, psychological, and health specialties. Leading authorities from the nation's top medical centers reported their findings in publications such as *The Wellness Encyclopedia* (University of California, Berkeley, Wellness Letter, 1991), *The Wellness Book* (Benson & Stuart, 1992), *Mind/Body Medicine* (Goleman & Gurin, 1993), and *Fresh Start: The Stanford Medical School Health and Fitness Program* (Stanford Center for Research in Disease Prevention, 1996). Top medical centers represented in these publications include Stanford University, Duke University, the University of Pittsburgh, Harvard, Johns Hopkins University, Vanderbilt University, the University of Massachusetts, Ohio State University, Case Western Reserve University, the University of California, Cornell University, the University of Michigan, the Sloan-Kettering Cancer Center, and the Mayo Clinic.

General topics from the research relating disease, health, and longevity include: mind/body basics; the mind's role in illness; emotions and health; nutrition; exercise; social support from family, friends, and groups; relaxation, stress management, and coping; personal health habits such as sleeping; self-care; and environment and safety.

Researchers and practitioners in these areas derive their knowledge and methodology from psychology and the biomedical sciences in general and have made significant contributions to understanding the optimal factors that reduce the risk of disease. They likewise further our understanding of the physical, mental, and social attributes that contribute to optimal health.

Stress Research

Stress research at first evolved very slowly and almost single-handedly from the pioneer work of Hans Selye (1974), who coined the term "stress." Although the term *stress* has long been associated with medical, psychosomatic, emotional, and interpersonal difficulties, as well as anxiety and burnout, there is no generally agreed-upon definition of stress. Considerable evidence regarding the effects of stress suggests that high stress levels, if chronically sustained, may contribute to a lowering of energy levels, ineffective mental functioning, performance failures, difficulty in interpersonal relationships, emotional disturbances, a weakened immune system, and illnesses of various kinds.

Two factors determine whether personal and environmental events might be stressful. First is the *cognitive appraisal* of the stressor. The formulation of this *appraisal* and the resulting *coping response* is best described by Lazarus and Folkman (1984) as "a relationship between the person and the environment that is appraised as taxing or exceeding his or her resources and endangering his or her well-being" (p. 21). The efficacy of the *coping response* is determined by the individual's *coping strategies and techniques*: coping behaviors such as stress monitoring, information seeking, and problem solving; and *coping resources* such as beliefs and values, self-esteem, and emotional-social support.

Stress appraisal and coping are part of a wellness model of health rather than a pathogenic orientation in which disease is the focus. A wellness orientation leads one to think in terms of factors promoting movement toward the healthy end of the disease–health continuum. It entails looking at how people stay healthy and what promotes well-being.

Quality-of-Life and Longevity Research

Quality-of-life and longevity research go hand in hand. The principles that play the most significant role in quality of life, with a few minor exceptions, are the very same ones necessary for achieving our biological potential (Bortz, 1991; Pelletier, 1981). What contributes to the quality of life tends to extend the longevity of life. Applying the results of these two avenues of research shifts the emphasis from pathology to longevity promotion that sustains an optimal quality of life. Research in this area includes longitudinal study of individuals or groups over years and the cross-sectional study of older persons and their habits and lifestyles, for example, centenarian communities such as the Georgians in the Caucasus Mountains of Georgia, formerly part of the Soviet Union.

Three extensive studies of wellness were conducted in the 1970s. Research by Belloc (1973) and Belloc and Breslow (1972) focused on the positive health behaviors of over 7,000 adults who were studied over a period of five and one-half years. Seven factors were significantly related to life expectancy and health: (a) three meals a day and no snacking, (b) breakfast every day, (c) moderate exercise two or three times a day, (d) adequate sleep (seven or eight hours a night), (e) no smoking, (f) moderate weight, and (g) no alcohol or only in moderation.

Flanagan (1978), operating out of the American Institute for Research (Palo Alto, CA), found that 15 needs areas were significantly related to the quality of life, including physical health; economic status; relationships with family, friends, and community; helping others; intellectual development; work role; and leisure and recreational activities.

Another research effort to assess well-being in the United States was conducted by Angus Campbell (1981) and the staff at the Institute for Social Research, University of Michigan. Personal, social, educational, occupational, and environmental factors made up 12 domains of life that were correlated as to their influence on the satisfaction of life in general. Findings from these studies and those described next characterize the quality-of-life indicators that also contribute to longevity.

Genetic, lifestyle, and environmental factors all play a part in longevity. Among the common denominators of longevity in individuals and cultures throughout the world are: (a) heredity or genetic influences; (b) dietary and nutritional factors; (c) being physically and mentally active throughout life; (d) abstinence from or moderate consumption of alcohol; (e) continued productive involvement in family and community affairs; (f) positive philosophical or religious attitudes (e.g., optimistic); (g) work satisfaction; and (h) an enduring sense of the meaning and purpose in life (Bortz, 1990, 1991; Pelletier, 1981; Peterson & Bossio, 1991; Santrock & Bartlett, 1986). Additional predictors are having parents or grandparents living past the age of 80, living in a rural area, being married, having at least two close friends, having high socioeconomic status, sleeping six to eight hours every night, and not smoking.

The environment, healthcare (especially of the young and old), and safe working conditions are other factors that interact with those just noted. Although no single choice, habit, or condition may make a huge difference (except smoking and substance abuse), they add up when put together, and have a significant impact on the quality of life and longevity. This additive and interactive effect makes it difficult to explain differences between individuals, cultures, and nations on characteristics of wellness.

Positive Psychology

The theme for the 1998 convention of the American Psychological Association was prevention. Certain psychologists recognized that the disease model prevalent for the previous 50 years did not move psychology closer to prevention of serious personal and relationship problems. Two years later, the journal *American Psychologist* (2000) published a special issue on happiness, excellence, and optimal human functioning.

Researchers were learning that there are human strengths that act as buffers against mental illness: courage, future mindedness, optimism, interpersonal skill, faith, work ethic, hope, honesty, perseverance, and the capacity for flow and insight. Martin Seligman, widely regarded as the "father of positive psychology," wrote that the challenge for the new century "will be to create a science of human strength whose mission is to foster these virtues in young people" (Seligman & Csikszentmihalyi, 2000, p. 7).

THE WORLD'S LONGEST-LIVED PEOPLE: THE OKINAWA LIFESTYLE

What we eat, do, think, and believe largely determine our health and longevity.

Okinawa is a string of islands southwest of Japan in the East China Sea. It was an independent kingdom until the Japanese took possession in 1879. It is the home of the longest-lived people in the world. Coronary heart disease, stroke, and cancer occur in Okinawa with the lowest frequency in the world. More than 400 centenarians live in a population of 1.3 million, many of them still healthy, active, and living independently. More important than their *life expectancy* is their *health expectancy*, the number of years they expect to live in good health. The Okinawa lifestyle is a unique approach to health and life based upon centuries of Eastern tradition and wisdom. *The Okinawa Program* is a report by a team of internationally known experts who have scientifically documented the Okinawa Centenarian Study over a 25-year period (Wilcox, Wilcox, & Suzuki, 2001). Their findings reveal the diet, exercise, and lifestyle practices that make the Okinawans the healthiest and longest-lived population in the world. The authors envision the Okinawa Program as a wellness model for the world.

Key Findings of the Okinawa Centenarian Study

After examining over 600 Okinawan centenarians and numerous "youngsters" in their 70s, 80s, and 90s, the researchers saw certain patterns emerge:

Eating Habits   A low-calorie, plant-based diet high in unrefined carbohydrates. The elders eat an average of seven servings of vegetables and fruits a day, seven servings of grains a day, two servings of flavonoid-rich soy products per day, fish products rich in omega-3 several times a week, and minimal dairy products and meat. The average body mass index for the elders ranges from 18 to 22.

Physical Activity   Exercise through the martial arts, traditional dance, gardening, and walking. Tai chi is also popular. They believe that health and longevity can be obtained by nurturing your *chi*, or "life energy," and living a balanced lifestyle that is in tune with nature's way.

Psychospiritual Outlook and Practices   Their philosophy affirms a faith in humanity, a sincere belief that all people are good, and it emphasizes both personal and group responsibilities. The elders retain remarkable mental clarity, even over the age of 100, partially due to diet. In personality testing, centenarians were low when it came to feelings of "time urgency" and "tension," and high in "self-confidence." Interviews revealed optimistic attitudes, adaptability, and an easygoing approach to life. Moderation was found to be a key cultural value. Health and longevity are celebrated, and health is a theme of most prayers. Low levels of negative emotions and depression are present.

Personal Care   They have integrated healthcare with the ancient Eastern and modern Western healing traditions. It focuses not just on the absence of disease but also on optimum health, both physical and psychospiritual. Alcohol is used moderately, if at all.

Social Integration   High levels of social contact. Cultural attitudes place the elderly in an exalted and respected position. Strong social networks and family ties exist, yet a fair amount of independence is retained. They believe in neighbor-sharing practices, where villagers cooperate to help one another in work and life tasks.

Source: Wilcox, B. J., Wilcox, D. C., & Suzuki, M. (2001). *The Okinawa Program.* New York: Three Rivers Press. Summary by Mel Witmer 4/5/09.

This new emphasis became known as positive psychology, which has become the scientific study of the strengths and the virtues that enable individuals and communities to thrive. It has three central concerns: positive emotions, positive individual traits, and positive institutions (Myers, 2000; Peterson, 2006; Seligman, 2002). Understanding positive emotion entails the study of contentment with the past, happiness in the present, and hope for the future. Understanding positive individual traits consists of the study of strengths and virtues, such as the capacity for love and work, courage, compassion, resilience, creativity, integrity, self-knowledge, moderation, self-control, and wisdom. The 24 character traits that contribute to optimal functioning are described in *Character Strengths and Virtues* (Peterson & Seligman, 2004). Understanding positive institutions entails the study of meaning and purpose as well as strengths that foster better communities, such as justice, responsibility, civility, parenting, nurturance, work ethic, leadership, teamwork, purpose, and tolerance. Positive psychology proposed to correct this imbalance by focusing on strengths as well as weaknesses, on developing the best things in life as well as repairing the worst.

Faith and Religious Practices

In a review of the accumulated literature on religion and health, Benson (1996) concluded that regardless of how traditional one's practice of religious beliefs, whenever faith is present, remembered wellness is triggered and health can be improved. Religion usually promotes healthy lifestyles. Religious commitment is consistently associated with better health. Benson summarizes the research: "The greater a person's commitment, the fewer his or her psychological symptoms, the better his or her general health, the lower the blood pressure, and the longer the survival" (p. 174). Regardless of age, ethnicity, specific religion, and patients with very different diseases and conditions, religious commitment brings with it a lifetime of benefits.

More recently, Harold Koenig at Duke University and his professional associates have reviewed the relationship between religious beliefs and lifestyle for their influence on physical and mental health (Koenig, 1999; Koenig & Lawson, 2004). The benefits cover illness prevention, illness recovery, and an overall sense of well-being. In their review of several hundred scientific studies comparing religious with nonreligious (or less religious) persons, the religious persons have lower diastolic blood pressure, are hospitalized less often, are less likely to suffer from depression, have healthier lifestyles, have a stronger sense of well-being and life satisfaction (especially older persons), have better health outcomes when suffering from a physical illness, have stronger immune systems, and live longer.

In reviewing the faith and mental health research, Koenig found that "religious beliefs and practices are usually associated with greater well-being, hope, and optimism; more purpose and meaning in life; greater quality of life; and more pro-social traits in terms of forgiveness, sociability, and altruism" (Koenig, 2005, p. 51). Also, religious involvement is consistently related to both a higher level and a higher quality of social support. Even in areas of the world where religion plays a less significant role than in the United States, religious activity still correlates with greater well-being.

In summary, a positive relationship exists between religious faith and health benefits. This effect appears to hold up in different cultures and across various faiths in the United States and other major religions of the world.

Energy Psychology and Medicine

Energy psychology is the integration of quantum physics, psychology, and Eastern medicine (Feinstein, Eden, & Craig, 2005). The body is seen as an energy system that strives to maintain harmony and balance in governing our every movement, feeling, and thought. Growing understanding about the relationship between electromagnetic energy and the molecules that carry information is causing practitioners and researchers in conventional medicine and psychotherapy to update their understanding of healing and health. For example, tapping into disturbing electrochemical patterns can bring about changes in a wide range of physical and psychological disorders. Energy psychology focuses on energy disturbance as well as the memory. Stimulating specific electro-magnetically sensitive points on the skin while imagining and bringing to mind a disturbing event can change the chemistry in certain areas of the brain.

Changing the internal wiring in relation to a clear-cut problem or symptom can be learned. One method for intervening in a disturbing flow of energy is to stimulate an acupuncture point in the body. This can change brain wave activity, deactivate an area of the brain associated with an undesirable condition, and in some locations cause the secretion of serotonin. More intrusive means such as the insertion of needles, electrical stimulation, or the application of heat can be applied. The accupoints are called "windows" into the body's energy system. The body's energy system can be affected by rubbing, tapping, stretching, holding, or tracing specific points or areas on the surface of the skin. Tapping is a common procedure that is being used in clinical treatment and research.

The promise of energy psychology presents powerful tools for personal development, too. Combined with conventional techniques such as affirmations, visualizations, and positive thoughts, the use of energy interventions can improve self-image, evoke potentials, and enhance performance. It is safe and noninvasive, as effective as or more effective than other available therapies for a number of mental health conditions, and also an effective tool in the self-management of thoughts, emotions, and behavior for personal development (Feinstein et al., 2005).

A broader application of the human energy field findings is described by Valerie Hunt in *Infinite Mind: The Science of Human Vibration* (1995). She demonstrates how electromagnetic radiation changes during human interaction and with environmental conditions. Through field research and extensive clinical studies, she provides insight into mind–body interaction, the emotions and creativity, extrasensory human capacities in higher consciousness, and the mystical connections of spirit.

Other Disciplines

Additional and interrelated disciplines have made contributions to understanding illness and the factors that contribute to health and wellness. Research on burnout and occupational stress has provided strategies for reducing physical and mental distress and introducing health-promotion programs in work settings. Biofeedback, as a means of monitoring physiological states such as skin temperature, muscle tension, and brain waves, provides visual and auditory information to alter mind–body connections to increase self-awareness and self-control. Its main focus is relaxation of the mind and body systems that are aroused by the sympathetic nervous system. Biofeedback has been used in treating a variety of stress-related conditions, such as headaches, muscle tension related to low back pain, and general anxiety.

Psychoneuroimmunology, the integration of three fields of research, has contributed to some major breakthroughs in our understanding of how thoughts can influence the functioning of the immune system. This new science is charting a labyrinth of mind–body connections, chemical messengers, emotions, and immune-system cells. Negative thinking can adversely affect moods as well as depress the immune system, therefore making us more vulnerable to an array of illnesses.

Research in the areas of nutrition and exercise has generated extensive scientific data on factors that improve the quality and longevity of life. We now understand how dietary excesses contribute to major health problems in our society. Exercise can assist in healing, aid in prevention, and enhance the functioning of the body and the mind. Regular exercise and a nutritional diet are two of the greatest contributors to our overall well-being. Sports psychology has demonstrated performance enhancement by combining such techniques as a positive attitude, relaxation, mental rehearsal, breath control, and physical fitness.

PERSISTENCE OF THE PLACEBO

The placebo effect is probably as old as humankind. Belief-inspired healing has been a part of the healing process practiced by healers and physicians in every culture and time one might study. Benson (1996) has studied the presence of the placebo in the history of healing and notes that, "[i]n large measure, the history of medicine is the history of the placebo effect" (p. 109). Even though a substance or procedure may in and of itself have no medical value, the *belief* that it will help has therapeutic value. Believing that the treatment will remediate a condition seems to activate a natural response within the individual's own health maintenance system. Benson prefers to call the intense desire for health and wholeness "remembered wellness," because it more accurately describes the mental process involved in caring for oneself.

Up until about a hundred years ago, remembered wellness was the treatment of choice. Benson believes that the scientific community is wrong in its dismissal of this phenomenon in its pejorative usage of "just the placebo effect." The facts are that the patient, caregiver, or both of them believing in the treatment conditions contributes to better outcomes. Andrew Weil (1995) observes that the placebo, far from being a nuisance, is potentially the greatest ally doctors can find in their efforts to mitigate disease. He has written extensively on how to discover and enhance the body's natural ability to maintain and heal itself.

Today, the "placebo effect" is the benchmark for new drugs and techniques. If a new drug or procedure is no better than a placebo, the new treatment is considered a failure. Studies of the placebo effect over the last half-century confirm that they are 30 to 70 percent effective, depending upon the nature of the illness and compliance. In every incident of remembered wellness, the catalyst is belief. The placebo has three components: the beliefs of the person, the beliefs of the health practitioner, and the relationship between the person and the practitioner. When these are positive, a placebo has a 37 percent chance of working as well as an active medicine (Benson & Stuart, 1992). History and scientific research confirm the universal presence of the mind–body effect on our health.

EARLY CONTEMPORARY WELLNESS EFFORTS

Wellness as a term in the English language has its origin in the mid-17th century. The recent development of the wellness concept using the language of *"wellness"* has been reviewed by Myers and Sweeney (2005). The World Health Organization (WHO)as early as 1947 defined health as being more than the absence of disease and in 1964 emphasized the well-being aspect with its definition of optimal health as "a state of complete physical, mental, and social well-being and not merely the absence of disease or infirmity" (WHO, 1964, p. 1).

Perhaps the oldest wellness operation promoting health-conscious behavior in the United States is the YMCA. The organization almost from its inception in the United States in 1851 began to emphasize the physical, mental, social, and spiritual aspects of a healthy lifestyle. As the organization evolved, various sports, bodybuilding, swimming, and aquatic activities were implemented. By 1979, the YMCA began doing fitness evaluations and offering exercise and fitness activities. Educational, social, and spiritual opportunities are still part of the YMCA's core offerings, with character development and physical activities being highlighted. Today more than 2,600 centers offer health-promoting activities for all persons without discrimination as to gender, age, race, ethnic background, or religion.

Halbert Dunn, a physician and professor, is widely credited with being the founding father of the modern wellness movement. His wellness philosophy and principles were presented in a series of short talks published in a book called *High Level Wellness* (Dunn, 1961). In Dunn's view, the ethic of self-responsibility and the integration of body, mind, and spirit are at the foundation of fulfilling one's potential. Dunn's holistic view is inherent in his definition of wellness as "an integrated method of functioning which is oriented to maximizing the potential of which an individual is capable, within the environment where he is functioning."

Another person whose work gave further impetus to the early wellness movement was Don Ardell, a medical researcher, professor, and health planner. He gives credit to Drs. Halbert Dunn and John Travis for their professional influence on his own work. Ardell's 1977 and 1979 (revised) books, each titled *High Level Wellness*, depict a model conceptualized as a circle, with self-responsibility in the center. The four characteristics surrounding the circle and contributing to high-level wellness are nutritional awareness, stress management, physical fitness, and environmental sensitivity. The most recent revision is more comprehensive and redefines the wellness circle with three parts: the physical domain, mental domain, and meaning and purpose, each with multiple subcomponents ranging from nutrition to emotional intelligence to relationships. His emphasis has been on the practical use of the model rather than studies to provide empirical support for the hypothesized components and their relationships. Ardell's book is a valuable resource for early references to persons and publications from a variety of disciplines during the 1960s and 1970s.

A third comprehensive approach to assessing wellness as a lifestyle was developed in the latter 1970s by Travis and Ryan (1977, 1981, 1988). Ardell (1979) describes the Wellness Resource Center as the most thorough portrait of what wellness looks like at a health-promotion center at this period of time. Their Wellness Resource Center, located in Mill Valley, California, published *Wellness Workbook*. The model includes a *Wellness Index* that has 12 components illustrated in a Wellness Index Wheel: Self-Responsibility and Love; Breathing; Sensing; Eating; Moving; Feeling; Thinking; Playing/Working; Communicating; Sex; Finding Meaning; and Transcending. His wellness model is illustrated by an Illness/Wellness Continuum, which shows premature death at the left end and high-level wellness at the right end. The center is the neutral point with no discernible illness. To the left are disabilities, symptoms, and signs of illness; to the right are increasing levels of health and well-being. Wellness is viewed as a process and never a static state.

The book includes a chapter on each of these wellness components, with explanations, information, and exercises for one's personal wellness development. The *Wellness Inventory*, an abridged version of the *Wellness Index*, was also made available, as was a later publication titled *Wellness*. It describes a step-by-step process covering areas from nutrition to exercise to preventive healthcare to self-awareness (Ryan & Travis, 1991).

The National Wellness Institute founded by Bill Hettler and his colleagues in the 1970s in Stevens Point, Wisconsin, was one of the early wellness centers to establish a comprehensive assessment of health and wellness. The National Wellness Institute continues to host an annual national wellness conference in Stevens Point.

A significant milestone for wellness was the 1985 publication of Dr. Mel Witmer's book *Pathways to Personal Growth: Developing a Sense of Worth and Competence*, in which he discusses wellness as a "way of life" and high-level health strategies. Also during the late 1980s and early 1990s, wellness counseling model began to be developed. These models will be discussed in some detail in the next chapter.

In the 1990s, mainstream medicine also began to acknowledge the importance of the wellness movement as evidenced by the National Institutes of Health opening its Office of Alternative Medicine (OAM) in 1991 (this office was renamed the National Center for Complementary Medicine and Alternative Medicine in 1998). Also, throughout the 1990s, more mental health practitioners and physicians were learning about and adopting primary prevention and holistic medicine approaches as part of their practices (Pert, 1997).

In the last decade, we have seen a significant growth in the wellness healthcare paradigm. This has been the case in part due to economic reasons, as wellness is now seen as a potentially viable means of cost containment, but also due to an increase in the public's desire for wellness and alternative healthcare services. Finally, there has also been a growth in empirical research concerning wellness as an approach to healthcare. The National Center for Complementary Medicine and Alternative Medicine has funded much of this research, along with private foundations and other government agencies. In the next chapter we will examine the underlying theory concerning wellness and some wellness models.

REFLECTION ACTIVITIES

1. What do you think future trends will be in health and wellness? Can you identify any themes from the evolution of wellness that will influence these future trends?
2. Many different professions were mentioned in this chapter. Identify two or three additional professions that influence the development of health and wellness. How do these professions impact the state of wellness of Americans?
3. Describe how your personal conception of health and wellness has changed over time. What factors influenced your conception of wellness?

References

Adler, A. (1927/1954). *Understanding human nature* (W. B. Wolfe, Trans.). New York: Fawcett Premier. (Original work published 1927)

AACD strategic plan. Alexandria, VA: Author. American Counseling Association. (1992). *Journal of Counseling & Development, 71*, 113–254.

Ardell, D. (1977). *High level wellness: An alternative to doctors, drugs, and disease*. Emmaus, PA: Rodale Press.

Ardell, D. (1979). *High level wellness: An alternative to doctors, drugs, and disease* (rev. ed.). Emmaus, PA: Rodale Press.

Belloc, N. B. (1973). Relationship of health practices and mortality. *Preventive Medicine, 2*, 67–81.

Belloc, N. B., & Breslow, L. (1972). Relationship of physical health status and health practices. *Preventive Medicine, 1*, 409–421.

Benson, H. (1996). *Timeless healing: The power of biology and belief*. New York: Scribner.

Benson, H., & Stuart, E. M. (1992. *The wellness book: The comprehensive guide to maintaining health and treat-ing stress-related illness*. New York: Fireside, Simon & Schuster.

Bernard, L. C., & Krupat, E. (1994). *Health psychology: Biopsychosocial factors in health and illness*. New York: Harcourt Brace.

Bortz, W. M. (1990). The trajectory of dying: Functional status in the last year of life. *Journal of the American Geriatrics Society, 38(2)*, 146–150.

Bortz, W. M. (1991). *We live too short and die too long*. New York: Bantam.

Campbell, A. (1981). *The sense of well-being in America: Recent patterns and trends*. New York: McGraw-Hill.

Charitonidou, A. (1978). *Epidaurus: The sanctuary of Asclepios and the museum*. Epidaurus, Greece: Clio Editions.

Chin, R. M. (1992). *The energy within: The science behind every Oriental therapy from acupuncture to yoga*. New York: Paragon House.

Dossey, L. (1999). *Reinventing medicine: Beyond the mind-body to a new era of healing*. San Francisco: Harper.

Dunn, H. L. (1961). *High-level wellness*. Arlington, VA: R. W. Beatty.

Eisenberg, D. M., Kessler, R. C., Foster, C., Norlock, F. E., Calkins, D. R., & Delbanko, T. L. K. (1993). Unconventional medicine in the United States: Prevalence, costs, and patterns of use. *New England Journal of Medicine, 328*, 246–252.

Feinstein, D., Eden, D., & Craig, G. (2005). *The promise of energy psychology*. New York: Tarcher/Penguin.

Flanagan, J. (1978). A research approach to improving our quality of life. *American Psychologist, 33*, 138–147.

Goleman, D., & Gurin, J. (Eds.). (1993). *Mind/body medicine: How to use your mind for better health*. Yonkers, NY: Consumer Reports Books.

Gordon, J. S. (1996). *Manifesto for a new medicine*. Reading, MA: Addison-Wesley.

Hattie, J. A., Myers, J. E., & Sweeney, T. J. (2004). A factor structure of wellness: Theory, assessment, analysis, and practice. *Journal of Counseling & Development, 82*, 353–364.

Hettler, W. (1984). Wellness: Encouraging a lifetime pursuit of excellence. *Health Values: Achieving High Level Wellness, 8*, 13–17.

Hunt, V. H. (1995). *Infinite mind: The science of human vibrations*. Malibu, CA: Malibu Publishing.

Ingelfinger, F. J. (1977). Health: A matter of statistics of feeling. *New England Journal of Medicine, 296*, 448–449.

Kelsey, M. (1985). *Foreword*. In K. L. Bakken (Ed.), *The call to wholeness* (p. viii). New York: Crossroad.

Koenig, H.G. (1999). *The healing power of faith: Science explores medicine's last frontier*. New York: Simon & Schuster.

Koenig, H. G. (2005). *Faith & mental health*. Philadelphia: Templeton Foundation Press.

Koenig, H. G., & Lawson, D. M. (2004). *Faith in the future: Healthcare, aging, and the role of religion*. Philadelphia: Templeton Foundation Press.

Krippner, S. (1995). Cross-cultural comparison of four healing models. *Alternative therapies in health and medicine, 1*(1), 21–29.

Lazarus, R. S., & Folkman, S. (1984). *Stress, appraisal, and coping*. New York: Springer.

Maslow, A. H. (1968). *Toward a psychology of being* (2nd ed.). New York: D. van Nostrand.

Maslow, A. H. (1970). *Motivation and personality* (2nd ed.). New York: Harper & Row.

Maslow, A. H. (1971). *The farther reaches of human nature*. New York: Viking Press.

Mokdad, A. H., Marks, J. S., Stroup, D. F., & Gerberding, J. L. (2004). Actual causes of death in the United States 2000. *Journal of the American Medical Association, 291*, 1238–1245.

Myers, D. (2000). *The American paradox*. New Haven, CT: Yale.

Myers, J. E., & Sweeney, T. J. (2005). The indivisible self: An evidence-based model of wellness (reprint). *Journal of Individual Psychology, 61(3)*, 269–279.

Myers, J. E., & Sweeney, T. J. (2005a). *Counseling for wellness: Theory, research, and practice*. Alexandria, VA: American Counseling Association.

Myers, J. E., & Sweeney, T. J. (2005b). The indivisible self: An evidence-based model of wellness. In J. E. Myers & T. J. Sweeney (Eds.), *Counseling for wellness: Theory, research, and practice* (pp. 29–37). Alexandria, VA: American Counseling Association.

Myers, J. E., & Sweeney, T. J. (2008). Wellness counseling: The evidence base for practice. *Journal of Counseling & Development, 86*, 482–493.

Myers, J. E., Sweeney, T. J., & Witmer, J. M. (2000). The Wheel of Wellness for counseling: A holistic model for treatment planning. *Journal of Counseling & Development, 78*, 251–266.

National Wellness Institute (1983). *Testwell*. Stevens Point, WI: Author.

Ornstein, R., & Sobel, D. S. (1990). The brain as a health maintenance organization. In R. Orstein & C. Swencionis (Eds.), *The healing brain: A scientific reader* (pp. 10–21). New York: Guilford Press.

Parsons, F. (1909). *Choosing a vocation*. Boston: Houghton Mifflin.

Pelletier, K. R. (1981). *Longevity: Fulfilling our biological potential*. New York: Delacorte Press/Seymour Lawrence.

Pert, C., 1997. *Molecules of emotion*. New York, NY: Simon & Schuster

Peterson, C. (2006). *Primer in positive psychology*. New York: Oxford University Press.

Peterson, C., & Bossio, L. M. (1991). *Health and optimism*. New York: Free Press.

Peterson, C., & Seligman, M. E. P. (Eds.). (2004). *Character strengths and virtues: A handbook and classification*. Washington, DC: American Counseling Association.

Preamble to the Constitution of the World Health Organization as adopted by the International Health Conference, New York, 19–22 June, 1946; signed on 22 July 1946 by the representatives of 61 States (Official Records of the World Health Organization, no. 2, p. 100) and entered into force on 7 April 1948.

Rogers, C. R. (1951). *Client-centered therapy*. Boston: Houghton Mifflin.

Rogers, C. R. (1961). *On becoming a person.* Boston: Houghton Mifflin.

Rogers, C. R. (1983). *Freedom to learn for the 80s.* Columbus, OH: Charles E. Merrill.

Ryan, R. S., & Travis, J. W. (1991). *Wellness: Small changes you can use to make a big difference.* Berkeley, CA: Ten Speed Press.

Santrock, J. W., & Bartlett, J. C. (1986). *Developmental psychology: A life cycle perspective.* Dubuque, IA: Wm. C. Brown.

Seligman, M. E. P. (2002). *Authentic happiness: Using the new positive psychology to realize your potential for lasting fulfillment.* New York: Free Press/Simon and Schuster.

Seligman, M. E. P., & Csikszentmihalyi, M. (2000). Positive psychology: An introduction. *American Psychology, 55,* 5–14.

Selye, H. (1974). *Stress without distress.* New York: Lippincott.

Shealy, C. N., & Church, D. (2006). *Soul medicine: Awakening your inner blueprint for abundant health and energy.* Santa Rosa, CA: Elite Books.

Stanford Center for Research in Disease Prevention. (1996). *Fresh start: The Stanford Medical School health and fitness program.* San Francisco: KQED Books.

Stanger, F. B. (1978). *God's healing community.* Nashville: Abingdon.

Stone, A. A., Cox, D. S., Valdimarsdottir, A., Jandorf, L., & Neale, J. M. (1987). Evidence that IgA antibody is associated with daily mood. *Journal of Personality and Social Psychology, 52,* 988–993.

Storr, A. (1983). *The essential Jung.* Princeton: Princeton University Press.

Sweeney, T. J. (1998). *Adlerian counseling: A practitioners approach* (4th ed.). Philadelphia: Taylor & Francis.

Sweeney, T. J. (2001). *Counseling: Historical origins and philosophical roots.* In D. C. Locke, J. E. Myers, & E. L. Herr (Eds.), *The handbook of counseling.* CA: Thousand Oaks.

Sweeney, T. J., & Witmer, J. M. (1991). Beyond social interest: Striving toward optimal health and wellness. *Individual Psychology, 47,* 527–540.

Time. (Nov. 4, 1991).

Travis, J. W. (1977). *Wellness workbook: A guide to attaining high level wellness.* Mill Valley, CA: Wellness Resource Center.

Travis, J. W., & Ryan, R. S. (1981). *Wellness workbook.* Berkeley, CA: Ten Speed Press.

Travis, J. W., & Ryan, R. S. (1988). *Wellness workbook* (2nd ed.). Berkeley, CA: Ten Speed Press.

University of California, Berkeley, Wellness Letter (Eds.). (1991). *The wellness encyclopedia.* Boston: Houghton Mifflin.

U.S. Department of Health and Human Services, Centers for Disease Control and Prevention, National Center for Chronic Disease Prevention and Health Promotion. (2004). *Fact sheet: Actual causes of death in the United States, 2000.* http://www.hhs.gov/healthcare/facts/factsheets/

U.S. Department of Health and Human Services, Public Health Service. (1990). *Healthy people 2000: National health promotion and disease prevention objectives.* Washington, DC: Superintendent of Documents, Government Printing Office.

Warburton, N. (1999). *Philosophy: The basics* (3rd ed.). New York: Routledge.

Weil, A. (1995). *Spontaneous healing.* New York: Alfred A. Knopf.

Witmer, J. M. (1985). *Pathways to personal growth.* Muncie, IN: Accelerated Development.

Witmer, J. M. (1989). Reaching toward wholeness. In T. J. Sweeney (Ed.), *Adlerian counseling: A practical approach for a new decade* (3rd ed., pp. 31–79). Muncie, IN: Accelerated Development.

Witmer, J. M., & Sweeney, T. J. (1992). A holistic model for wellness and prevention over the life span. *Journal of Counseling and Development, 71,* 140–148.

World Health Organization. (1958). *Constitution of the World Health Organization.* Geneva, Switzerland: Author.

3 | A MODEL OF WELLNESS

Paul F. Granello & Mel Witmer

Life is not merely being alive, but being well.

MARCUS AURELIUS, (ROMAN EMPEROR, BEST KNOWN FOR HIS
MEDITATIONS ON STOIC PHILOSOPHY, AD 121–180)

*Medical authorities have recognized that at least
50 percent, some say 80 percent, of the patients they
see have a condition that has a stress component.*

WELLNESS THEMES

The 10 themes described in this section are descriptive of a wellness approach to life.

Striving for Wellness and Well-Being

The central goal of a wellness lifestyle is to promote overall health across all of the domains of our functioning. Individuals who practice wellness as a lifestyle seek to prevent illness, minimize disease, improve the overall quality of life, and increase longevity. Wellness-oriented individuals focus on challenges that continually strive for the highest level of multidomain health possible (not simply the remission of a particular set of presenting symptoms in one domain of functioning).

Unity of All Dimensions of Human Existence

Wellness-oriented individuals believe that the well-being of the person is an inter-weaving of all the dimensions of human experience. The individual exists on many different levels or domains—cognitive, affective, behavioral, social, spiritual, and physical. All the components are interrelated and interdependent. The level of func-tion (or dysfunction) of one affects the functioning of the others. A person is more than one's body. Every human being is a holistic being, comprised of interdependent relationships of body, mind, emotions, and spirit. The goals for living a wellness-oriented lifestyle encompass the whole person in all spheres of human existence, including the physical, cognitive, emotional, social, cultural, vocational, and spiritual aspects of life.

Concern for Both Quality and Longevity of Life

Three real questions for wellness living are: *How long* will I live? *How healthy and vigorous* will my life be while living it? And a third existential question, "*How* do I want to live? With medical science and lifestyle changes extending the longevity of life, many times the quality of life suffers. Conversely, by seeking to help clients improve the quality of their lives, wellness-oriented individuals believe that there will be an increase in the length of life. The wellness model values *adding more life to living* as much as extending the life that one lives.

Person Oriented Rather than Disease Oriented

Each person must be seen as a unique individual and treated in a way appropriate to that person. Positive regard, understanding of the total person, and genuineness in the relationship are essential ingredients in any health or healing endeavors. Wellness-oriented individuals are democratic and tolerant rather than authoritarian, understanding that the quality of relationships between individuals exerts a powerful influence on their health.

Developmentally All Inclusive

Wellness-oriented individuals can make positive adjustments to their lifestyles at any age or stage of life. They believe that all people can adapt, change, and practice new lifestyle habits in order to increase their well-being. No individual is too old or too young to learn new ideas or behaviors, and in doing so improve some aspect of their lives. However, sound health practices cannot begin in adult life, as by this time much damage may have already been done. When they are nurtured, the traits of wellness naturally unfold early in life and continue to develop throughout the lifespan. Characteristics such as a sense of humor, an optimistic and trusting attitude, physical activity, and living in the present moment are all characteristics of healthy children and can contribute to our well-being until the end of life.

Cross-Cultural Universal Qualities

Wellness-oriented individuals believe that the dimensions of wellness apply universally to all humankind. The opportunity to pursue high-level wellness is a fundamental right of all human beings, not just those from select or privileged groups.

Sensitivity to Context

Contextual variables impact the health of the individual through local, institutional, environmental, and global events. We are not immune or isolated from such influences. Events in the environment, often beyond our control, impact our daily lives and the quality of living. Wars, poverty, natural disasters, crime, violence, disease, environmental pollution, economic exploitation, unemployment, and competition for limited resources are all stressors. A holistic approach to wellness requires that the individual be understood in the context of political, social, economic, and environmental factors that affect every one of us, day in and day out.

Integrated Multidisciplinary Approaches and Methods

Wellness-oriented individuals believe that they can benefit from breaking down the silos of sub-specialization that dehumanize the present-day medical system. Modern medical technology and perennial wisdom are both given an honorable place. Knowledge and practices are accepted from multiple professional disciplines. Current medical science and practices are also respected. Cultural wisdom and religious practices (e.g., meditation, yoga) may also be seen as sources of knowledge for creating healthier persons. The holistic approach is pragmatic in its criterion of using "what works" and doesn't require that a particular process be fully understood, although processes that have supportive research are highly desirable. Wellness-oriented individuals are open to seeking treatment and consulting with professionals from many different healthcare and social institutions. These professionals may include those in medicine, education, religious organizations, government and public service, recreation or physical development, allied health, business, and many others. Whatever methods are used should contribute to the well-being of the individual and his or her desire to become a more fully functioning person.

Personal Responsibility and Self-Care

Primary care is self-care. Wellness requires that individuals take responsibility for their own health over the lifespan. It teaches us to mobilize our power to heal ourselves and enhance our well-being. Personal control, empowerment, and self-efficacy may be the ultimate determinants in human health and aging. We are to make full use of the extraordinary capacity of our minds to influence the body. Although we still have much to learn about just how we can improve the quality and length of life, our current knowledge far exceeds our commitment to live a "healthy lifestyle." Wellness-oriented individuals believe that by applying what is known today, they can improve the quality of life significantly. Our understanding of health is shifting from dependence upon a "healer" to taking full responsibility for good health attitudes and practices. We are the writer, producer, director, and actor in fulfilling our own biological potential, social contribution, and spiritual destiny.

Proactive Rather than Reactive

Organizations must take the initiative and responsibility for healthcare systems that emphasize primary prevention rather than crisis intervention. Parental, school, community, and religious teachings should encourage healthy lifestyle behaviors. Wellness-oriented individuals encourage the client to be an active participant in a collaborative process in their healthcare, not just a passive recipient of care. Although the individual has the responsibility for choosing a healthy lifestyle, professionals in the healthcare field must also see their role as part of a holistic view of the person's well-being. Wellness-oriented healthcare providers should proactively advocate on behalf of their clients and the overall community to encourage organizational systems to promote a wellness approach to health.

Social Connectivity

Wellness-oriented individuals value the health effects of positive social support systems. A sense of belonging and connection to other people is a basic human need. Altruism, "the helping gene," provides health benefits for those who give and help others. Wellness-oriented individuals encourage social connections and the great untapped power that ordinary people have to understand and help one another through the family, neighborhood, small support groups, civic organizations, churches, schools, and the workplace.

In summary, the basic themes just outlined reflect a philosophy that asserts a positive view of humanity. Humans are viewed as holistic beings operating across many interrelated dimensions of life and as having the ability to strive to achieve enhanced levels of health and well-being.

Humans can learn, adapt, change, and create. This philosophy serves as the core of a wellness approach to lifestyle.

COUNSELING MODELS OF WELLNESS

Just as it is important to have a theoretical orientation in all mental health interventions (Young, 2008), so too is it important to have a theoretical road map when working toward a healthier lifestyle. Wellness models that indicate specific psychological and sociological variables can be used as the basis for structuring wellness work with clients.

Several authors have suggested models with specific psychological and sociological variables that contribute to an individual's wellness, as discussed next.

Zimpher Wellness Model

Zimpher (1992) proposed a wellness model based upon his treatment of clients with cancer. The model includes seven areas of treatment important for client wellness: medical health, immune function, lifestyle management, spiritual beliefs and attitudes, psychodynamics, energy forces, and interpersonal relations. Specific techniques are related to each category. An example under the interpersonal area would be the encouragement of a client to meditate with a partner, thereby assisting the client to maintain a social support network (Zimpher, 1992). The Zimpher model may be best suited to working with clients who are already diagnosed with a serious illness and who are looking to receive therapy as an adjunct to their medical care.

Hettler Hexagonal Model of Wellness

A second wellness model developed by Hettler attempts to provide specific factors that comprise wellness (Opatz, 1986). This model has a broader focus than the Zimpfer model and was developed and implemented for a college campus environment (Hettler, 1980). The six dimensions of wellness that are specifically defined in this model are intellectual, emotional, physical, social, occupational, and spiritual wellness (Figure 3.1). Further, each of the categories is divided into subtasks, for example, under the category of social wellness, behavior of an individual that involves actively seeking interdependent relationships is viewed as contributing to wellness. This model

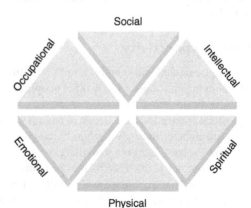

FIGURE 3.1 Hettler's Six-Dimension Hexagonal Model of Wellness

has been used in a variety of industrial and college settings (Mareno, 2010) and is used by the National Wellness Institute at Stevens Point, Wisconsin (Granello, 2000; Hettler, 1980).

The Lifespan Model of Wellness

The lifespan model is much more comprehensive than either of the two models just described. The Adlerian concepts of social interest and striving for mastery are used as the theoretical basis of this model and provide a rationale to explain why individuals wish to achieve a wellness lifestyle (Sweeney & Witmer, 1991).

The model, developed by Witmer and Sweeney (1991), uses five "life task" categories that are viewed as necessary to wellness: spirituality, self-direction, work and leisure, friendship, and love. Each of the life tasks is further separated into a total of 16 subscales (spirituality, sense of worth and sense of control, realistic beliefs, emotional responsiveness, intellectual stimulation, sense of humor, exercise, nutrition, self-care, gender identity, cultural identity, stress management, work, leisure, friendship, and love). For example, the life task of friendship is separated into two components: social interest and connectedness, and social support, interpersonal relations, and health. The authors provide cited research to support the logic of including each of the 15 subcomponents in the overall wellness model (Witmer & Sweeney, 1991). This model is well grounded in research and may be the most useful for practitioners wishing to do wellness counseling with the general public (Myers, Sweeney, & Witmer, 2000).

The Indivisible-Self Wellness Model (5-F WEL)

After 10 years of research involving four separate and increasingly more useful versions of the Wellness Evaluation of Life (WEL) measure, 17 discrete factors of wellness were determined. The lack of factor-analytic studies with the original WEL limits its usefulness for research, but it still has usefulness for educational and workshop purposes. Its successor, the Five-Factor Wellness Inventory (5-F WEL), grew out of the factor-analytic studies of the original WEL database. The lead researchers, Myers and Sweeney, describe the five factors of wellness assessment in their publication *Counseling for Wellness* (Myers, 2005).

The 5-F WEL is a paper-and-pencil instrument that includes 73 items measuring a single-order factor, Total Wellness, and five second-order factors. Reliability data along with convergent and divergent validity support the usefulness of the instrument for research purposes and its implications for clinical use (Myers & Sweeney, 2005). The 37 studies using the WEL and the 5-F WEL are summarized in a table that reflects its wide application to a variety of settings and clients of different ages, gender, marital status, socioeconomic status, and cultures (Myers, 2005). The five second-order factors to emerge from the exploratory and confirmatory studies are as follows, with the descriptive dimensions used in the original WEL indicating the content of each factor. The initial 17 scales of the WEL did emerge as independent factors but did not group according to the initial five life tasks of the hypothesized wheel (Figure 3.2). Using the Adlerian (Sweeney, 2009) concept of the unity and indivisibility of the self, the researchers named the five factors that emerged empirically as facets of wellness; these are summarized in Table 3.1.

The clinical and research editions of this wellness assessment have created a foundation for theoretical, measurement, and clinical application to healthcare and understanding optimal wellness. Currently, it is one of the most comprehensive wellness models and assessments in the field of counseling and holistic health (Myers, 2005, 2008).

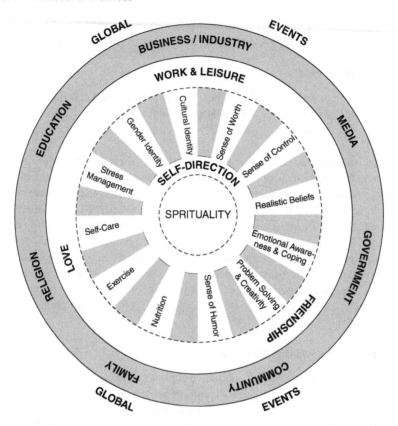

FIGURE 3.2   The Wheel of Wellness

TABLE 3.1   Indivisible-Self Model (Five-Factor Wellness Model)

Five Factors	Wellness Evaluation of Lifestyle Subscales
Creative Self	Problem Solving and Creativity; Sense of Control; Emotional Awareness and Coping; Sense of Humor; Work
Coping Self	Leisure; Stress Management; Sense of Worth; Realistic Beliefs
Social Self	Friendship; Love
Essential Self	Essence of Spirituality; Self-Care; Gender Identity; Cultural Identity
Physical Self	Nutrition; Exercise

FIGURE 3.3   Clinical and Educational Model of Wellness

Clinical and Educational Wellness Model

When applying wellness counseling with clients in my practice, I found the need to have a clinical wellness model that was simple to explain. So, I developed the wellness model portrayed in Figure 3.3. The model is heavily based on the lifespan model (Witmer & Sweeney, 1991), with my own adaptations. The model consists of eight domains of human functioning that contribute to the overall well-being of the individual, which are summarized in Table 3.2.

These eight domains are of course not discrete and are highly interactive with each other. The domains are only separated for the purposes of helping clients to examine areas where they might have strengths or have a need to improve their functioning. Clients should be viewed holistically, with the understanding that all aspects of their lives interact and influence all others. The third section of this book is comprised of chapters that examine each of the wellness domains in some detail.

TABLE 3.2   Eight Domains of the Clinical and Educational Wellness Model

Cognition	Encompasses all of the mental activities of the individual's brain that create consciousness, such as perception, memory, attribution, and appraisal. Example: Ability to purposefully appraise potential stressors.
Emotional Regulation	The ability of an individual to monitor and modify emotions for the purpose of controlling his or her level of arousal. Example: Managing arousal from negative emotions by engaging in an activity such as yoga or through breathing exercises.
Physical Activity and Nutrition	The positive use of exercise and diet to achieve and maintain a healthy body and mind. Example: Eating a well-balanced diet.
Preventative Self-Care	Engaging in health and safety habits that promote mental and physical health. Examples: Yearly physical examinations, wearing seat belts, brushing your teeth.
Spirituality and Meaning	An individual's system of beliefs or values that provide a sense of purpose in life. Example: The belief in an organizing principle or creator of the universe.
Cultural and Environmental Context	The impacts that the setting in time and place in which an individual exists have upon his or her health. For example: Access to healthcare, availability of safe drinking water, beliefs about women's rights.
Social Relationships	The influences of interactions with others on the health of the individual. Example: The ability to draw on and provide tangible or emotional support to/from others.
Creativity	Process of novel problem solving, cognitive flexibility, and creation of purposeful new ways of relating, understanding, and interpreting. Example: The arts, research, experimentation, product development.

References

Granello, P. (2000). Integrating wellness work into mental health private practice. *Journal of Psychotherapy in Independent Practice, 1*(1), 3–16.

Hettler, B. (1980). *Wellness promotion on a university campus.*

Hettler, B. (1986). Strategies for wellness and recreation program development. In F. Leafgren (Ed.), *Developing campus recreation and wellness programs.* San Francisco: Jossey-Bass.

Mareno, N. (2010). *Wellness characteristics and health risk behaviors of young adult university students.* http://www.resourcenter.net/images/snrs/files/sojnr_articles2/Vol10Num04Art05.pdf

Myers, J. E. (2005). *Counseling for wellness: Theory, research, and practice.* American Counseling Association, Alexandria, VA.

Myers, J. E. (2008). *Wellness counseling: The evidence base for practice.* American Counseling Association, Alexandria, VA.

Myers, J. E., & Sweeney, T. J. (2005). The indivisible self: An evidence-based model of wellness (reprint). *Journal of Individual Psychology, 61*(3), 269–279.

Myers, J. E., Sweeney, T. J., & Witmer, J. M. (2000). The wheel of wellness counseling for wellness: A holistic model for treatment planning. *Journal of Counseling & Development, 78*(3), 251–266.

Opatz, J. P. (1986). Stevens Point: A longstanding program for students at a midwestern university. *American Journal of Health Promotion*: Premier Issue, Vol. 1, No. 1, pp. 60–67.

Sweeney, T. J. (2009). *Adlerian counseling and psychotherapy: A practitioner's approach* (5th ed.). New York: Routledge, Taylor, and Francis Group.

Sweeney, T. J., & Witmer, M. J. (1991). Beyond social interest: Striving toward optimum health and wellness. *Individual Psychology, 47*(40), 527–540.

Witmer, M. J. (1985). *Pathways to personal growth.* Muncie, IN: Accelerated Development Inc.

Witmer, M. J., & Sweeney, T. J. (1991). A holistic model for wellness and prevention over the life span. *Journal of Counseling and Development, 71*, 140–148.

Yevchak, A. M., Loeb, S. J., & Fick, D. M. (2008). Promoting cognitive health and vitality: A review of clinical implications. *Geriatric Nursing, 29*(5), 302–310. doi:10.1016/j.gerinurse.2007.10.017

Young, M. E. (2008). *Learning the art of helping: Building blocks and techniques* (4th ed.) Upper Saddle River, NJ: Prentice Hall.

Zimpher, D. G. (1992). Psychosocial treatment of life-threatening disease: A wellness model. *Journal of Counseling & Development, 71*, 203–209.

4 | CREATING GOOD GOALS AND SUSTAINING MOTIVATION: TOOLS FOR LASTING BEHAVIOR CHANGE

Stephen C. Davis

Cat: Where are you going?
Alice: Which way should I go?
Cat: That depends on where you are going.
Alice: I don't know.
Cat: Then it doesn't matter which way you go.

ALICE IN WONDERLAND, BY LEWIS CARROLL

The Cheshire cat from *Alice in Wonderland* was an aloof and often formless being that only added to Alice's vexation as she wandered through the bewildering wonderland. Health and wellness can often feel like wonderlands. Daily, there is a media barrage of both information and marketing that adds more details and nuances to the health and wellness landscape of the United States. It can be overwhelming to think about developing well-being in life as we deal with the demands for our time and attention. Motivation can dwindle quickly when we feel overwhelmed and uncertain about the prospect of changing health habits.

Our goals, especially, may feel aloof and unformed like the Cheshire Cat, disappearing before our eyes. The landscape of health and well-being is so vast that it can feel impossible to pinpoint one goal to work toward. People feel as though they have to use all of this information and address every concern they can, which leads to poorly defined and unachievable goals. As behavior change, motivation, and goal setting are interconnected, poor goal setting can halt our efforts right out of the gate. It becomes very important, then, to start working toward new behaviors by developing effective goals and creating tools for maintaining motivation.

WELLNESS, MOTIVATION, AND GOAL SETTING

Wellness is an approach to living that emphasizes longevity and well-being through habitual behaviors that contribute to the quality of life. Cultivating and maintaining wellness requires active assessment of behavior and goal development. Individuals must be able to accurately perceive the impact of their behaviors and attitudes on their health and wellness. This assessment requires education concerning healthful behaviors and an ability to perceive inner experience. These skills are addressed in other chapters throughout this book (specifically, Chapter 6: Emotional Regulation, and Chapter 9: Preventative Self-Care: Benefits of Modern Medicine).

Assessment creates motivation for change, but motivation must be sustained once action is taken. Discouragement halts motivation and is the biggest impediment to lasting behavior change (Young, 2009). Motivation can be difficult to maintain because our minds and bodies want to maintain homeostasis. Most often we behave a certain way because it is safe, pleasurable, or comfortable. Change is threatening to our minds and bodies, and we have to find ways to persevere in the face of resistance. We have to learn to forestall immediate gratification so that we may establish real and lasting wellness. Resistance may also come from external sources such as families, friends, and the culture at large. Sustained motivation may be difficult in the face of environmental pressures.

Perpetuating wellness requires the establishment of a number of methods for maintaining motivation. These methods may include everyday reminders, regular incentives, or having a mentor or role model. As people explore the ways they can cultivate wellness in their lives, they will also have to explore which motivators work best for them. Motivators come in all shapes and sizes, and what works best for one person may not work well for another. It is important for a person to understand how he or she has successfully changed his or her behavior in the past. This understanding will provide a person with clues as to how he or she can best maintain motivation.

There is one way to help ensure motivation that everyone can do: set good goals. Any time a person sets out to change his or her behavior, he or she should thoughtfully develop good goals. Often, people set out to meet ill-defined goals with no benchmarks for achievement. Establishing good goals will help sustain motivation, as good goals leave no wiggle room. Without alternatives or reasons for avoiding action, goals are achieved more readily. Good goal development makes the paths toward each goal clear and the achievement of the goal obvious. Intentional goal development minimizes the ambiguity and doubt that often dismantle motivation. In this chapter, I will present a number of characteristics that define effective goals. I will also discuss additional ways to help maintain motivation.

DEVELOPING WELLNESS GOALS

The idea of increasing health and wellness may seem overwhelming. Wellness is a paradigm that highlights the importance of creating habits across several domains (see Chapter 3: A Model of Wellness). Addressing each of these domains may seem like an insurmountable task. With effective goal setting, though, the monolith of change is made smaller. Goal setting divides large-scale change into smaller, easier-to-work-toward pieces (Young, 2009). When one domain of wellness is impacted, a ripple effect occurs, and change is seen across multiple domains (Granello, 2012). Thus, working toward a goal that is only a subunit of the larger overall change affects the nature of the overall change as well as the nature of each subgoal.

THE IMPORTANCE OF GOOD GOALS

Wellness is centered on the notion of personal responsibility (Hafen & Hoeger, 1997). Each individual is responsible for taking steps to ensure his or her personal health and well-being. The reality of the world is that many people experience very severe barriers to resources while others experience undue privilege. The wellness paradigm seeks to empower people by calling them to work toward realistic and accessible change in their lives. Goal setting helps form a foundation for personal responsibility and is thus an essential piece of wellness. When individuals begin to form and work toward good goals, they exhibit self-determination and autonomy.

Beyond empowerment, effective goal setting helps identify a number of details important to understanding a person's position along the wellness path. One important function of goals is that they establish a baseline. When a person cannot meet a goal or meets a goal with little difficulty, he or she becomes more aware of his or her skill set. This awareness may lead to feelings of affirmation and identify areas for growth. Knowing his or her skill set and areas for growth will further illuminate how the individual can cultivate personal wellness.

Although it may seem obvious, only clearly defined goals can be achieved. If goals are ambiguous or ill-defined, it is impossible to know when they have been met because no parameters exist to differentiate achievement from nonachievement. Good goal setting combats this issue and is essential because we can only know when to move on to a new endeavor when we have completed the previous endeavor. Achieving a goal can be seen as a challenge to remain ambitious and continually work on wellness. In this way, goals keep individuals from resting on their past achievements and becoming lax in their wellness practices.

In addition to identifying strengths, areas for growth, and new wellness challenges, effective goals make it clear what things must be done to achieve the goals. For example, if a person's goal is to decrease his or her blood pressure to a specific level in a specific amount of time, it is much easier to identify how often the person should exercise, what dietary changes should be made, and which adjunctive interventions should be used (e.g., meditation, yoga, and other stress relief). It is difficult to work toward something when the methods to do so are unclear. Developing goals that have the characteristics outlined later in this chapter makes the steps toward goal achievement obvious.

Beyond identifying skill sets, areas for growth, and achievements, good goals can help increase positive feelings toward the self. Affirmation is an important positive experience that can help sustain motivation. When a goal is met, especially a goal that was difficult to attain, an individual may experience pride and feel empowered. Feeling empowered can lead to taking on new goals and approaching challenges with confidence. An individual's sense of self-efficacy increases each time he or she meets a goal. Through goal attainment, a person may begin to believe that he or she *does* have the ability to make meaningful and lasting changes in his or her life.

SOME THINGS TO KEEP IN MIND

Before I describe the characteristics of good goals, I want to share some ideas that can meaningfully add to the process of goal attainment. These ideas can help create a working mindset that lends itself to maintaining motivation. First, it is okay to design a goal for early success. A victory can add to feelings of self-efficacy and further desire to change. However, people have to be honest about whether they need a victory or a challenge. Working on goals that are not challenging is a sign that the goals may not be meaningful or additive to individual wellness. Be mindful of what is really needed and establish goals accordingly.

Second, individuals should think about how they have met goals in the past. These goals can be related to anything in life, not necessarily health and wellness. Reviewing how a person has achieved goals unrelated to health and wellness may help them get out of rigid thinking patterns. People can identify times when they had to get creative or struggle to complete an academic, professional, or personal project. These memories can serve as motivating proof of a person's ability to make change and supply him or her with ideas for meeting present challenges.

Third, brainstorm different goals or ways of achieving goals without criticizing. Goal setting can be described as a long-term form of problem solving. Creativity is an essential piece of problem solving. Creativity as a characteristic is often measured by describing the fluency (number of ideas) and flexibility (difference from the status quo) of a set of ideas (Hennessey & Amabile, 2010). If a person limits either of these dimensions by giving up on his or her ideas before there is time to reflect on them, he or she is necessarily limiting creative capacity.

The last point is crucial for goal attainment: patience is invaluable. Challenging goals will take time and effort. Without patience, individuals may not be able to withstand the struggles inherent in any attempt to form new behaviors. To help cultivate patience, a person should keep his or her expectations realistic. A person should ask, "Given the circumstances and the amount of effort I am putting into the goal, is the progress I am expecting to make realistic?" Other people can help a person develop patience. Finding other people who have worked toward a similar goal can provide a venue for discussing frustrations and gaining insight.

CHARACTERISTICS OF GOOD GOALS

There are a number of characteristics of good goals. These characteristics include achievable and controllable, believable, measurable, stated in the positive with no alternative, desirable, and growth facilitating. Each characteristic contributes to goal attainment by strengthening commitment and increasing motivation. Individuals can refer back to this list to ensure their goals will meaningfully contribute to the cultivation and maintenance of wellness in their lives.

Reflection 4.1

Before you read about the characteristics of good goals, write down a goal you are working toward currently. Keep that goal in mind as you read through this section.

Achievable and Controllable

Ambition is important to personal development, but goals have to be achievable to contribute to long-term wellness. To be achievable, the demands of the goals have to match the developmental level, skill set, and available resources of the individual. When there is a mismatch between the goal and these factors, it is likely that the goal cannot be reached. Continually working toward unachievable goals can diminish confidence and drain motivation. Achievability is important because achieving goals can increase a person's sense of self-efficacy.

There are multiple ways to ensure a goal is achievable. The first method involves having all of the information needed to make an informed decision. As a person sets goals, he or she should be gathering information regarding the time and money needed to complete each goal. Additionally, he or she should know how much education or training is needed to reach each goal. The demands of each goal must be compatible with the internal and external resources of the individual. When there is a mismatch between these variables, a goal can be broken down into smaller parts. While achieving the subgoals, a person is gathering the skills and other resources needed to meet the original goal.

Similar to the issue of mismatch between goals and resources in the issue of paradoxical goal setting. A person is unlikely to earn a Ph.D., for example, if he or she is unwilling to increase the amount of time spent studying at the library. In this scenario there is a paradox: the person has a stated goal, but is unwilling to do the work needed to make the goal realistic. A person must be honest about what he or she is willing to put into goal attainment. To decrease paradox and mismatch between resources, a person can seek out the help of a professional whose work relates to the nature of his or her goal (e.g., nutritionist for goals about diet; career counselor for goals about career, etc.). Regularly assessing progress can also help ensure that an individual is working toward an achievable goal.

Part of achievability is controllability. For a person to achieve a goal, it has to be within his or her power to remove the barriers preventing achievement. Many barriers can exist, ranging from interpersonal constraints (e.g., your partner may not want you to spend more time at the gym) to cultural constraints (e.g., gender stereotypes) and financial constraints. When developing achievable goals, a person has to be realistic about his or her ability to remove an obstacle. Creativity is very important when developing goals, as some barriers cannot be removed and will require novel solutions and alternatives. An individual may not be able to pay a monthly gym membership, for instance, but he or she can find creative ways to exercise, such as playing sports or using household items to work out.

Believable

Achievability describes external environmental constraints upon goal attainment. Believability describes the internal constraints of the mind upon goal attainment. Numerous factors contribute to a person's perception of whether he or she can attain a goal. Environmental constraints such as cultural expectations or obligations to work and family impact whether a person believes he or she can complete a goal by limiting a person's perception of what he or she can put into the process. A person's belief about him- or herself also impacts goal attainment.

Self-efficacy is a person's tendency to believe he or she can do something. Self-efficacy is important during goal setting, as people with self-efficacy are more likely to commit to a goal (Locke & Latham, 2002). Thus, a cycle exists in which people with high self-efficacy are more committed to a goal, which increases the likelihood the goal will be achieved. In turn, the self-efficacy of the person increases as he or she completes the goal. Increasing believability can be done by ensuring goals are achievable. By setting achievable goals, a foundation of self-efficacy can be formed, which contributes to the attainment of goals across a variety of domains.

Hopelessness severely limits self-efficacy, as people experiencing hopelessness often believe that they cannot affect their circumstances. When people experience hopelessness, they tend to participate in conditional goal setting (Hadley & MacLeod, 2010). Conditional goal setting is a practice in which a person believes he or she will only be happy if he or she achieves certain goals. People who create conditional goals may rigidly pursue those goals based on this belief. The help of a professional counselor may be necessary when an individual exhibits hopelessness and conditional goal setting, as these have been linked to depression and may inhibit actual goal attainment.

Self-efficacy and believability can be increased by breaking goals down into smaller units, similar to the process used to increase the achievability of a goal. As a person attains small goals, he or she can begin to believe that the overall goal is also attainable. Another important way to increase the believability of a goal is for individuals to increase their awareness of the messages they tell themselves regarding their abilities. Individuals often participate in negative self-talk, repeatedly telling themselves that they cannot achieve their goals and that they are to blame for their circumstances (Beck, Rush, Shaw, & Emery, 1979). These thoughts are often automatic. Becoming aware of these thoughts and intentionally stopping the process can halt the decrease in self-efficacy that results. Two methods for halting negative self-talk are identifying evidence contrary to the message of the self-talk and saying the word "stop" aloud when participating in negative self-talk (Erford, Eaves, Bryant, & Young, 2010).

Reflection 4.2

Think of an important goal you have worked toward in the past or are working toward currently. On a piece of paper, create two columns. In the left-hand column, list the negative messages you tell yourself about your ability to achieve this goal. On the right-hand side, develop a countermessage for each negative message. Counters should use the words "I" and "me," should be stated positively in the present tense, and should be realistic (Erford et al. , 2010). The following is an example to guide you through your own exploration of negative self-talk:

Negative Self-Talk	Positive Countermessages
• I will never be able to exercise enough to lose weight.	• I can exercise for 30 minutes four times per week.
• I am just not a creative person. I cannot draw, paint, or write anything.	• I can be creative in my own way in whichever medium I enjoy most.

Now that you have created your list, practice using your counters when you notice negative self-talk. It is likely that the negative self-talk is unfounded and the confirming evidence is minimal or nonexistent. Remember to continually assess whether or not your self-talk is rational.

Measurable

One hallmark of a high-quality goal is measurability. When a goal is measurable, it is easy to answer the questions, "How can a person work toward this goal?" and "Will it be obvious when this goal has been achieved?" Individuals are more likely to commit to a goal and persevere when a method of observing progress is built into the goal (Granello, 2012). Remember that wellness is cultivated when people work toward and achieve behavior change. Because measurability makes it more likely that a person will commit to a goal, creating a measurable goal increases the likelihood of cultivating wellness.

The best way to ensure easy answers to the previously noted questions is to write highly specific goals that address the methods by which the goal will be attained and the benchmark for achievement. Addressing these questions requires that observable behaviors for goal attainment are stated, the frequency of the behaviors is discussed, the method by which progress will be measured is specified, and role of others is made clear. An ambiguous health goal would be "to lose weight." It is not obvious from the way this goal is written what steps a person would take to achieve it and how the person would know the goal was achieved. Nothing about the goal is measurable. Losing one pound every week for 10 weeks (a total of 10 pounds) by doing cardiovascular exercise on Monday, Wednesday, Friday, and Saturday is a much more specific and measurable goal.

The revised weight-loss goal is written in a way that outlines an obvious method for tracking weight loss (recording weight lost each week). Tracking progress is an important function of the measurability characteristic. Not only is it necessary for knowing when the goal has been attained, but it can sustain motivation. As a person works toward a goal, he or she is likely to feel encouraged if progress is observed. This progress is an indication that the goal is attainable and the individual does have the power to meet the goal. Tracking progress provides a means by which believability can be increased.

Stated in the Positive and with No Alternative

When people talk about changing behavior, it is not uncommon to hear the axiom "Old habits die hard." This is such a popular saying because it has an air of truth around it. People develop behaviors that make them feel safe and comfortable. Our minds and bodies resist changing those behaviors. When approaching goal development, it is important to keep this resistance in mind. It will be necessary to develop goals that seek to increase a behavior or add a new behavior. Goals that only seek to *stop* a behavior will be ineffective.

The mechanism at work in this characteristic is called *reciprocal inhibition*, the inability to think or behave in two opposite ways at the same time (Wolpe, 1968). Incorporated into this notion is the idea that thinking about doing something, smoking for example, and thinking about not doing something mentally expose a person to the behavior equally as often. Here is an exercise to illustrate this point. First, think of a pink dog. Reflect on how odd it is to see a dog with pink fur walking down the sidewalk. Now, do not to think of the pink dog at all. My guess is that you are still thinking of the pink dog. Think about the pink dog again for a moment or two. Now think of a giant green bear. I assume your imagination turned to the green bear and away from the pink dog.

An effective goal using this characteristic would be to squeeze a stress ball when you desire a cigarette. The goal is written in a way that moves attention from cigarettes to the stress ball. The goal also describes a behavior that is incompatible with smoking. Squeezing a stress ball continuously makes it very hard to hold a cigarette in hand. This goal is also stated with no alternative. People often look for outs when they develop their goals, such as making gym attendance conditional on the weather. If a person has an escape route, he or she will use it the minute he or she begins to experience the normal discomfort involved with creating new habits.

Desirable

I mentioned throughout this chapter the importance of motivation during goal attainment. Goal setting is only effective as a means to a wellness end. Goal setting in itself is not enough to cultivate wellness. Therefore, individuals have to be able to persevere and delay gratification to reap the benefits of effective goal setting. One of the most effective ways to ensure sustained motivation is to develop personally desirable goals. There are many sources of expectations for individuals in the world—families and loved ones, coworkers and employers, and educators all have ideas for what people should be working toward. However prominent these sources of expectations are, individuals may feel overwhelmed when they work toward goals out of line with their personal motivations (Ward & Reuter, 2011).

Desirability is related to a concept known as *intrinsic motivation*. Intrinsic motivation arises from a person's interest in and enjoyment of a behavior in its own right, without thought of reward (Eccles & Wigfield, 2002). Intrinsic motivation can be used to increase commitment to difficult goals. When writing specific goals, a person can include strategies and behaviors for goal attainment for which he or she is intrinsically motivated. For example, a person who wishes to lose weight may experience little or no motivation for running on a treadmill. However, this person may be intrinsically motivated to compete with others and may find sports to be a great match between his or her desired goal and intrinsic motivation.

Intrinsic motivation appears to be linked to an experience known as *flow* (Eccles & Wigfield, 2002), in which an individual's mood is slightly elevated, attention is focused on the task at hand, and time seems to move quickly and go unnoticed (Funder, 2007). The experience of flow can be rewarding and may make the work of goal attainment feel less daunting. When an individual develops goals, he or she should reflect on past experiences of flow. Individuals should seek to incorporate behaviors that lead to the flow experience into their goal statements. This incorporation will enhance commitment, sustain motivation, and perhaps lead to enjoyment.

It is important for individuals to be aware of whether or not a goal is meaningful to them. Knowing this can help clarify if the goal is the individual's goal or the goal of another person. The following questions have been adapted from Young (2009) and the answers can be used to help determine the personal significance of a goal:

- How likely am I to work on this goal consistently?
- How important is this to me?
- What difference would it make if I accomplished this goal?
- Will I make excuses to avoid accomplishing this goal?
- Is this my goal, or does someone else want me to work on this?

Individuals take on the goals of others for many reasons. At times, people are made to believe others know best. In some situations, another person may be in a position of authority and we cannot avoid working toward his or her goals (this is most likely to occur in the workplace). When developing good goals, it is important to note where these varying circumstances occur and how they impact commitment and motivation.

Growth Facilitating

The last characteristic of effective goals is that they are growth facilitating. A central premise of wellness is that humans have within in them the ability to cultivate well-being and longevity in their lives, provided they create meaningful goals toward these ends (Granello, 2012). Goals that increase behaviors that can damage mental and physical health do not move people in a wellness direction. Goals of this nature detract from meaningful involvement with the world.

In order for goals to be growth facilitating, they will need to be consistent with an individual's personal set of values. As values are relative to cultures and individuals, a goal that is growth facilitating for one person will not necessarily be growth facilitating for another. When goals are consistent with values, a person is more likely to maintain commitment toward goal attainment (Davis, Robbins Eshelman, & McKay, 2008). Additionally, if a person is working toward a number of goals, optimal growth can be facilitated by ensuring that the goals are balanced across a number of wellness domains and life activities. A person can experience stress when goals are unbalanced (Davis et al., 2008), which detracts from motivation.

Whether or not a goal is growth facilitating will not always be obvious. Certainly, the goal of eating more saturated fat is not growth facilitating. Less clear are the answers to questions about whether or not working toward a specific degree or job is growth facilitating. This determination will require assessing personal strengths, motivations, and desired outcomes. Often, people work toward non-growth-facilitating goals when compelled by external forces such as families or partners. Other times, people feel overwhelmed and participate in destructive behaviors as a way of coping. To cultivate wellness, it will be necessary to honestly examine whether or not a goal is growth facilitating.

S.M.A.R.T. Goals

Goal setting is a constant process, and the characteristics described thus far are nuanced. The information in the previous sections may feel overwhelming or inefficient for short-term, everyday goal development. The S.M.A.R.T. acronym used here (adapted from Doran, 1981), however, is simple to remember and can quickly be referenced when developing short-term, day-to-day goals.

- **S**imple: Addresses one specific area for change; avoids addressing multilevel, systemic changes.
- **M**easurable: Outlines how the goal will be attained and specifies methods for measuring progress.
- **A**chievable: Considering available resources and barriers to achievement, this goal can be reached.
- **R**elevant: The goal is desired by the person who will work toward it. Additionally, this goal addresses holistic health concerns relevant to the person's well-being and longevity.
- **T**imely: The goal can be achieved in a relatively short amount of time. Emphasizes the need for subgoals when working toward long-term behavior change.

Reflection 4.3

Look at the goal you wrote down at the beginning of the chapter. How can you change that goal to include the characteristics represented by S.M.A.R.T.? Do you react differently to your goal after changing it? Does it seem more attainable now?

SUSTAINING MOTIVATION

Motivation describes the factors that lead an individual to initiate and direct behavior (Petri, 1989). Individuals have motives for avoiding behavior and exhibiting behavior with a certain level of intensity. These motives differ from person to person and are the result of the experience of having an inner life (the mind) and a life in relationship to other individuals, institutions, and cultures. Understanding motivation and how it can be sustained requires that a person examine the forces at work at each level of his or her experience. Once an awareness of the impact of these levels of experience has been developed, motivational strategies can be crafted to increase the frequency and intensity of behavior or alter the direction of behavior. Direction of behavior can be thought of as the means by which behavior satisfies motivation. For example, a person who experiences relief from anxiety when he or she eats would direct his or her behavior toward food when he or she is nervous.

INTRAPERSONAL STRATEGIES FOR SUSTAINING MOTIVATION

A person's intrapersonal experience is comprised of learning, ideals, values, emotions, and thoughts. Each of these constructs is impacted by a person's awareness of his or her environment. Through the course of everyday life, individuals are constantly observing and reacting to their environments. Consequently, the intrapersonal experience of any individual is dynamic and may change as time goes on. Some constructs, such as emotions and thoughts, are reactive and may change regularly. Other constructs, such as ideals and values, are more static. These constructs often form the foundation of a person's personality.

Awareness and Learning

All motivation begins with awareness (Petri, 1989). Motivation to meet homeostatic needs such as eating and drinking only comes with awareness of hunger or thirst. Similarly, motivation to work toward wellness goals only comes with an awareness of how an individual can benefit from goal attainment. The Transtheoretical Model of Change suggests five stages that people progress through when making a change (Prochaska & Diclemente, 1983). The first stage, precontemplation, occurs when individuals have no awareness of the need for change, and must be worked through before change can occur.

Awareness, and thus motivation, can be developed through learning. This is the assumption on which major health initiatives are founded (O'Donnell, 2005). Individuals interested in cultivating personal wellness should seek credible sources on health and wellness. These sources can include physicians, health-oriented individuals, and other health professionals, as well as continuing education on health and wellness. Additionally, most newspapers provide daily information regarding health and wellness. The National Institute of Health publishes wellness guidelines developed in accordance with research regarding health and wellness.

Seeking out credible information can form the initial motivation for change, but it can also sustain motivation once a person begins working toward a goal. Initially, wellness goals may be described as performance goals. Performance goals are worked toward in a way that only focuses on the outcome. Generally, the standard is established by an entity outside of the person working toward the goal. Research shows that performance goals are poorly correlated with intrinsic motivation (Elliot & Harackiewicz, 1994). As stated previously, intrinsic motivation is the motivation to do something for the enjoyment of doing it. Intrinsic motivation may facilitate goal attainment more readily than extrinsic motivation by facilitating maximal effort during goal attainment.

Extrinsic motivation is poorly correlated with performance goals, but highly correlated with mastery goals. Mastery goals are intended to lead to a high level of ability. The unit of measurement is related to the way in which a behavior is performed. For example, a performance goal related to running may be to run three miles. A mastery goal related to running may not use distance as the standard for goal attainment, but rather running form. Mastery of an activity or behavior can be achieved through continuous learning. When an individual learns with an aim toward mastery, motivation may increase, as the goal is no longer to just perform an activity. Rather, the goal is to perform the goal with intention and precision. In this way, the behaviors needed for goal attainment may become less monotonous and more interesting.

Motivation and Emotions

Emotions are a central experience to everyday life. Individuals experience emotions in reaction to a range of environmental changes. In this way, emotions serve to increase the evolutionary fitness of humans (Lazarus, 1994). Emotions draw a person's focus to changes in the environment that may be threatening. Increased awareness and focus on an environmental threat allows for a reaction that decreases the danger of the threat. Emotions can arouse or under-arouse an individual (Averill, 1997). Shame, for example, motivates people to hide from the shame-inducing situation (Tangney & Dearing, 2002) and may be considered under-arousing, as the person is not motivated to make a change. Anger, however, may be considered arousing, as it often motivates people to seek reparation for a perceived insult (Lazarus, 1994). Thus, emotions can contribute to or detract from motivation for goal attainment.

Emotions contribute to motivation when an emotional experience energizes a person to direct behavior toward goal attainment. As a person gathers information related to health and wellness, he or she may have cognitive and emotional responses. An older man who smokes make react with fear when he learns of a statistic that suggests men his age who smoke are at increased risk of heart attack. The older man's fear is an emotional reaction that motivates him to stop smoking. As the intensity of emotional reactions increases, the motivational power of the reaction increases. If the older man just mentioned had lost his own father to heart attack, for instance, he may feel remorse and empathy for his own children in addition to fear. The combination of these strong emotions may increase his motivation to make a change.

Emotions can also inhibit motivation. As mentioned, people tend to hide from the sources of their shame. By doing so, people lose the opportunity to change the situation that perpetuates their shame. Similar scenarios could be envisioned regarding wellness. An individual experiencing depression may desire to increase his or her wellness by seeking treatment from a mental health professional. However, the intense sadness and feelings of worthlessness associated with depression may inhibit his or her motivation to contact a professional. In some instances, the same emotion may contribute to motivation in one scenario and detract from motivation in another. The scenario in the previous paragraph described how fear might motivate an individual to work toward a wellness goal. However, fear in another context may diminish motivation. A person wishing to cultivate health through an exercise regimen may fear hurting him- or herself, and thus lose the motivation to exercise.

This idea highlights an important point when considering strategies for increasing motivation. Mindful awareness of emotional states can contribute to emotion regulation and sustained motivation. Intense emotions can distract a person from everyday activities. A person can be distracted to the point that the emotional dysregulation could be considered debilitating. The converse of this experience, inhibiting emotions to the point that they lose all motivation value, can also be debilitating. Emotion regulation is a strategy for positively managing the impact of emotions on a person's life, including his or her motivation (Linehan, 1993).

Linehan (1993) suggests a seven-part process for emotional regulation.

1. *Identify and Label Emotion*: Use knowledge of the situation that leads to the emotion, the personal interpretation of the event, the bodily sensations accompanying the emotion, and the impact of the emotion on functioning to accurately label the emotion.
2. *Identify Barriers to Emotional Change*: Increased awareness of how a person benefits from an emotional experience (functions and reinforcers) can give insight into strategies for regulation.
3. *Reduce Vulnerability to Intense Emotion*: Identification of the life stressors (e.g., little sleep, sickness) that contribute to emotional dysregulation provides clues for change.
4. *Increase Positive Emotions*: Increasing the number and awareness of positive events can help increase emotion regulation.
5. *Increase Mindfulness to Current Emotion*: Experiencing emotions without judging them or inhibiting them decreases secondary emotions (such as being ashamed for being afraid), which can lead to less intense emotional experiences.
6. *Take Opposite Action*: Behaving in a way contrary to an emotion can lead to the experience of the opposite emotion. For example, if a person is ashamed of his or her artistic talent, he or she may feel motivated to never display pieces of art. However, if the person displays his or her works, he or she is open to the chance of feeling pride.
7. *Increase Ability to Tolerate Distress*: Strong emotions can cause distress. When people are unable to manage the distress associated with strong emotion, they may act impulsively. Goal attainment requires intention and design. Impulsive behavior may detract from ultimate goal attainment.

These seven steps outline a process for managing negative and often under-arousing emotions that can detract from motivation. By practicing the steps, a person can diminish the distracting nature of intense emotions. This can lead to increased focus, sustained motivation, and goal attainment. In addition to regulating the experience of negative emotions related to wellness goals, individuals can increase the positive emotions relevant to goal-directed behavior.

Csikszentmihalyi (1996) outlined a number of characteristics research participants used to describe experiences that were enjoyable to them. Following are some of these characteristics with suggestions for their application to increasing motivation:

1. *Clear goals at every step with no contrary demands*: To increase motivation, write clear goals with no contrary language. Individuals should work toward one end so that energy and resources are not misspent.
2. *There is a balance between challenges and skills*: Motivation can be increased by ensuring that a goal is challenging enough to be novel and sustain interest while providing opportunity for the use of skills already acquired. This opportunity adds to a person's self-efficacy and prevents feelings of being overwhelmed and incapable.
3. *Intention and focus are present during action*: Develop strategies for goal attainment that require continued engagement in the behaviors being performed. One method for ensuring focus is to work toward mastery goals that focus on *how* the behavior is being executed, not merely *what* is being worked toward.
4. *No worry of failure*: Patience allows a person to work toward a goal with the belief that there is time for work. When thoughts of failure are diminished, increased attention can be given to goal attainment.

Establishing strategies for attaining wellness goals that lend themselves to these characteristics may increase the enjoyment derived from goal attainment. In turn, enjoyment may contribute to sustained motivation.

INTERPERSONAL STRATEGIES FOR SUSTAINING MOTIVATION

The interpersonal experience of an individual is comprised of his or her interactions with other people. There are a number of levels of interpersonal connection that impact wellness. These levels include the family, the community, and the culture (Bronfenbrenner, 1979). More is said about the impact of culture on wellness in Chapter 11: Cultural and Environmental Aspects of Wellness. Just as intrapersonal experiences can be used to sustain motivation, interpersonal strategies can be used to cultivate motivation. These strategies rely heavily on the human desire for connection with and affirmation from other people.

Role Models

Observational learning is the process by which humans and other animals learn by studying the behaviors of others and the resultant consequences (Funder, 2007). Role models provide sources for observational learning by exhibiting behaviors relevant to goal attainment. A role model can be a person who exhibits behaviors useful for goal attainment (Funder, 2007), or an individual whose behavior does not lead to goal attainment. In both cases, a person can learn the behaviors that impact achievement. Learning from a role model sustains motivation by decreasing anxiety and increasing ability to achieve.

Role models can function beyond observational learning, though. Role models can also provide direct instruction and immediate feedback for behaviors. The information related to health and wellness is abundant and can be overwhelming. Individuals may feel as if they do not know where to begin with their wellness goals because of the number of available facts, figures, and opinions related to health and wellness. Having a role model who can provide direct instruction can help minimize the anxiety associated with working through health and wellness information. Additionally, the feedback given by role models is important for gauging progress. This feedback may be especially important when working toward mastery goals that require a level of technique for completing.

Positive role models can help strengthen support networks. In some instances, a role model may be an individual who has worked through similar challenges. As such, role models may provide empathy and support for individuals struggling to create lasting behavior changes. Additionally, role models may have access to resources related to goal attainment. A role model for a person working to develop his or her drawing ability may know of drawing classes open to the public. In this way, role models are often gateways to further education relevant to goal attainment.

Incentivizing

Incentivizing relies on the use of reinforcers when goals are met or behaviors are exhibited. Reinforcement can be positive or negative. *Positive reinforcers* involve the application of a desired stimulus as a response to behavior. *Negative reinforcers* involve removing unpleasant stimuli when desired behavior is enacted. Reinforcers are often used by interested parties to elicit desired behaviors from individuals—for example, students and employees are frequently given incentives for accomplishing tasks and meeting certain standards. Individuals can also create reinforcers to give themselves when goals are met or behaviors are enacted.

Incentivizing reinforcers can be built into any step of the goal-attainment process. An individual whose goal is to lose 20 pounds by going to the gym four times per week could sustain motivation by incentivizing each trip to the gym. The individual could also give him- or herself an incentive for every five pounds lost. The desirability of the incentive should correlate with the difficulty of the behavior or goal achieved. The person going to the gym four times a week may incentivize by watching one episode of a favorite TV show every time he or she goes to the gym, or by going on a vacation when the goal is met.

Incentives sustain motivation by providing something to look forward to when performing difficult tasks. They are a celebration of accomplishment. It is important, though, to ensure that incentives are in line with wellness goals (Hafen & Hoeger, 1997). Incompatible incentives, such as incentivizing exercise with doughnuts, ultimately hinder goal attainment. Incentives can add to wellness while helping sustain motivation.

CONCLUSION

Individuals have a responsibility to maintain their personal wellness. However, goal attainment can be difficult and requires perseverance. The cornerstone of perseverance and motivation is effective goal setting. Effective goals should be achievable and controllable, believable, measurable, stated in the positive with no alternative, desirable, and growth facilitating.

Motivation can be sustained using additional strategies such as learning techniques of emotion regulation, enhancing activity enjoyment, using a role model, and incentivizing. Implementing these strategies during goal attainment increases the likelihood of lasting behavior change and the cultivation of wellness.

References

Averill, J. R. (1997). The emotions: An integrative account. In R. Hogan, J. Johnson, & S. Briggs (Eds.), *Handbook of personality psychology* (pp. 513–541). San Diego: Academic Press.

Beck, A. T., Rush, A. J., Shaw, B. F., & Emery, G. (1979). *Cognitive therapy of depression.* New York: The Guilford Press.

Bronfenbrenner, U. (1979). *The ecology of human development: Experiments by nature and design.* Cambridge, MA: Harvard University Press.

Csikszentmihalyi, M. (1996). *Creativity: Flow and the psychology of discovery and invention.* New York: HarperCollins.

Davis, M., Robbins Eshelman, E., McKay M., (2008). *The relaxation and stress reduction workbook.* Oakland, CA: New Harbinger Publications.

Doran, G. T. (1981). There's a S.M.A.R.T. way to write management's goals and objectives. *Management Review, 70*(11), 35.

Eccles, J. S., & Wigfield, A. (2002). Motivational beliefs, values, and goals. *Annual Review of Psychology, 53,* 109–132.

Elliot, A. J., & Harackiewicz, J. M. (1994). Goal setting, achievement orientation, and intrinsic motivation: A mediational analysis. *Journal of Personality and Social Psychology, 66*(5), 968–980. doi: 10.1037/0022-3514.66.5.968

Erford, B. T., Eaves, S. H., Bryant, E. M., & Young, K. A. (2010). *35 techniques every counselor should know.* Upper Saddle River, NJ: Pearson.

Funder, D. C. (2007). *The personality puzzle.* New York: W. W. Norton & Company.

Granello, P. F. (2012). *Wellness counseling.* Upper Saddle River, NJ: Pearson.

Hadley, S. A., & MacLeod, A. K. (2010). Conditional goal-setting, personal goals, and hopelessness about the future. *Cognition & Emotion, 24*(7), 1191–1198.

Hafen, B. Q., & Hoeger, W. W. K., (1997). *Wellness: Guidelines for a healthy lifestyle.*

Hennessey, B. A., & Amabile, T. M. (2010). Creativity. *Annual Review of Psychology, 61,* 569–598. doi: 10.1146/annurev.psych.093008.100416

Lazarus, R. S. (1994). *Emotion and adaptation.* New York: Oxford University Press.

Linehan, M. M. (1993). *Cognitive-behavioral treatment of borderline personality disorder.* New York: The Guilford Press

Locke, E. A., & Latham, G. P. (2002). Building a practically useful theory of goal setting and task motivation: A 35-year odyssey. *American Psychologist, 57*(9), 705–717.

O'Donnell, M. P. (2005). A simple framework to describe what works best: Improving awareness, enhancing motivation, building skills, and providing opportunity. *American Journal of Health Promotion, 20*(1), 1–6.

Petri, H. L. (1989) *Motivation: Theory and research.* Belmont, CA: Wadsworth Publishing.

Prochaska, J. O., & DiClemente, C. C. (1983). Stages and processes of self-change of smoking: Toward an integrative model of change. *Journal of Consulting and Clinical Psychology, 51*(3), 390–395. doi: 10.1037/0022-006X.51.3.390

Tangney, J. P., & Dearing, R. L. (2002). *Shame and guilt.* New York: The Guilford Press.

Ward, C. C., & Reuter, T. (2011). *Strength-centered counseling: Integrating postmodern approaches and skills with practice.* Thousand Oaks, CA: Sage.

Wolpe, J. (1968). Psychotherapy by reciprocal inhibition. *Conditioned Reflex: A Pavlovian Journal of Research and Therapy, 3*(4), 234–240.

Young, M. E. (2009). *Learning the art of helping: Building blocks and techniques.* Upper Saddle River, NJ: Pearson

5 | COGNITION: RULES FOR REALITY

Paul F. Granello

What we think, we become.

BUDDHA, HINDU PRINCE GAUTAMA SIDDHARTHA,
THE FOUNDER OF BUDDHISM, 563–483 BC

Cognition can be defined to encompass all those brain activities that comprise an individual's ability to process information from and act in the environment (Waldstein & Elias, 2003). The word *cognition* is often used as an umbrella term for all of the processes the brain performs (including attention, perception, memory, association, and language skills).

Each cognitive process, or "module," has evolved to perform a specific task, such as facial recognition or the perception of emotions in others. When these cognitive modules work in conjunction with other cognitive modules, we can accurately perceive and function in our environment. Almost all of these cognitive processes work without our awareness of them, and in fact work so well together that the seamless experience we call the "mind" or "consciousness" is created. Perhaps it is because our lived experience is of one unified mind that we forget there are really many modules making up a mind. In fact, we have over 100 billion neurons in our brains that are organized into sophisticated networks (cognitive modules), each charged with performing a cognitive process that we need to survive.

The idea that "mind" (cognitive function) and body are somehow separate is fundamentally biologically inaccurate. The activities of the brain directly affect the body and, conversely, the systemic health of the body impacts the functioning of the brain (Day, McGuire, & Anderson, 2009). Research has demonstrated that individuals with a cognitive impairment, such as dementia, suffer from over double the number of chronic health conditions that same-aged individuals without dementia suffer (Day et al., 2009). For some time now, healthcare providers have readily acknowledged that systemic diseases (e.g., cancer and cardiovascular, pulmonary, renal, and hepatic diseases) can cause physiological damage to the brain and have dramatic effects on cognitive function (Waldstein & Elias, 2003). These alterations have negative impacts on cognition, perceptions of well-being, mood, and even on the performance of the basic activities of everyday life.

The majority of people today would accept that those individuals afflicted with chronic illnesses may experience significant psychological impacts. For example, we would think it strange if someone who was recently diagnosed with cancer did not experience some anxiety, anger, sadness, or depression. Yet, historically, healthcare providers have had more difficulty in accepting that the cognitive activities of the brain can directly impact our physical health. Being unable to measure brain activity made the workings of the brain seem somehow unrelated, special, or different from other biological processes we could more readily observe.

At present, however, with the advent of new brain-scanning technologies such as functional magnetic resonance imaging (fMRI) and positron emission tomography (PET), it has become much easier to observe the brain at work. Brain-imaging technologies have now made it possible to directly link brain activity to physiological changes in the body, such as secretion of stress response hormones (cortisol), immune cell mobilization, blood pressure, skin conductance, oxytocin production, and many more.

In addition to our knowledge gained through brain-imaging technologies, better longitudinal health research is uncovering the long-term effects of our cognitive functioning on our longevity and quality of life (Waldstein & Elias, 2003). Research has supported the idea that certain stable patterns of cognition that individuals utilize over the lifespan have significant impacts on individual health. Hostility, optimism (Alloy, Abramson, & Chiara, 2000), and realistic thinking styles have all been shown to relate to health status (Dickerhoof, 2007; Zautra, Davis, & Smith, 2004).

At present, therefore, there exists a rapidly growing body of research that has demonstrated significant links between our cognitive activities and our wellness (Brosschot, Gerin, & Thayer, 2006; Cordova, Cunningham, Carlson, & Andrykowski, 2001; Crosby, 1996; Dickerhoof, 2007; Hevey, 2005; Juster, McEwen, & Lupien, 2009; Marcus, Gurley, Marchi, & Bauer, 2007; Nachev, 2006). In this chapter we will look first at the biological underpinnings of our cognitive functioning. Next, we will look at the significant impacts on our cognition made by the social nature of our lives. Last, we will share some examples of techniques for developing cognitive flexibility.

COGNITION AND WELLNESS: BIOLOGICAL UNDERPINNINGS

Genetic Parameters

All of us are born with a defined genetic inheritance from our parents. Just as our predisposition for many diseases, such as cancer, heart disease, and schizophrenia, are genetically based, so too our genetics also significantly impact our cognitive abilities. After all, it is our DNA that contains the sequences of genes that are responsible for organizing the cells that constitute our brains. In fact, it is currently thought that almost two-thirds of the genes in the human genome are related to guiding brain function (Petrella, Mattay, & Doraiswamy, 2008).

The basic cognitive foundations (as used here, the term *cognitive* includes everything the brain does, including thoughts and emotions) of our personalities are set by our genetic inheritance. Genes are thought to establish "set-points" for many of our personality traits. A set-point is the stable point around which a trait varies over an extended period of time (Carr, 2004). Monozygotic twin studies have shown that there is up to a 50 percent genetic contribution to individuals' sense of well-being, life satisfaction, and happiness. Our genes, then, establish the baseline biological parameters of our cognitive capacities and our stable cognitive patterns (personality traits) (Carr, 2004). Generally, it can be said that some of us are born to be more "cognitively well" than others. Another way of saying this is that some of us are born with a genetic inheritance that predisposes us to think and feel in ways that will contribute to improved health outcomes. So in a very fundamental way, our genes influence our health from the very start of our lives.

Biogenic Principles of Cognition

Cognition, like any other biological function, has evolved through natural selection in such a way as to enhance the survival of the individual and ultimately the reproduction the species. In this light, healthy cognition can be viewed as enhancing our well-being by helping us to accurately perceive, construct, process, interpret, and behave in advantageous ways. Conversely, when our cognitive processes are compromised (such as when an individual has dementia or a psychotic disorder), we may experience problems in relating to the world around us and ultimately suffer harmful impacts on our well-being.

One way to organize our thinking about the advantageous contributions of cognitive processes to our wellness is to employ a set of biogenic principles. *Biogenic* simply means biologically derived. Biogenic principles are broad rules that illustrate how cognitive processes help us to meet a biological need. Used here, they are simply rules for simplifying and illustrating the very complex relationship between our cognitive processes and our well-being.

Four biogenic principles about cognition are illustrated in the following discussion. Each principle is briefly explained and then examples of how cognitive processes might relate to that principle are given. It is hoped that the reader will understand that human cognition has evolved to help us navigate our world in ways that can preserve and enhance our health.

BIOGENIC PRINCIPLE 1: CONTROL: *Cognition directly or indirectly modulates the physio–chemical-electrical processes that constitute an organism.*

Explanation: Presently, we understand that the brain communicates with the major organs of the body in three ways. The first is through nerve impulses sent down the spinal cord out to the peripheral nervous system. Similarly, a stimulus (light, sound, temperature, etc.) from the environment is converted into nerve impulses and is sent to the brain. The second channel of brain and body communication is chemical, which occurs through hormones released into the bloodstream by the pituitary gland (sometimes called the master gland), which is located on the underside of the brain. Pituitary hormones, such as cortisol, act on the organs of the body, regulating their activities. The third way the brain communicates with the body is through the production of small proteins, called neuropeptides, which are also distributed via the bloodstream (Pert, 1997). Through these channels of communication the brain controls all bodily functions from voluntary muscle movement, to organ function, and even perhaps regulation of specific cells.

Example: The stress response, or as it is sometimes called our "fight-or-flight" response, is our mind/body's adaptation to a perceived danger (stressor) in the environment. The stress response produces significant biochemical changes in all bodily systems, allowing us to either fight off a potential threat or to flee to some safe location. The chemical state within our bodies created by chronic stress has been documented to relate to the acquisition of many diseases (Brosschot et al., 2006; Juster et al., 2009). Richard Lazarus, in his book *Emotion & Adaptation* (1994), proposes two critical cognitive processes for regulating the stress response, which he calls "appraisals." The first of these, or the primary appraisal, takes place when the organism (in this case us) perceives some event in the environment. The individual must decide if the event is a threat that requires a response. This first cognitive appraisal activates the stress response system. The second cognitive appraisal takes place once a potential threat has been perceived and involves the individual determining if he or she can cope with the threat. If, due to specific skills, prior experience, or other factors, the threat can be successfully coped with by the individual, then the severity of the stress response is reduced. The cognitive processes of primary and secondary appraisal are key components of the stress response that directly modifies our bodies' biochemistry. It would seem that our thoughts do affect our bodies!

BIOGENIC PRINCIPLE 2: VALANCE: *Relative to the organism's needs and/or experience, different properties of the environment will be invested with different degrees of significance, both positive and negative.*

Explanation: We learn to discriminate those properties (people, things, situations) in the environment that are positively reinforcing, neutral, or punishing. We develop "beliefs" (schemas, frames, constructs), which are stable ways of interpreting information from the world concerning ourselves, others, and the environment. A belief can be defined as representing a specific state of things or interpretation of reality on which the individual bases action; that is, a belief is considered to have predictive reliability for planning and performing further actions (Paglieri, 2003). We therefore can use our stored beliefs about the reality of the world to inform ourselves on how to behave in similar circumstances.

Example: One example of how our exposure to different learning experiences can affect our wellness might be the way our parents taught us about the importance of health. If, for example, we were strongly encouraged to be healthy by our parents as children and received positive reinforcement for those behaviors considered healthy, it is then likely we will develop a set of stable beliefs about health. Because of these beliefs, we will likely emphasize the importance of eating fruits and vegetables, having a regular bed time, brushing our teeth regularly, and generally avoiding unhealthy behaviors.

In relation to wellness, the health beliefs of individuals have been widely studied. Health beliefs are thought to be very important for influencing behavior concerning preventative healthcare, perception of health risks, and help-seeking behavior (Hevey, 2005; Lawton, Conner, & Parker, 2007; Patterson, 2001; Shumaker, Ockene, & Riekert, 2009).

BIOGENIC PRINCIPLE 3: JUDGMENT: *Cognition relates to the (more or less) continuous assessment of system needs relative to prevailing circumstances, the potential for interaction, and whether the current interaction is working or not.*

Explanation: In order to survive and thrive, we are constantly monitoring our own needs (food, belonging, security, etc.) and evaluating our ability to meet those needs in the environment (physical and social). Humans therefore have evolved executive cognitive modules that help organize and evaluate how well other cognitive modules are performing. This ability to think about our own thinking is known as **metacognition**.

Metacognitive modules monitor how well we are doing in achieving our goals. A goal may be defined as an anticipatory representation of reality that has the power of driving an individual's behavior; that is, the person is willing to behave in such a way as to act to modify the state of his or her beliefs or the world according to his or her anticipatory representation. It is important to note that both beliefs and goals may vary in importance. Namely, the strength of our beliefs and the perceived value of our goals may vary throughout our lives. In general, we would expect rational people to act in relation to their goals, on the basis of their beliefs (Paglieri, 2003). It seems matter of fact, therefore, to state that people are likely to act on beliefs they hold strongly in relation to goals they value greatly.

Example: Attribution is a cognitive process that assigns causality to events. Attribution theory (Weiner, 1980, 1992) emphasizes the idea that individuals are strongly motivated by the pleasant outcome of being able to feel good about themselves. It emphasizes that the individual's current self-perceptions will strongly influence interpretation of the success or failure of current efforts, and hence the individual's future tendency to perform these same behaviors.

According to attribution theory, the explanatory styles that people tend to make to justify successes or failures can be analyzed in terms of three sets of characteristics:

- First, the cause of the success or failure may be *internal* or *external*. Individuals may believe that the factors producing success or failure have their origins within themselves or they may believe that factors originate outside themselves in the environment.
- Second, the cause of the success or failure may be either *stable* or *unstable*. If individuals attribute a cause as stable, then the outcome is likely to be the same on a later occasion. If the cause for success or failure is unstable, then the outcome is likely to be the same on a later occasion.
- Third, the factors related to success or failure can either be global or specific. Global attributions indicate that the individual believes the same results will occur across a wide variety of circumstances. Specific attribution indicates that a factor will only apply to a circumstance with very similar characteristics.

An important assumption of attribution theory is that people will interpret their environments in such a way as to maintain a positive self-image. That is, they will *attribute* their successes or failures to factors that will enable them to feel as good as possible about themselves. In general, this means that when individuals succeed at a task, they are likely to want to attribute this success to their own efforts or abilities (internal); but when they fail, they will want to attribute their failure to factors over which they have no control, such as bad teaching or bad luck (external).

Explanatory style shows us that two people can experience the same event and have significantly different interpretations of it based on their style of cognitive processing about that event. Further, explanatory styles have been linked to perceptions of well-being, productivity, job turnover, and self-esteem (Proudfoot, Corr, Guest, & Dunn, 2009).

BIOGENIC PRINCIPLE 4: RANDOMNESS REDUCTION: *Cognition is an important mechanism by which biological systems reduce and modulate the influence of random perturbations on their functioning and are, thereby, robust to perturbation.*

Explanation: Cognitive processes for succeeding in the environment become ingrained in us. The term **schema** is often used to define a series of cognitive processes that have been grouped together to form a unit. Schemas are employed to help us quickly assess and cope with the environment. Further, they do not immediately change or become discarded when a new problem presents itself. For example, when a schema for perceiving an individual is formed many times, it is generalized to all individuals who might share some characteristic with the original individual—this is how stereotypes arise. Also, when a problem-solving strategy is learned in one context, that same strategy schema may be generalized or "tried out" in other contexts. It may be more efficient to draw upon our already learned cognitive processes and behavioral repertoire than to continuously create new strategies for each experience we encounter.

However, sometimes people can be very stubborn about their opinions (beliefs, schemas) despite significant evidence that those opinions are wrong or inaccurate. **Cognitive dissonance** is a term that is often used to describe a confused or anxious state in which a schema is being challenged by new information. If the cognitive dissonance becomes great enough, such that the individual can no longer rely on the accuracy of the schema (its predictive utility to assist in

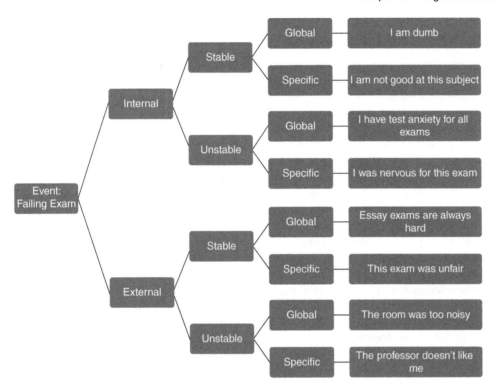

FIGURE 5.1   Explanatory Style Example: Failing an Exam

coping with reality), then one option is for the individual to modify his or her way of thinking about a specific situation. Of course, another option is for the person to try to modify or control the environment (other people, things) in such a way as to fit into his or her schema.

It is of course probably good that our cognitive patterns (values, beliefs, and worldview) are relatively stable, or else we would all be constantly changing our personalities with every new situation. Such a state of affairs would be very confusing, making it very hard for individuals to relate to each other in any kind of predictable or consistent manner.

Example: The stability of our cognitive processes may actually be a disadvantage to our wellness. A significant amount of research, public health programming, and money has been put into figuring out how to get people to change their beliefs (cognitive schemas) concerning health behaviors. Examples of these efforts include trying to get people to stop smoking, wear seatbelts, drink responsibly, get mammograms and prostate exams, and, more recently, eat nutritionally balanced diets and engage in physical activity.

Perhaps as a testimony to the tenacious stability of our cognitive processes in the face of dissonant information, these efforts aimed at altering health beliefs of the populace often take many years of public education, social marketing campaigns, product control (restricting advertising), and the creation environmental disincentives (e.g., raising taxes on cigarettes or levying heavy fines for driving under the influence) to produce noticeable effects.

COGNITION AND WELLNESS: SOCIAL AND CULTURAL IMPACTS

So far in this chapter we have been learning about the biological basis for and influences upon our cognition and ultimately on our wellness and health. Now we will alter our viewpoint and see that even though there are basic biological parameters placed on our cognitive abilities, our patterns of thinking are very much shaped by learning from the experiences we have in the environment. There are two major ways in which our cognition is affected by the environment. First, in childhood, our neural networks are significantly altered by the environment. Human infants are born with approximately twice the number of neurons as adults. Depending on our exposure to experiences in the environment, certain neural networks are reinforced and maintained, whereas others are not used and eventually die off. Perhaps that is why children can learn music, languages, and other processes more easily than adults: they have a built-in ability to simply absorb information. So, in a very real way, the environment (our social, cultural, familial, and community) shapes our brains' cognitive processes and the neural networks that function to produce them.

Second, drawing on dominant theory from evolutionary psychology, it appears that the modules of cognition in the human brain have evolved to help us live in close social groups. One of the unique things about primates and human beings in particular (*Homo sapiens sapiens*) is that we like to live in groups. Living in groups has survival advantages for us. There are more eyes and ears for detecting predators, and there are much better chances of a group of us fending off a lion than one of us. So, those individuals who were able to live productively with others in groups had an evolutionary advantage over those who could not. However, living with others in a group (especially groups the size of those in which humans now live) requires some special cognitive modules (processes). First, we need to keep track of who is in our group, so we need cognitive modules for facial recognition, and we need a lot of memory ability to store that information. Also, it would be useful to track whom we do things for (altruism) and who owes us, so memory is again important, as well as a sense of fairness. Finally, it would be really great to communicate with others in our group, so cognitive modules for producing and decoding language would sure come in handy. According to evolutionary psychologists, many of our cognitive abilities have evolved to aid us with the tasks of living successfully with others. Our minds are naturally attuned to others, having evolved in a social context. Perhaps that is why we experience powerful negative emotions such as loneliness when we feel socially isolated (Cacioppo & Patrick, 2008). Conversely, it has been demonstrated that social engagement and activity help maintain our cognitive abilities (Smith & Christakis, 2008). Although subsequent chapters in this book examine social and cultural impacts on our wellness, it is important to note here that we have cognitively evolved to live in connection with others.

STRATEGIES FOR DEVELOPING WELLNESS THROUGH COGNITION

As amazing as our brains are in helping us to navigate the environment, we can still make many cognitive errors. We can inaccurately perceive the environment, or distort and/or deny the information we perceive through our own belief systems. We can also be blinded by our drive to achieve our goals and fail to attend to the realities of the world around us. I often think of a man I knew who so adamantly pursued his goal of romancing the girl of his dreams that he could not see that his efforts were actually alienating her. Human cognition is far from infallible, and faulty processing of information can lead to complex problems, emotional upset, and the need for change. Change of

Special Focus

Intellectual Stimulation: Does It Help Us Maintain Our Cognitive Capacity into Old Age?

The median age of the American population is climbing upward, and the average lifespan for both men and women is now in the 80s. As a result, the rates of medical diseases that affect cognitive function in old age are rising at a rapid rate. Dementia and Alzheimer's disease are two such illnesses. Currently, 1 in 10 people age 65 and older is afflicted with Alzheimer's disease, which is characterized by many cognitive deficits, including memory loss, confusion, and disorientation (Cook, 2007; Wilson et al., 2010). These factors and others have raised the interest among the general public and researchers concerning the discovery of interventions that will contribute to healthy cognitive functioning into old age (Granello, Fleming, & Granello, 2008; Laditka, Beard, & Bryant, 2009).

Several strategies have been identified for promoting cognitive health as we age: prevention and management of chronic conditions (especially those related to blood flow to the brain), proper nutrition, physical activity, intellectual stimulation, and social engagement (Fillit et al., 2002; Masley, Weaver, Peri, & Phillips, 2008; Yevchak, Loeb, & Fick, 2008).

The cognitive intervention of intellectual stimulation, or "brain exercises," has been shown to improve cognitive functioning (Cook, 2007; Edwards et al., 2005). Intellectual stimulation involves keeping the brain active not only in old age, but throughout the lifespan. Intellectual stimulation training programs focusing on memory activities have been shown to produce positive gains in the specific areas related to the training at follow-up after five years (Willis et al., 2006).

However, a recent longitudinal study conducted over a 12-year period produced some disappointing findings concerning the efficacy of intellectual stimulation as an intervention (Wilson et al., 2010). The results of the study indicated that although intellectual stimulation forestalled the development of dementia initially, those subjects with high intellectual stimulation as a regular part of their lifestyles actually had significantly accelerated deterioration once they developed cognitive impairments (Wilson et al., 2010).

Therefore, although promising, it appears that the research is currently mixed on the beneficial effects of intellectual stimulation for warding off cognitive diseases such as dementia and Alzheimer's.

any type can be difficult for people, and cognitive change is no exception. It takes self-awareness (metacognition) and lots of new learning experiences (practice) to modify long-established and ingrained beliefs about "reality."

Following are three examples of how a person can increase his or her wellness through cognitive interventions. This list is far from exhaustive but should serve as a means to illustrate the usefulness of developing flexible cognition concerning health and wellness.

1. *Develop flexible, realistic beliefs and goals.* Beliefs and goals need to be "permeable" and open for discussion and change. The more rigidly you hold onto faulty or unrealistic beliefs and goals, the less able you will be to respond to changes in your environment. Work on your own or with a professional counselor to identify, refute, and substitute more realistic beliefs and goals for faulty ones. Emmons (1986) found that having goals, making progress toward goals, and having goals that did not conflict with each other were all predictors of subjective well-being and happiness.

2. *Affirm yourself for having identified and adapted beliefs and goals to improve.* You should not only identify and refute unrealistic beliefs and goals, but also give yourself encouragement

and affirmation for adaptive cognitive changes, flexibility, creative problem solving, and problem-focused coping.

3. *Develop metacognition regarding self-generated stress-inducing demands*. Self-monitoring is a technique that may promote metacognition. Track your cognitions and behaviors with journals, diaries, or other methods for collecting data.

There is a twofold benefit: first, your awareness (metacognition) is raised regarding the beliefs or behaviors, and second, baseline data is collected that can be used to help set goals for change. A research study that involved having adults self-monitor their health cognitions and behaviors revealed significant improvements in health locus of control, health value, personal control over and self-regulation of development-related cognitions, and well-being, as well as reductions in psychosomatic complaints and feelings of hopelessness (Krampen, 1996). On your own or with a professional counselor, learn and rehearse cognitive stress-reducing self-care skills. Cognitive self-care skills are powerful stress-reducing resources that can prevent psychological stress and that can promote a sense of wellness (Lyon, 2002). One example of a cognitive self-care skill is mindfulness meditation. In this type of meditation, the goal is to change one's relationship to thoughts instead of changing the content of thoughts themselves (Teasdale et al., 1995).

Summary

There are of course many reasons that individuals may achieve high-level health or succumb to disease. Some of these reasons include health habits, environmental conditions, genetic factors, access to healthcare, and social supports. This chapter has focused on one of these reasons: cognitive function.

In this chapter we have reviewed aspects of our cognitive functioning's contribution to our health from both a biological and environmental perspective. The information shared here is just the beginning for developing a deeper understanding of how our cognitive abilities relate to our health. The human brain is a very powerful evolutionary development, and to date we are only just beginning to understand its full abilities and potential. In the future, it is hoped that wellness-oriented individuals will utilize and demonstrate the efficacy of cognitive interventions with clients to improve their quality of life, perceptions of wellness, and coping abilities, and lower their risk for disease.

Reflection Activities

1. Identify a time when you were stuck in one way of thinking and it led you to a disappointment. Can you identify other ways of thinking about that situation?
2. What are some ways of thinking about the world that you know came from your upbringing? What would it take for these patterns to change?
3. List some situations and how you think people will behave in those situations. Can you challenge these assumptions? What are some different ways of looking at the situations?

References

Alloy, L. B., Abramson, L. Y., & Chiara, A. (2000). *On the mechanisms by which optimism promotes positive mental and physical health: A commentary on Aspinwall and Brunhart.* West Conshohocken, PA: Templeton Foundation Press.

Brosschot, J., Gerin, W., & Thayer, J. (2006). The perseverative cognition hypothesis: A review of worry, prolonged stress-related physiological activation, and health. *Journal of Psychosomatic Research, 60*(2), 113–124. doi:10.1016/j.jpsychores.2005.06.074

Cacioppo, J. T., & Patrick, W. (2008). *Loneliness : Human nature and the need for social connection* (1st ed.). New York: W.W. Norton & Co.

Carr, A. (2004). *Positive psychology: The science of happiness and human strengths* (illustrated ed.) New York: Routledge.

Cook, B. L., McGuire, T., & Miranda, J. (2007). Measuring trends in mental health care disparities, 2000–2004. *Psychiatric Services, 58*(12), 1533–1540. doi:10.1176/appi.ps.58.12.1533

Cordova, M. J., Cunningham, L. L. C., Carlson, C. R., & Andrykowski, M. A. (2001). Social constraints, cognitive processing, and adjustment to breast cancer. *Journal of Consulting and Clinical Psychology, 69*(4), 706–711.

Crosby, R. A. (1996). Cognitive processing and the prevention of HIV transmission: A synthesis of theory into a ten-step model. *Journal of Wellness Perspectives, 12*(3), 140.

Day, K. L., McGuire, L. C., & Anderson, L. A. (2009). The CDC healthy brain initiative: Public health and cognitive impairment. *Generations, 33*(1), 11–17.

Dickerhoof, R. M. (2007). *Expressing optimism and gratitude: A longitudinal investigation of cognitive strategies to increase well-being.* ProQuest Information & Learning. *Dissertation Abstracts International: Section B: The Sciences and Engineering, 68*(6), 4174.

Edwards, J. D., Wadley, V. G., Vance, D. E., Wood, K., Roenker, D. L., & Ball, K. K. (2005). The impact of speed of processing training on cognitive and everyday performance. *Aging & Mental Health, 9*(3), 262–271. doi:10.1080/13607860412331336788

Emmons, R. A., & Diener, E. (1986). Influence of impulsivity and sociability on subjective well-being. *Journal of Personality and Social Psychology, 50*(6), 1211–1215. doi:10.1037/0022-3514.50.6.1211

Fillit, H. M., Butler, R. N., O'Connell, A. W., Albert, M. S., Birren, J. E., Cotman, C. W., . . . Tully, T. (2002). Achieving and maintaining cognitive vitality with aging. *Mayo Clinic Proceedings, 77*(7), 681–696. doi:10.4065/77.7.681

Granello, P. F., Fleming, M. S., & Granello, P. F. (2008). Providing counseling for individuals with Alzheimer's disease and their caregivers. *Adultspan Journal, 7*(1), 13–25.

Hevey, D. (2005). Contextual, cognitive and emotional influences on risk perception for illness. *Irish Journal of Psychology, 26*(1–2), 39–51.

Juster, R. P., McEwen, B. S., & Lupien, S. J. (2009). Allostatic load biomarkers of chronic stress and impact on health and cognition. *Neuroscience and Biobehavioral Reviews.* doi:10.1016/j.neubiorev.2009.10.002

Krampen, G. (1996). The program for systematic self-monitoring and reflection of health behavior and health attitudes (SySeRe): Conception and empirical evaluation of a group program on health promotion. *Swiss Journal of Psychology/Schweizerische Zeitschrift Fur Psychologie/Revue Suisse De Psychologie, 55*(4), 227–240.

Laditka, J. N., Beard, R. L., & Bryant, L. L. (2009). Promoting cognitive health: A formative research collaboration of the healthy aging research network. *The Gerontologist, 49*(S1), S12–S17.

Lawton, R., Conner, M., & Parker, D. (2007). Beyond cognition: Predicting health risk behaviors from instrumental and affective beliefs. *Health Psychology, 26*(3), 259–267.

Lazarus, R. S. (1994). *Emotion and adaptation.* New York: Oxford University Press.

Lyon, B. L. (2002). Cognitive self-care skills: A model for managing stressful lifestyles. *The Nursing Clinics of North America, 37*(2), 285–294.

Marcus, D. K., Gurley, J. R., Marchi, M. M., & Bauer, C. (2007). Cognitive and perceptual variables in hypochondriasis and health anxiety: A systematic review. *Clinical Psychology Review, 27*(2), 127–139.

Masley, S. C., Weaver, W., Peri, G., & Phillips, S. E. (2008). Efficacy of lifestyle changes in modifying practical markers of wellness and aging. *Alternative Therapies in Health and Medicine, 14*(2), 24–29.

Nachev, P. (2006). Cognition and medial frontal cortex in health and disease. *Current Opinion in Neurology, 19*(6), 586–592. doi:10.1097/01.wco.0000247609.36482.ae

Paglieri, F., & Castelfranchi, C. (2008). More than control freaks: Evaluative and motivational functions of goals. *Behavioral and Brain Sciences, 31*(1), 35–36. doi:10.1017/S0140525X07003275

Patterson, R. (2001). *Changing patient behavior: Improving outcomes in health and disease management* (1st ed.) San Francisco: Jossey-Bass.

Pert, C., 1997. *Molecules of emotion*. New York, NY: Simon & Schuster.

Petrella, J. R., Mattay, V. S., & Doraiswamy, P. M. (2008). Imaging genetics of brain longevity and mental wellness: The next frontier? *Radiology, 246*(1), 20–32.

Proudfoot, J. G., Corr, P. J., Guest, D. E., & Dunn, G. (2009). Cognitive-behavioural training to change attributional style improves employee well-being, job satisfaction, productivity, and turnover. *Personality and Individual Differences, 46*(2), 147–153. doi:10.1016/j .paid.2008.09.018

Shumaker, S. A., Ockene, J. K., & Riekert, K. A. (2009). *The handbook of health behavior change* . New York: Springer Pub. Co.

Smith, K. P., & Christakis, N. A. (2008). Social networks and health. *Annual Review of Sociology, 34*(1), 405–429. doi:10.1146/annurev.soc.34.040507.134601

Teasdale, J. (1995). How does cognitive therapy prevent depressive relapse and why should attentional control (mindfulness) training help? *Behaviour Research and Therapy Behaviour Research and Therapy, 33*(1), 25–39.

Waldstein, S. R., & Elias, M. F. (2003). Introduction to the special section on health and cognitive function. *Health Psychology,* Vol 22(6), 555–558.

Weiner, B. (1980). The role of affect in rational (attributional) approaches to human motivation. *Educational Researcher, 9*(7), 4–11.

Weiner, B. (1992). History of motivational research in education. *Journal of Educational Psychology, 82*(4), 616–622.

Willis, S. L., Tennstedt, S. L., Marsiske, M., Ball, K., Elias, J., Koepke, K. M., . . . ACTIVE Study Group. (2006). Long-term effects of cognitive training on everyday functional outcomes in older adults. *JAMA: The Journal of the American Medical Association, 296*(23), 2805–2814. doi:10.1001/jama.296.23.2805

Wilson, R. S., Beckett, L. A., Barnes, L. L., Schneider, J. A., Bach, J., Evans, D. A., Bennett, D. A. (2002). Individual differences in rates of change in cognitive abilities of older persons. *Psychology and Aging,* Vol 17(2), 179–193.

Yevchak, A. M., Loeb, S. J., & Fick, D. M. (2008). Promoting cognitive health and vitality: A review of clinical implications. *Geriatric Nursing, 29*(5), 302–310. doi:10.1016/j.gerinurse.2007.10.017

Zautra, A. J., Davis, M. C., & Smith, B. W. (Eds.). (2004). Emotions, personality, and health. Introduction to the Special Issue. *Journal of Personality, 72*: 1097–1104.

6 EMOTIONAL REGULATION

Karen Michelle Hunnicutt-Hollenbaugh

The strangest and most fantastic fact about negative emotions is that people actually worship them.

P. D. OUSPENSKY, RUSSIAN PHILOSOPHER

Although many people would regard emotions as a component of our mental health, rarely do we think about the processes we engage in to regulate our emotions, and the effect this may have on our health and well-being. In this chapter we seek to illuminate the importance influence of emotions and emotion regulation on wellness. In addition, we discuss the interventions that can be used with clients as well as in our own lives to increase our ability to effectively manage emotions. Although emotion regulation can be reviewed in the context of regulating others' emotions as well as our own, here emotion regulation will only be explored regarding the regulation of one's own emotions.

EMOTIONS

At its most basic characterization, *Merriam Webster* (2008) defines emotion as:

> a: the affective aspect of consciousness : **feeling** b: a state of feeling
> c: a conscious mental reaction (as anger or fear) subjectively experienced
> as strong feeling usually directed toward a specific object and typically
> accompanied by physiological and behavioral changes in the body.

This definition gives us a starting place, but we can go further. Biologically, emotions begin in the brain, although exactly how emotions work continues to be researched and is mired with uncertainty. It is widely believed that emotions are based in the limbic system, although some current theories suggest the involvement of many different systems (Le Doux, 2000). It is posited that emotions are not something we can control, but instead are a phenomenon that happens to us, and we often react to them before we realize it. Most research supports the involvement of the amygdala, a small almond-shaped brain structure, which studies show has a significant relationship with emotional meaning and memory. Clearly, we have conscious reactions to emotions—for example, making the decision to spend less time with one's mother-in-law, as she often elicits feelings of irritation and anger. However, the brain works rapidly to send important information through the thalamus (a part of the brain that is considered to be a relay point and translator of information) to the amygdala (which remembers key factors regarding situations and emotions.) Before the message actually reaches the neocortex (the conscious part of the brain where we normally intervene with our response to the emotion), this information has already been sent to different parts of the brain—for example, the hypothalamus, which releases hormones such as adrenalin. Why? Biologically, humans often need to elicit a rapid behavioral response before making a connection between a stimulus and an emotional response. The amygdala is also thought to be a major component in classical conditioning, as it sends messages to the prefrontal cortex regarding the association between the conditioned stimulus and the unconditioned stimulus before the individual has conscious realization of this association (Le Doux, 1996).

These biological processes have significant implications for wellness and emotion regulation. Our emotion systems were created at the very beginning of our biological evolution to manage emotions and increase rates of survival in very basic ways (i.e., the prominent "fight-or-flight" response.) Today, however, these emotions can frequently lead to dysfunctional ways of thinking and behaving (Baumeister, DeWall, & Zhang, 2007). We must condition ourselves to regulate our emotions in a healthy manner, or fall victim to methods of regulating emotion that can decrease wellness and spin out of control. Take, for example, the fear of heights (acrophobia). Someone afflicted with acrophobia may have once faced a traumatic experience related to heights, such as being in danger of falling and getting injured. The amygdala then sent messages to the hypothalamus to release adrenal steroids, which increased arousal enough to elicit an immediate response—presumably stopping all physical movement or moving toward safety (McEwen & Sapolsky, 1995). Although this may be helpful during situations of actual danger, the amygdala keeps the memory of this highly stressful emotional response and will initiate the same reaction to similar situations, regardless of actual danger (e.g., elevators or planes). This highly emotional reaction can also make it difficult to think clearly, and as result, the individual may develop unhealthy coping responses, such as avoiding all situations involved with height, to regulate his or her emotions. (Le Doux, 1996).

Emotion Regulation

Everyone regulates emotions differently. In conjunction with the biological processes of emotions themselves, regulation of these emotions also takes place in the limbic system, and involves communication between the amygdala, hippocampus, and neocortex (Beer & Lombardo, 2007; Davidson, Fox, & Kalin, 2007). As mentioned, emotion regulation can be unconscious and automatic (e.g., looking away from the couple kissing in the library because it makes us uncomfortable), but can also be very conscious and deliberate (e.g., suppressing unhappiness with receiving Aunt May's unlikable fruitcake as a gift once again) (Gross & Thompson, 2007). These automatic and conscious processes also differ by culture. For example, North American culture holds the belief that it is weak for a man to cry, whereas individuals in other societies believe showing emotions is seen as a strength, regardless of gender (Mauss, Bunge, & Gross, 2008). Emotion regulation also varies based on the individual and is at least in part related to how we were raised to act (which behaviors were reinforced and which were not) and our biological level of emotions, as some of us experience higher levels of emotions than others (Linehan, 1993; Mauss, Cook, Cheng, & Gross, 2007; Mikolajczak, Nelis, Hansenne, & Quoidbach, 2008).

There is also significant research that suggests men and women may differ in their skill levels with and approaches to regulating emotions. In a recent U.S. study, men exhibited less brain activity while using emotion regulation techniques than women, suggesting men may either be more bio-logically apt to regulate emotions than women or (the more likely hypothesis) that men were taught culturally to regulate emotions more than women (McRae, Ochsner, Mauss, Gabrieli, & Gross, 2008). This finding coincides with the results of other research that women are more expressive with emotions than men (Kring & Gordon, 1998). This information can have significant implications for our own lives and for our clients, as it suggests that men and women choose different emotion regulation techniques, and these different approaches to emotions can have an effect on how people communicate and function in daily life.

There are five basic categories of emotion regulation. Some of these groups are cognitive, and others are behavioral. The first, *situation selection*, refers to the act of looking ahead to choose situations based on our past experiences and the effect these situations may have on our emotions—for example, making the decision to view a comedy as opposed to a horror movie (Gross & Thomson, 2007). This method of regulating emotion can be difficult to use successfully, as we often misjudge how we might react emotionally to any given situation (Lowenstein, 2007). The next group of pro-cesses, *situation modification*, is the act of changing the current situation to manage emotions—for example, instead of leaving when feeling irritated with one's mother-in-law, one might instead change the topic of discussion. However, it should be noted that the differences between situation selection and situation modification are often blurred, as modifying the situation could be considered selecting a new situation. The third category, *attention deployment* (or attention control), encompasses the use of distraction as well as concentration. When unable to change the current situation, we instead redirect our attention to manage emotions. As with all methods of regulating emotions, this can have positive or negative results (e.g., concentrating on things that make you happy, or ruminating on an event that elicits sadness). Fourth, the method of *cognitive change* involves reappraisal, the act of changing the way we think about something in order to regulate how we feel about it (e.g., the sayings "every cloud has a silver lining," and "making lemonade of lemons"). Reappraisal has been widely studied, and will be discussed later in this chapter as a healthier approach to regulating emotions (Nezleck & Kuppens, 2008). Last, *response modulation* encompasses any method of altering our responses to our emotions. This includes taking medication, but also how we express our emotions (e.g., finding a healthier way to manage anger than yelling or throwing things.)

Gross (1998) identifies these categories based on a continuum of when they appear along a timeline. It begins with the situations we choose (situation selection and modification), then moves to where we focus our attention once we are in that situation (attention deployment), how we appraise or evaluate the situation (cognitive change), and then our response to the elicited emotions (response modulation). Although he uses a linear model to demonstrate the processes, he also postulates that this process is not linear but a recurring cycle, as our emotions themselves are cyclical. Emotions can be activated and re-activated based on our cognitive and behavioral responses to these emotions. In addition, many of these regulation processes can occur in the brain simultaneously (e.g., feeling sad about my poor performance on the test, but blaming the profes-sor for unfair questions to regulate my sadness, then feeling angry, and at the same time feeling envious of a fellow student who performed better, and then feeling guilty for feeling that way). Again, how we modulate our responses to emotions can be considered adaptive or maladaptive, and varies based on one's age, situation, and culture (Gross & Thompson, 2007).

EMOTION REGULATION AND WELLNESS

Our ability to regulate our emotions has a direct relationship with every portion of the Wheel of Wellness (Witmer & Sweeny, 1992). This includes spirituality, relationships, family, mental health, physical well-being, and career. Thus, effective strategies to regulate emotion can improve every aspect of our wellness, whereas negative strategies can be unhealthy and detrimental to wellness.

Mental Health

Emotion regulation has a strong connection to mental health. Individuals who are unable to use emotion regulation skills to accept emotional distress have higher levels of anxious arousal and worry (Kashdan, Zvolensky, & McLeish, 2008). Emotion regulation affects mental health, and, conversely, mental illness can negatively affect emotion regulation skills (this is cyclical—each impacts the other). Further, a study of emotion regulation skills in children diagnosed with bipolar disorder showed distinct biological differences in their ability to regulate emotions as compared with children who have not been diagnosed with a mental illness (Dickstein & Leibenluft, 2006). In an interview of adolescent girls diagnosed with conduct disorder, it was found that the subjects had few, if any, methods of regulating emotions that actually achieved relief from negative emotions, suggesting an important relationship between emotion dysregulation and the etiology of conduct disorder, which may also limit healthy social and behavioral growth during this crucial period of human development (Kostiuk & Fouts 2002).

Relationships

Interpersonal relationships are a major facet of our overall wellness, and when we cannot control our emotions effectively, relationships may be the first aspect of our lives to suffer the consequences. Research has shown that emotion regulation plays a significant role in social difficulties of young boys with developmental delays. Those who showed less ability to tolerate frustration, for example, struggled more in interactions with peers and adults (Wilson, Fernandes-Richards, Aarskog, Osborn, & Capetillo, 2007). Men who used emotion regulation in childhood exhibited higher social functioning in adulthood than those who did not, and, conversely, individuals who are unable to manage and reduce social anxiety have been found to experience low levels of positive emotions (Kashdan & Breen, 2008; Pulkkinen, Nygren, & Kokko, 2002). Indeed, in the *Diagnostic and Statistical Manual of Mental Disorders* (DSM-IV) of the American Psychiatric Association (2000), many psychological disorders, including personality disorders, include criteria related to the individual's inability to manage emotions in the context of relationships (Gross & Munoz, 1995). For example, individuals with borderline personality disorder are often plagued with real or imagined fear of abandonment, a fear that they are often unable to control, with deleterious results. These individuals may push loved ones away completely, or become so completely attached that loved ones feel that they have no choice but to pull away (American Psychiatric Association, 2000.)

In the discussion of social relationships, we must also consider romantic partners, as our ability (or inability) to regulate emotions can have a direct impact on the health of intimate relationships. Specifically, the use of suppression (the act of ignoring or pushing away emotions) can be found to reduce the strength of relationships and limit intimacy (Butler et al., 2003; Gross & John, 2003). Suppressing emotions while discussing relationship conflicts has been found to decrease memory of what was said, and instead increase memory of the emotions experienced. On the other hand, reappraisal (changing our beliefs about a situation) was shown to increase memory of what was said (Richards, Butler, & Gross, 2003). The point is, if we use suppression as a major method of regulation, we may find ourselves feeling more angry or upset after an argument with our partner, while forgetting things that were said, thus possibly damaging the relationship further. Research also suggests that the ability to regulate anger and sadness may reduce the likelihood of domestic violence in newlywed couples, important information to consider for ourselves and for our clients (McNulty & Hellmuth, 2008).

Family

The negative consequences associated with our inability to manage our emotions in relationships affect family relationships as well. That being said, there is also evidence that we learn how to regulate our emotions from our nuclear families. For example, individuals who are more emotionally expressive also report higher levels of emotional expression in their families than other respondents (Kring & Gordon, 1998). Conversely, if our families of origin engaged in unhealthy methods of emotion regulation, such as suppression, overeating, or drug and alcohol use, we may learn these behaviors as well. The implications are clear: regulating our own emotions can not only affect our wellness, but the wellness of those around us, especially our children (Morris, Silk, Steinberg, Myers, & Robinson, 2007).

Spirituality

Spiritual beliefs can have profound effects on our ability to regulate emotions and thus affect our wellness. For example, higher levels of spirituality are related to a higher ability to cope with stress, as well as reduced symptoms of distress in cancer patients (Laubmeier, Zakowski, & Bair, 2004) The most obvious method of spiritual emotion regulation—prayer—as well as other religious coping methods (such as forgiveness) were found to have positive associations with greater well-being in patients with chronic pain (Moreira-Almeida & Koenig, 2008). Further, in families that engaged in religious and spiritual emotion regulation activities (such as prayer and meditation), the children's mental and physical health was greater, as were academic success and the frequency of healthy social interactions (Schottenbauer, Spernack, & Hellstrom, 2007).

Nutrition

It has been found that individuals will engage in impulsive behaviors if they believe these will improve their mood—for example, eating desirable foods (Tice, Bratslavsky, & Baumeister, 2001). Research also shows a significant relationship between negative moods and binge-eating behaviors in college students (Lynch, Everingham, Dubitzky, Hartman, & Kasser, 2000). Although eating and procrastination may boost positive emotions in the short term, using these behaviors can be detrimental when considering long-term consequences. Consistent use of eating to manage emotions can develop into eating disorders and poor physical health, and the stress that results from repeated procrastination can also have negative effects on health.

Compulsive and Addictive Behaviors

Many addictive behaviors are directly related to dysfunctional methods of regulating emotions, and the consequences can be great. A review of research on tobacco and nicotine addiction shows that many individuals use smoking as an affect-regulation strategy, making it more difficult for them to quit and maintain cessation, especially when experiencing anxiety and depression. Precipitating further damage to wellness, many turn to alcohol and other drugs to regulate emotions, and there is a higher relapse rate for those with a co-morbid mental illness (Khantzian, 1990; Kushner et al., 2005). A study of college students found that men who struggled with the ability to effectively regulate their emotions also had higher levels of alcohol use than those who reported being able to effectively manage emotions (Fischer, Forthun, Pidcock, & Dowd, 2007). Further, studies have shown alcohol use to be related to short- and long-term increases in emotion dysregulation, in addition to the other innumerable negative consequences regular alcohol use has on wellness (Sher & Grekin, 2007).

Career

The way we regulate our emotions can also have consequences for our careers. Invariably, in order to attain and maintain employment, we must be able to effectively manage our emotions. This ability is comprised of the knowledge of which emotions to express (e.g., happiness and excitement over a promotion or reaching departmental goals) and which to reappraise and regulate (e.g., disappointment at not receiving a requested raise) (Gross & Munoz, 1995). Further, being unable to regulate emotions in a healthy manner may have implications for work performance and satisfaction. Here again, suppression rears its ugly head—research shows a significant relationship between emotion suppression at work and unhappiness with the job and intentions to quit (Cote & Morgan, 2002). In a related study, individuals who reported suppressing anger and depression were more likely to report occupational problems than those who did not. These individuals also reported more anxiety and more interpersonal problems, troubles that are often consequences of poor emotion regulation skills (Hutri & Lindeman, 2002) Finally, it is thought that higher levels of emotional intelligence (a concept discussed later in the chapter) may lead to improved career decision making and heightened satisfaction with career decisions (Emmerling & Cherniss, 2003).

Physical Health

There is a significant amount of research that indicates a relationship between physical health and regulating emotions, especially negative emotions. Research shows that anger, aggression, and hostility can be considered risk factors for coronary heart disease (Smith, Glazer, Ruiz, & Gallo, 2004). Further, studies show that optimism about life and the future results in fewer problems with physical health symptoms (Scheier & Carver, 1985). Research also supports the idea that optimists are more likely to engage in healthy behaviors than those who are pessimistic (Scheier & Carver, 1992). In the company of optimism and positive emotion regulation comes the feeling of hope. Individuals who reported more feelings of hope had less likelihood of physical health problems or illnesses over the course of several years (Richman et al., 2005). High levels of negative emotions have a significant relationship with less physical activity, and those who report negative emotions also engage in higher rates of alcohol consumption and saturated fat consumption (Anton & Miller, 2005). These results are not restricted solely to adults—longitudinal study of emotions in children found that young girls who reported experiencing higher levels of mood swings and anger also reported higher levels of pain and fatigue later in life (Kokkonen, Pulkkinen, & Kinnunen, 2001). In a systematic review of available studies, it was found that one of the top causes of heart disease was chronic exposure to stress. As reviewed in the section on emotion regulation, situation selection can be a form of emotion regulation, and removing ourselves from consistently stressful situations can not only help regulate our emotions but also increase our wellness (French, Senior, Weinman, & Marteau 2001). The conclusions we wish to draw from this section are that not only is there a connection between poorly regulated negative emotions and poor health, but that regulating our emotions will help us feel better, therefore making us more likely to engage in health-related behaviors, and thus increasing our physical health and wellness.

RUMINATION, SUPPRESSION, AND LOCUS OF CONTROL

Benefits to our wellness come not just from regulating our emotions, but also from how we do so. Studies show that people may believe that worrying and ruminating about something may be helpful for them emotionally; however, the results are quite the opposite—the more time subjects spent ruminating on negative events, the longer they experienced depressed and negative feelings, and in a similar but separate study, subjects were found to feel more depressed when ruminating on the negative feelings, whereas those who engaged in distraction reported experiencing significantly less depression (Campbell-Sills & Barlow, 2007; Nolen-Hoeksema & Morrow, 1993; Nolen-Hoeksema, Morrow, & Fredrickson, 1993).

There also seems to be a relationship between whether we believe we can control our emotions and our overall wellness. In a study of incoming college freshmen over the course of their first year at college, students who reported less belief that they could control their emotions also reported higher levels of negative emotions, less social adaptation and support, less satisfaction, and less well-being than those who felt they could manage their emotions (Tamir, John, Srivastava, & Gross, 2007). In addition, students who felt they could control their emotions reported using reappraisal more than other types of emotion regulation.

As previously mentioned, suppressing our emotions has been found to be detrimental to wellness in a variety of ways. One study demonstrated that reappraisal as a method of regulating emotions was found to increase aspects of wellness for participants in comparison to the act of suppressing emotions, which created the opposite effect (Nezleck & Kuppens, 2008). Suppressing emotions can also lead to increases in bodily stress and increases in blood pressure (Butler et al., 2003). In addition, suppressing emotions puts more stress on many systems in the body, including the cardiovascular system, which could lead to significant health problems in the future (Mauss & Gross, 2004). As mentioned in the earlier discussion of relationships and emotion regulation, studies have also shown that suppressing emotions significantly reduces our memories regarding the events that took place, and this is not just true for social situations but also when viewing something that might be upsetting or elicit emotional expression (Richards & Gross, 2006).

As if these studies were not evidence enough that suppression is damaging to our wellness, in a comparison of suppression and reappraisal as venues to regulate our emotions, research supports that participants who used suppression reported higher levels of depression, less satisfaction with life, lower self-esteem, and less optimism than those who utilized reappraisal (Gross & John, 2003). On the other hand, participants who used reappraisal responded more positively on all of the aforementioned aspects, in addition to reporting higher levels of personal growth and self-acceptance, and having a clear purpose in life.

INTERVENTIONS

The relationship between emotion regulation and wellness is clear. The next step is to focus on ways we can improve emotion regulation processes, in our own lives and the lives of our clients.

Because of the reciprocal nature of emotions and wellness, improvements in any one area will affect the other. For example, increases in physical health activities can help us feel better, and can improve and maintain our employment situation. Abstaining from addictive substances and attending to our relationships in all areas of our lives can also help us to experience more positive emotions. Learning to regulate our emotions can improve our physical energy and enhance our relationships.

Spirituality and Meditation

Spirituality can provide meaning and purpose during stressful and harrowing times, helping to regulate emotions and increasing coping skills in the face of hardship. Many religions include practices such as prayer and meditation. Prayer, in many ways, can be considered reframing, as the individual engaged in prayer also engages in identification of events in which he or she cannot control, which then may help the individual to accept the things that may be causing intense and interfering emotions.

Meditation, often considered a spiritual practice, incorporates controlling one's thoughts and behaviors to regulate and control impulsive and unwanted thoughts often related to emotions, and can have important implications for emotion regulation (Watts, 2008). Studies show that individuals who use meditation regularly experience less anxiety and lower heart rates when using meditation skills in the face of a stressful situation that those who do not (Goleman & Schwartz, 1976).

Mindfulness and Dialectical Behavior Therapy

Mindfulness, the act of controlling one's attention and thoughts to become more aware of current thoughts and feelings, has been shown repeatedly to be associated with an increased ability to manage negative emotions, decreased physical symptoms, and increased coping skills and well-being (Carmody & Baer, 2008; Carmody, Reed, Kristeller, & Merriam, 2008; Coffey & Hartman, 2008). Mindfulness can be considered the basis for regulating emotions, supplemented by other valuable skills (Linehan, Bohus, & Lynch, 2007). Invariably, emotion regulation is a major module included in dialectical behavior therapy. Although this therapy is directed toward patients with borderline personality disorder, these abilities can be helpful for anyone working to improve the regulation of their emotions. The techniques are directed toward several points in the emotion and response continuum, commencing with reducing vulnerability to negative emotions by increasing wellness in other areas (e.g., engaging in physical health activities, engaging in activities that increase feelings of competence) and increasing positive emotions on a daily basis. The skills are then directed toward understanding the emotions that are experienced, using mindfulness to tolerate them, and managing painful emotions effectively by acting opposite to the current emotion—for example, watching a comedy when feeling sad (Linehan, 1993). Other skills employed in dialectical behavior therapy can contribute significantly in attempts regulate emotions as well, including interpersonal effectiveness and distress tolerance skills (Linehan et al., 2007). Using emotion regulation skills in treatment interventions based on cognitive-behavioral theories has shown to be beneficial not only by increasing mental health outcomes but also by increasing the applicability of skills learned (Berking et al., 2008).

Cognitive-Behavioral Interventions

In a study of the relationship between social anxiety and methods of emotion regulation, it was found that it was not merely lower levels of anxiety that resulted in an increase in positive emotions, but also the act of openly expressing emotions as opposed to suppressing (Kashdan & Breen, 2008). Although both techniques proved to be effective in emotion regulation, cognitive-behavioral techniques have shown to be more effective than mindfulness in increasing subjects' ability to cope with pain and stress (Zautra et al., 2008). Emotions and our reactions to those emotions are based on our appraisal of any given situation (Seimer, Mauss, & Gross, 2007). In addition, people who engage in reappraisal have been found to not only experience fewer and less extreme negative emotions (e.g., anger and sadness) but also to experience more positive emotions in the face of frustrating or irritating tasks (Mauss et al., 2007).

Emotional Intelligence

Emotional intelligence (EI) is another method of helping clients to increase their ability to regulate their thoughts and emotions. EI began with Gardner's *Frames of Mind* (1983) when he postulated that there were several types of intelligence. From this point, EI grew into many forms and resulted in a significant amount of research. One of the most popular models is conceptualized by Salovey and Mayer (1990), who define EI as "the ability to monitor one's own and others' feelings and emotions, to discriminate among them and to use this information to guide one's thinking and actions" (p. 5). They go further to divide EI into four branches: perception of emotion, using emotion to facilitate thought, understanding emotion, and managing emotions. There are many ways to increase one's emotional intelligence based on Salovey and Mayer's model, including increasing skills such as self-awareness, emotion regulation, empathy, and managing relationships (Goleman, 1995). For example, it has been found that participants with higher levels of EI were more likely to utilize adaptive strategies to decrease a variety of negative emotions as well as increase and maintain positive emotions (Mikolajczak et al., 2008).

Indeed, although the importance of emotion regulation as an intervention in our counseling cannot be argued, emotion regulation skills can and should be implemented as a preventative measure as well, at the very base of prevention models pursuing wellness. Higher levels of effective emotion regulation equate to less emotion dysregulation, fewer occurrences of severe negative emotions that spin out of control, and thus fewer disorders involving depression, anxiety, impulse control, and addiction (Gross & Munoz, 1995).

CONCLUSION

Although emotion regulation may not receive as much scrutiny as other aspects of wellness, it is connected with nearly all facets of our health. We have discussed that while there are many things we can control, our emotions are not one of those things. We can, however, regulate them—and our ability to regulate our emotions can limit or enhance our physical health, careers, relationships, and decision making on several levels. The complexities continue, as it is not only regulating these emotions but also the manner in which we regulate them that affect wellness—we have shown that although suppression is often used, it can decrease wellness, whereas reappraisal can increase wellness in every area of our lives. There are many ways to increase our wellness through emotion regulation, including increasing our emotional intelligence and engaging in meditation and cognitive strategies. What is most important is not only that we use this information for ourselves but also for our clients, in facilitating their ability to manage their own emotions and thoughts for happiness in every facet of their lives.

References

American Psychiatric Association. (2000). *Diagnostic and statistical manual of mental disorders-Text revision* (4th ed.) Washington, DC: Author.

Anton, S. D., & Miller, P. M. (2005). Do negative emotions predict alcohol consumption, saturated fat intake, and physical activity in older adults? *Behavior Modification, 29*(4), 677–688.

Beer, J. S., & Lombardo, M. V. (2007). Insights into emotion regulation from neuropsychology. In J. J. Gross (Ed.), *Handbook of emotion regulation.* New York: The Guilford Press.

Berking, M., Wupperman, P., Reichardt, A., Pejic, T., Dippel, A., & Znoj, H. (2008). Emotion-regulation skills as a treatment target in psychotherapy. *Behaviour Research*

& Therapy, 46(11), 1230–1237. Butler, E. A., Egloff, B., Wilhelm, F. H., Smith, N. C., Erickson, E. A., & Gross, J. J. (2003). The social consequences of expressive suppression. Emotion, 3(1), 48–67.

Campbell-Sills, L., & Barlow, D. H. (2007). Incorporating emotion regulation into conceptualizations and treatments of anxiety and mood disorders. In J. J. Gross (Ed.), Handbook of emotion regulation. New York: The Guilford Press.

Carmody, J., & Baer, R. A. (2008). Relationships between mindfulness practice and levels of mindfulness, medical and psychological symptoms and well-being in a mindfulness-based stress reduction program. Journal of Behavioral Medicine, 31(1), 23–33.

Carmody, J., Reed, G., Kristeller, J., & Merriam, P. (2008). Mindfulness, spirituality, and health-related symptoms. Journal of Psychosomatic Research, 64(4), 393–403.

Coffey, K. A., & Hartman, M. (2008). Mechanisms of action in the inverse relationship between mindfulness and psychological distress. Complementary Health Practice Review, 13(2), 79–91.

Cote, S., & Morgan, L. M. (2002). A longitudinal analysis of the association between emotion regulation, job satisfaction, and intentions to quit. Journal of Organizational Behavior, 23(8), 947–962.

Davidson, R. J., Fox, A., & Kalin, N. H. (2007). Neural bases of emotion regulation in nonhuman primates and humans. In J. J. Gross (Ed.), Handbook of emotion regulation. New York: The Guilford Press.

Dickstein, D. P., & Leibenluft, E. (2006). Emotion regulation in children and adolescents: Boundaries between normalcy and bipolar disorder. Development and Psychopathology, 18(4), 1105–1131.

Emmerling, R. J., & Cherniss, G. (2003). Emotional intelligence and the career choice process. Journal of Career Assessment, 11(2), 153–167.

Fischer, J. L., Forthun, L. F., Pidcock, B. W., & Dowd, D. A. (2007). Parent relationships, emotion regulation, psychosocial maturity, and college student alcohol use problems. Journal of Youth and Adolescence, 36, 912–926.

French, D. P., Senior, V., Weinman, J., & Marteau, T. M. (2001). Causal attributions for heart disease: A systematic review. Psychology & Health, 16(1), 77–98.

Gardner, H. (1983). Frames of mind. New York: Basic Books.

Goleman, D. (1995). Emotional intelligence: Why it can matter more than IQ. New York: Bantam Books.

Goleman, D. J., & Schwartz, G. E. (1976). Meditation as an intervention in stress reactivity. Journal of Consulting and Clinical Psychology, 44(3), 456–466.

Gross, J. J. (1998). The emerging field of emotion regulation: An integrative review. Review of General Psychology, 2(3), 271–299.

Gross, J. J., & John, O. P. (2003). Individual differences in two emotion regulation processes: Implications for affect, relationships, and well-being. Journal of Personality and Social Psychology, 85(2), 348–362.

Gross, J. J., & Munoz, R. F. (1995). Emotion regulation and mental health. Clinical Psychology: Science and Practice, 2(2), 151–164.

Gross, J. J., & Thompson, R. A. (2007). Emotion regulation: Conceptual foundations. In J. J. Gross (Ed.), Handbook of emotion regulation. New York: The Guilford Press.

Hutri, M., & Lindeman, M. (2002). The role of stress and negative emotions in an occupational crisis. Journal of Career Development, 29(1), 19–36.

Kashdan, T. B., & Breen, W. E. (2008). Social anxiety and positive emotions: A prospective examination of a self-regulatory model with tendencies to suppress or express emotions as a moderating variable. Behavior Therapy, 39, 1–12.

Kashdan, T. B., Zvolensky, M. J., & McLeish, A. C. (2008). Anxiety sensitivity and affect regulatory strategies: Individual and interactive risk factors for anxiety-related symptoms. Journal of Anxiety Disorders, 22, 429–440.

Khantzian, E. J. (1990). Self-regulation and self-medication factors in alcoholism and the addictions: Similarities and differences. In M. Galanter (Ed.), Recent developments in alcoholism. New York: Plenum Press.

Kokkonen, M., Pulkkinen, L., & Kinnunen, T. (2001). Low self-control of emotions as an antecedent of self-reported physical symptoms: A longitudinal perspective. European Psychologist, 6(1), 26–35.

Kostiuk, L. M., & Fouts, G. T. (2002). Understanding of emotions and the emotion regulation in adolescent females with conduct problems: A qualitative analysis. The Qualitative Report, 7(1). Retrieved from http://www.nova.edu/ssss/QR/QR7-1/kostiuk.html

Kring, A. M., & Gordon, A. H. (1998). Sex differences in emotion: Expression, experience, and physiology. Journal of Personality and Social Psychology, 74(3), 686–703.

Kushner, M. G., Abrams, K., Thuras, P., Hanson, K. L., Brekke, M., & Sletten, S. (2005). Follow-up study of anxiety disorder and alcohol dependence in comorbid alcoholism treatment patients. Alcoholism: Clinical and Experimental Research, 29(8), 1432–1443.

Laubmeier, K. K., Zakowski, S. G., & Bair, J. P. (2004). The role of spirituality in the psychological adjustment to cancer: A test of the transactional model of stress and coping. International Journal of Behavioral Medicine, 11(1), 48–55.

Le Doux, J. E. (1996). The emotional brain: The mysterious underpinnings of emotional life. New York: Simon & Schuster.

Le Doux, J. E. (2000). Emotion circuits in the brain. *Annual Review of Neuroscience, 23*, 155–184.

Linehan, M. (1993a). *Cognitive-behavioral treatment of borderline personality disorder.* New York: The Guilford Press.

Linehan, M. (1993b). *Skills training manual for treating borderline personality disorder.* New York: The Guilford Press.

Linehan, M., Bohus, M., & Lynch, T. (2007) Dialectical behavior therapy for pervasive emotion dysregulation: Theoretical and practical underpinnings. In J. J. Gross (Ed.), *Handbook of emotion regulation.* New York: The Guilford Press.

Lowenstein, G. (2007). Affect regulation and affective forecasting. In J. J. Gross (Ed.), *Handbook of emotion regulation.* New York: The Guilford Press.

Lynch, W. C., Everingham, A., Dubitzky, J., Hartman, M., & Kasser, T. (2000). Does binge eating play a role in the self-regulation of moods? *Integrative Physiological & Behavioral Science, 35*(4), 298–313.

Mauss, I. B., Bunge, S. A., & Gross, J. J. (2008). Culture and automatic emotion regulation. In S. Ismer, S. Jung, S. Kronast, C. van Scheve, & M. Vanderkerckhove (Eds.), *Regulating emotions: Culture, social necessity and biological inheritance.* London: Blackwell Publishing.

Mauss, I. B., Cook, C. L., Cheng, J. Y. J., & Gross, J. J. (2007). Individual differences in cognitive reappraisal: Experiential and physiological responses to an anger provocation. *International Journal of Psychophysiology.* doi: 10.1016/j.ijpsycho.2007.03.017.

Mauss, I. B., & Gross, J. J. (2004). Emotion suppression and cardiovascular disease: Is hiding feelings bad for your heart? In I. Nyklicek, L. Temoshok, & A. Vingerhoets (Eds.), *Emotional expression and health: Advances in theory, assessment, and clinical applications.* New York: Brunner-Routledge.

McEwen, B., & Sapolsky, R. (1995). Stress and cognitive functioning. *Current Opinion in Neurobiology, 5*, 205–216.

McNulty, J. K., & Hellmuth, J. C. (2008). Emotion regulation and intimate partner violence in newlyweds. *Journal of Family Psychology, 22*(5), 794–797.

McRae, K., Ochsner, K. N., Mauss, I. B., Gabrieli, J. J. D., & Gross, J. J. (2008). Gender difference in emotion regulation: An fMRI study of cognitive reappraisal. Manuscript submitted for publication.

Merriam Webster's Online Dictionary. (2008). Retrieved from http://aolsvc.merriam-webster.aol.com/dictionary/emotion

Mikolajczak, M., Nelis, D., Hansenne, M., & Quoidbach, J. (2008). If you can regulate sadness, you can probably regulate shame: Associations between trait emotional intelligence, emotion regulation, and coping efficiency across emotions. *Personality and Individual Differences, 44*, 1356–1368.

Moreira-Almeida, A., & Koenig, H. G. (2008). Religiousness and spirituality in fibromyalgia and chronic pain patients. *Current Pain and Headache Reports, 12*(5), 327–332.

Morris, A., Silk, J., Steinberg, L., Myers, S., & Robinson, L. (2007). The role of the family context in the development of emotion regulation. *Social Development, 16*(2), 361–388.

Nezleck, J. B., & Kuppens, P. (2008). Regulating positive and negative emotions in daily life. *Journal of Personality, 76*(3), 561–580.

Nolen-Hoeksema, S., & Morrow, J. (1993). Effects of rumination and distraction on naturally occurring depressed mood. *Cognition & Emotion, 7*(6), 561–570.

Nolen-Hoeksema, S., Morrow, J., & Fredrickson, B. L. (1993). Response styles and the duration of episodes of depressed mood. *Journal of Abnormal Psychology, 102*(1), 20–28.

Pulkkinen, L., Nygren, H., & Kokko, K. (2002). Successful development: Childhood antecedents of adaptive psychosocial functioning in adulthood. *Journal of Adult Development, 9*(4), 251–265.

Richards, J. M., Butler, E. A., & Gross, J. J. (2003). Emotion regulation in romantic relationships: The cognitive consequences of concealing feelings. *Journal of Social and Personal Relationships, 20*(5), 599–620.

Richards, J. M., & Gross, J. J. (2006). Personality and emotional memory: How regulating emotion impairs memory for emotional events. *Journal of Research in Personality, 40*(5), 631–651.

Richman, L. S., Kubzansky, L., Maselko, J., Kawachi, I., Choo, P., & Bauer, M. (2005). Positive emotion and health: Going beyond the negative. *Health Psychology, 24*(4), 422–429.

Salovey, P., & Mayer, J. D. (1990). Emotional intelligence. *Imagination, Cognition, and Personality, 9*, 185–211.

Scheier, M. F., & Carver, C. S. (1985). Optimism, coping, and health: Assessment and implications of generalized outcome expectancies. *Health Psychology, 4*(3), 219–247.

Scheier, M. F., & Carver, C. S. (1992). Effects of optimism on psychological and physical well-being: Theoretical overview and empirical update. *Cognitive Therapy and Research, 16*(2), 201–228.

Schottenbauer, M. A., Spernack, S. M., & Hellstrom, I. (2007). Relationship between religious behaviors and child well-being among third-grade children. *Mental Health, Religion, & Culture, 10*(2), 191–198.

Seimer, M., Mauss, I., & Gross, J. J. (2007). Same situation—different emotions: How appraisals shape our emotions. *Emotion, 7*(3), 592–600.

Sher, K. J., & Grekin, E. R. (2007). Alcohol and affect regulation. In J. J. Gross (Ed.), *Handbook of emotion regulation.* New York: The Guilford Press.

Smith, T. W., Glazer, K., Ruiz, J. M., & Gallo, L. C. (2004). Hostility, anger, aggressiveness, and coronary heart disease: An interpersonal perspective on personality, emotion, and health. *Journal of Personality, 72*(6), 1217–1270.

Tamir, M., John, O., Srivastava, S., & Gross, J. J. (2007). Implicit theories of emotion: Affective and social outcomes across a major life transition. *Journal of Personality and Social Psychology*, *92*(4), 731–744.

Tice, D. M., Bratslavsky, E., & Baumeister, R. F. (2001). Emotional distress regulation takes precedence over impulse control: If you feel bad, do it! *Journal of Personality and Social Psychology*, *80*(1), 53–67.

Tice, D. M., Baumeister, R. F., & Zhang, L. (2004). The role of emotion in self-regulation: Differing role of positive and negative emotions. In P. Philippot, R. S. Feldman (Ed.), (pp. 213–226). Mahwah, NJ, Lawrence Erlbaum Associates Publishers.

Vohs, K. D., Baumeister, R. F., & Loewenstein, G. (2007). *Do emotions help or hurt decision making?: A hedgefoxian perspective.* Russell Sage Foundation Publications.

Watts, J. H. (2008). Emotion, empathy and exit: reflections on doing ethnographic qualitative research on sensitive topics. *Medical Sociology Online, 3*(2) pp. 3–14.

Wilson, B. J., Fernandes-Richards, S., Aarskog, C., Osborn, T., & Capetillo, D. (2007). The role of emotion regulation in the social problems of boys with developmental delays. *Early Education and Development, 18*(2), 201–222.

Witmer, J. M., & Sweeney, T. J. (1992). A holistic model for wellness and prevention over the life span. *Journal of Counseling and Development, 71*, 140–148.

Zautra, A. J., Davis, M. C., Reich, J. W., Tennen, H., Nicassio, P., Finan, P., Kratz, A., Parrish, B., Tennen, H., & Irwin, M. R. (2008). Comparison of cognitive behavioral and mindfulness meditation interventions on adaptation to rheumatoid arthritis for patients with and without history of recurrent depression. *Journal of Consulting and Clinical Psychology, 76*(3), 408–421.

7 | PHYSICAL ACTIVITY AND PSYCHOLOGICAL WELL-BEING

Brian C. Focht & Michael Lewis

Everyone knows the effects of physical exercise on the mood: how much more cheerful and courageous one feels when the body has been toned up. . . Our moods are determined by the feelings that come up from our body. Those feelings are sometimes of worry, breathlessness, anxiety; sometimes peace and repose. It is certain that exercise will tend to train the body toward the latter feelings. The latter feelings are certainly an essential ingredient of all perfect human character

WILLIAM JAMES, 1899, PP. 220–221

Stress, anxiety, and depression have become increasingly prevalent in contemporary society. Recent estimates suggest that over 40 million adults in the United States suffer from clinically meaningful elevations in depressive and anxiety symptoms (Kessler et al., 1994). Emotional disturbance has adverse effects upon health and well-being and represents one of the leading causes of disability adjusted life years (i.e., years of life lived with meaningfully compromised function and well-being). Taken collectively, the deleterious effects of mood disturbance have serious social, economic, and public health implications. Although effective for many individuals, traditional medical and counseling approaches used in the treatment of mood disturbance are also time consuming and expensive, and have been associated with potentially adverse side effects. Consequently, there is considerable interest in identifying safe, effective, inexpensive behavioral interventions that can be implemented as either alternative or adjuvant approaches to the prevention and treatment of mood disorders.

The physical health benefits of physical activity are well established. Regular physical activity and exercise participation are linked with prevention of all-cause mortality and reductions in risks for a variety of chronic diseases, including coronary heart disease, cancer, and diabetes (Blair, Lamont, & Nichamon, 2004). Exercise therapy is advocated for inclusion in the treatment of many chronic diseases, such as heart disease, arthritis, and diabetes. Furthermore, physical activity is an integral

73

component of weight-management strategies and is widely considered an important part of countering the rising obesity epidemic and the mortality risk accompanying being overweight or obese (Bouchard, 2001; Focht, Rejeski, & Rejeski, 2005; Wing, 1999).

In addition to producing improvements in these valuable physical health outcomes, there is now mounting evidence that physical activity is also associated with significant improvements in psychological well-being. Accordingly, scientific and practical interest in determining the value of applying physical activity as an independent treatment, or integrating physical activity in conjunction with traditional mental health treatment approaches, has increased dramatically during the past 30 years. The primary purpose of the present chapter is to provide an overview of the relationship between exercise and psychological well-being. The specific objectives of this review include: (a) summarizing the extant literature addressing the effects of exercise on select psychological well-being outcomes, (b) providing an overview of the mechanisms proposed to explain the psychological benefits of exercise, and (c) addressing the role of psychological responses to exercise in promoting the adoption and maintenance of regular physical activity participation.

PHYSICAL ACTIVITY, EXERCISE, AND PSYCHOLOGICAL WELL-BEING: KEY DEFINITIONS AND DISTINCTIONS

As scientific and applied interest in the psychological benefits of a physically active lifestyle has developed, the importance of appropriately defining both the key aspects of physical activity behavior as well as the relevant psychological outcomes it influences has received increased attention. Accordingly, definitions of physical activity, exercise, and select psychological outcomes that have been investigated in conjunction with physical activity participation are provided in the following section.

Physical Activity and Exercise

Physical activity is defined as any bodily movement involving the skeletal muscles that results in an appreciable increase in energy expenditure (Blair et al., 2004; Caspersen, 1989). Consistent with this definition, physical activity is now recognized as an umbrella concept that comprises a wide variety of movement-related forms of activities, including, but not limited to, exercise, occupational activity, purposeful activity, sports participation, and other physically active leisure-time pursuits. By contrast, *exercise* is a subtype of physical activity that is defined as planned, repetitive involvement in various forms of structured physical activity (e.g., walking, running, cycling, group fitness, strength training, yoga) for the purpose of attaining desired fitness outcomes, such as improvements in cardiovascular endurance, muscular strength, muscle tone, flexibility, body composition, and weight management.

DEFINING PSYCHOLOGICAL WELL-BEING: DISTINGUISHING KEY OUTCOMES

There is evidence that exercise results in beneficial changes in a wide variety of psychological outcomes. Exercise has been linked with improvements in affect, mood, self-esteem, self-efficacy, depression, anxiety, and quality of life (Berger & Tobar, 2007; Dishman & Buckworth, 2002; Ekkekakis & Acevedo, 2007; Lox, Martin Ginis, & Petruzzello, 2006; McAuley & Blissmer, 2000;

Rejeski & Mihalko, 2001). As the empirical evidence addressing the mental health benefits of exercise has grown, considerable debate regarding the definition and appropriate measurement of many of these outcomes has emerged in the contemporary exercise psychology literature (Ekkekakis, 2008; Ekkekakis & Petruzzello, 2001; Gauvin & Rejeski, 2001). It has been contended that some researchers in the exercise psychology literature have frequently used terms such as affect, mood, and emotion synonymously when they actually represent unique psychological constructs with distinct, identifiable characteristics. A consensus regarding the most appropriate definition or measurement approach for each of the psychological constructs that are favorably influenced by exercise has yet to be reached. A comprehensive summary of the definition and measurement debate is beyond the scope of the present chapter. However, for the purposes of this chapter, *psychological well-being* is defined as an individual's perceptions and evaluation of his or her own life that reflects a general state of favorable mental functioning and well-being. Psychological well-being is characterized by the experience of greater positive affect, relative absence of negative affect, successful cognitive function, fulfilling relationships with others, and the ability to effectively cope with stress and adversity. Psychological well-being encompasses a wide range of psychological outcomes, including ratings of basic pleasure and activation (affect), mood, and distinct emotions (e.g., anxiety, depression, and anger). The idea that people feel better following exercise has become very well established. However, there are many different terms used to describe the psychological responses to exercise (Dishman & Buckworth, 2002; Lox et al., 2006). Recently, some researchers in the exercise psychology literature have placed considerable emphasis on resolving what they contend to be confusion, and potential misuse, of the terminology commonly used to describe the psychological outcomes most frequently assessed in conjunction with exercise participation (Ekkekakis, 2008; Ekkekakis & Acevedo, 2007; Ekkekakis & Petruzzello, 2001; Lox et al., 2006). Although some debate regarding the definition of key psychological constructs persists, there is sufficient consensus to operationally define many of these important outcomes. Thus, distinguishing key terms that are used to describe psychological responses to exercise is an important consideration in the exercise psychology literature. *Feelings* are subjective experiences that reflect bodily sensations, cognitive appraisals, or some combination of these responses (Dishman & Buckworth, 2002; Lox et al., 2006). *Emotions* (e.g., anxiety, depression, anger, fear, pride) are immediate responses that involve cognitive appraisal of an eliciting stimulus whereby a person, situation, or event is perceived as having a potential impact upon one's well-being. Similarly, *moods* are subjective states that also involve cognitive appraisal. However, moods are considered to be less intense and of longer duration than emotions. Additionally, moods can be experienced temporally more distant or removed from the eliciting stimulus relative to emotions. Conversely, *affect* is considered a more general valenced state involving basic ratings of pleasure and activation. Any valenced state is considered an affective response. Therefore, mood and emotions are often subsumed under the general rubric of affective responses. Irrespective of differences in terminology applied, there is sufficient evidence to contend that exercise produces meaningful improvements in each of these psychological outcomes.

Systematic study of the effects of exercise has been conducted on a variety of psychological outcomes, including affect (Ekkekakis & Petruzzello, 1999), mood (Berger & Motl, 2000), self-esteem (Lox et al., 2006), cognitive functioning (Netz, 2007), and quality of life (Berger & Tobar, 2007; Rejeski & Mihalko, 2001). The majority of recent research addressing the relationship between exercise and psychological well-being has focused upon the effects of *exercise participation* on changes in self-reported indices of *affect*, *depression*, and *anxiety*.

Exercise and Depression

Depression is a stress-related emotion characterized by feelings of sadness, despair, and discouragement (Dishman & Buckworth, 2002; Landers & Arent, 2007). Depressive symptoms are often linked with low self-esteem, withdrawal from interpersonal contact, and disturbances in sleep and eating behaviors. Depression is one of the most prevalent mental health issues in the United States, with estimates that over 19 million Americans experience significant depressive symptoms each year (Kessler et al., 1994).

There is considerable evidence linking physical activity participation with reduced risk of depression. Epidemiological findings demonstrate a significant inverse relationship between physical activity and depressive symptoms, with higher levels of activity being associated with lower levels of self-reported depressive symptoms and reduced risk of being diagnosed with depression (Dishman, Washburn, & Heath, 2004; Mutrie, 2000). Findings from the Harvard Alumni study also revealed that men who expended > 2500 kcal per week through physical activity had a 28 percent decrease in the risk of developing depression (Paffenbarger, Lee, & Leung, 1994). Taken collectively, inactivity is now acknowledged as being an independent risk factor for developing depressive symptoms and depressive disorders (Lox et al., 2006).

Whereas overall physical activity participation is strongly linked with reduced risk of developing depressive symptoms, exercise participation has also been consistently shown to produce meaningful reductions in depressive symptoms. Findings from meta-analytic reviews reveal that exercise resulted in significantly greater reduction in depressive symptoms (effect sizes ranging from –.53 to –1.01) when compared to comparison or control treatments (Craft & Landers, 1998; Lawlor & Hopker, 2001; North, McCullagh, & Tran, 1990). The meta-analytic findings indicate that comparable antidepressant benefits are observed for both aerobic exercise and resistance exercise. Additionally, no consistent differences emerged as a function of individual characteristics such as age, gender, ethnicity, or fitness level. However, the observation of higher effect sizes accompanying exercise in individuals with diagnosed depressive disorders (Craft & Landers, 1998) suggests that those exhibiting the highest baseline depressive symptoms may experience the most pronounced reductions in depression following exercise participation. No systematic differences in reductions in depressive symptoms were documented as a function of exercise program characteristics such as intensity, duration, frequency, or mode (Craft & Landers, 1998; Lawlor & Hopker, 2001; North et al., 1990).

Given the beneficial effects accompanying exercise, there has been interest in directly comparing the effects of exercise with those of common treatments for depression such as psychotherapeutic counseling interventions and antidepressant medications. Results from a limited number of studies also demonstrate that exercise is comparable to psychotherapy (Freemont & Craighead, 1987; Greist et al., 1979) and antidepressant medication (Blumenthal et al., 1999). In this regard, there are several findings of interest that warrant additional explanation. For example, it is interesting to note that although exercise has been shown to be similarly effective as traditional cognitive therapy, there does not appear to be any added antidepressant benefit when the treatments are combined (Freemont & Craighead, 1987).

Recent studies directly comparing the effects of exercise to antidepressant medications have yielded similar findings (Babyak et al., 2000; Blumenthal et al., 1999; Brenes et al., 2007). However, although findings of a recent study examining the effects of exercise alone, medication alone, and a combination of exercise and medication resulted in comparable antidepressant effects, there were unique trajectories in the timeline of change in depressive symptoms and maintenance of the observed treatment effects between the interventions (Blumenthal et al., 1999). Notably, whereas the intervention of antidepressant medication alone elicited the most rapid initial treatment response (Blumenthal et al., 1999), participants receiving exercise alone were less likely to have relapsed six months following the cessation of treatment (Babyak et al., 2000). Therefore, whereas exercise and medication produced comparable reductions in depressive symptoms, the combination of exercise and medication did not operate in a synergistic fashion to yield additional benefit over the implementation of either treatment alone. More important, the antidepressant effect persisted longer following exercise, and patients receiving exercise were less likely to experience a recurrence of depression when compared to those who received medication only. Although the mechanisms responsible for the superior maintenance of the treatment effect following exercise presently remain unclear, it is possible that features of the treatments, such as the ability to self-administer exercise and the potential development of tolerance to antidepressant medications, may contribute to the observed differences.

In contrast to meta-analytic findings (Craft & Landers, 1998; Lawlor & Hopker, 2001; North et al., 1990), there is emerging evidence suggesting that there may be a dose–response effect of exercise on depressive symptoms. Dunn and colleagues (Dunn, Trivedi, Kampert, Clark, & Chambliss, 2005) reported an exercise program in which participants achieved a weekly caloric expenditure consistent with public health recommendations (expenditure of 17.5 kcal/kg of body weight) that resulted in more favorable reductions in self-rated depressive symptoms relative to an exercise program that prescribed a lower dose of exercise (expenditure of 7 kcal/kg of body weight). Therefore, achieving public health recommendations for energy expenditure through physical activity is associated with a superior antidepressant effect than an exercise program that requires lower energy expenditure.

Parenthetically, in addressing dose–response effects of exercise on depression, it should be acknowledged that short periods of significantly increased exercise participation performed at or near maximal capacity, referred to as overtraining, have been linked with increases in mood disturbance and depressive symptoms (O'Connor, 1997). Staleness, which has been proposed to reflect an exercise-induced form of depression, is believed to be elicited by periods of exercise overtraining and is characterized by increases in overall mood disturbance, depression, anxiety, and fatigue, as well as concomitant reductions in energy and overall physical performance. It should be recognized that overtraining and staleness have only been observed among individuals who consistently participate in strenuous exercise training programs (i.e., competitive athletes). The volume and intensity adopted in such rigorous exercise training programs considerably exceeds the amount of physical activity advocated for the derivation of health and well-being benefits. The doses of activity associated with overtraining and the onset of staleness also considerably exceed the typical amount of physical activity performed by the average adult. Consequently, given that rates of sedentary behavior remain alarmingly high among U.S. adults, the risk of experiencing increased mood disturbance accompanying exercise overtraining and staleness is unlikely to be a concern for the majority of Americans, many of whom fail to achieve the minimum amount of moderate-intensity physical activity necessary to obtain health benefits.

In summary, epidemiological findings demonstrate that physical activity is associated with reduced risk of developing depression. Additionally, exercise participation is reliably associated with meaningful reductions in depressive symptoms that are comparable to benefits accompanying common treatments such as medication, psychotherapy, and counseling interventions. The antidepressant benefits of exercise are observed independent of differences in individual demographic factors or program characteristics. Thus, it appears that multiple types of exercise prescriptions can yield clinically meaningful antidepressant effects for a wide variety of people.

Taken collectively, exercise represents a promising adjuvant behavioral intervention to aid in alleviating depressive symptoms.

The Anxiolytic Effects of Exercise

Anxiety is an unpleasant emotion involving the appraisal of real or imagined threat to self. Anxiety is characterized by feelings of apprehension, self-doubt, and tension as well as physiological symptoms such as increased heart rate, sweating, and breathlessness. Overall, the various anxiety disorders represent the most common forms of mood disturbance in the United States, affecting over 20 million adults.

Over the past 30 years, reductions in anxiety have become one of the most frequently studied psychological effects of exercise participation. However, investigation of the anxiolytic effects of exercise and integration of exercise into treatment approaches designed to alleviate anxiety symptoms was impeded for some time by erroneous beliefs about the potentially anxiety-precipitating effects accompanying exercise and lactate accumulation among patients with anxiety disorders. Specifically, it was widely believed that the lactate accumulation accompanying exercise participation increases anxiety symptoms and precipitates panic attacks in patients with, or at risk for, anxiety disorders (Pitts & McClure, 1969). However, the Pitts–McClure hypothesis of the exercise–anxiety relationship has been ably refuted by over 30 years of research with virtually no documented incidence of exercise-induced panic attacks (O'Connor, Raglin, & Martinsen, 2000; O'Connor, Smith, & Morgan, 2000), as well as the consistent finding that exercise alleviates anxiety and stress symptoms (Raglin, 1997).

The anxiolytic effects of exercise have been widely investigated. Decreases in state anxiety (i.e., immediate, transient feelings of apprehension in response to perceived threat) following participation in single or acute episodes of aerobic exercise are one of the most frequently documented findings in the contemporary exercise psychology literature (Petruzzello, Landers, Hatfield, Kubitz, & Salazar, 1991; Raglin, 1997). Although studied far less frequently than the effects of acute exercise on state anxiety, exercise training interventions have also reliably yielded clinically meaningful reductions in trait anxiety (i.e., one's general disposition to appraising situations as threatening).

Results of meta-analytic (Petruzzello et al., 1991) and comprehensive narrative reviews (Landers & Arent, 2007; Raglin, 1997) suggest that acute bouts of aerobic exercise produce reductions in state anxiety (effect size = −.25 to −.50) that emerge almost immediately following the cessation of activity and persist for up to six hours post-exercise. More recently, findings from a series of investigations also provide support for the anxiolytic benefits of acute bouts of resistance exercise (Arent, Landers, Matt, & Etnier, 2005; Bartholomew & Linder, 1998; Focht, 2002; Focht & Arent, 2008; Focht & Koltyn, 1999; Focht, Koltyn, & Bouchard, 2000). The results of these studies suggest that the most favorable reductions in state anxiety were observed following moderate-intensity resistance exercise and the greatest benefits were obtained by those reporting the highest levels of pre-exercise anxiety levels (Focht, 2002; Focht & Arent, 2008). Together, these findings provide support for the anxiolytic benefits of single episodes of both aerobic and resistance exercise.

Meta-analytic findings (Petruzzello et al., 1991) also demonstrate that exercise training programs consistently result in significant reductions in trait anxiety (effect size = −.33). Individuals exhibiting the highest levels of anxiety prior to exercise report the greatest post-exercise reductions in trait anxiety. Additionally, although there is limited number of studies that directly compare the effects of exercise with other common treatments for anxiety disorders, preliminary evidence demonstrated that exercise and medication resulted in comparable anxiolytic benefits (Broocks et al., 1998).

It should be recognized that much of the existing exercise–anxiety research has been conducted in samples of nonanxious individuals reporting anxiety levels that are lower than age-related normative values. However, the magnitude of improvement in anxiety has been consistently greater among individuals exhibiting higher levels of anxiety prior to initiating exercise training (Focht, 2002; Petruzzello et al., 1991; Raglin, 1997). Thus, while there have been relatively few investigations examining the benefits of exercise for reducing anxiety symptoms in samples of individuals with diagnosed anxiety disorders, the limited available evidence (Broocks et al., 1998; Martinsen, Hoffart, & Solberg, 1989; Petruzzello et al., 1991) provides support for exercise as an efficacious adjuvant therapeutic strategy for those with elevated levels of anxiety. Clearly, given the alarming prevalence of anxiety disorders in the United States, further research addressing the benefits of exercise for reductions in trait anxiety and clinical anxiety symptoms is necessary to determine the scope and magnitude of benefit that exercise may have.

Affective Responses to Exercise

Investigation of the effects of acute exercise on the valence and activation dimensions of basic affect has recently emerged as a focal area of interest in the contemporary exercise psychology literature (Ekkekakis, 2003; Ekkekakis & Acevedo, 2007). Prior to 2000, much of the research investigating the relationship between exercise and psychological well-being focused upon categorical psychological responses such as state anxiety or select mood and feeling states. However, a trend in recent research has been to conceptualize and measure affective responses from a dimensional perspective utilizing the circumplex model of affect (Russell, 1980). Studies conducted within the context of the circumplex model of affect have examined changes in the bipolar dimensions of pleasure and activation (Ekkekakis, 2008) during and following single episodes of exercise.

Consistent with prior research addressing changes in categorical psychological states, findings from this line of inquiry generally demonstrate that moderate-intensity bouts of aerobic exercise result in improvements in ratings of pleasure following exercise (Ekkekakis, 2003; Ekkekakis & Petruzzello, 1999). However, important individual differences have been observed. For example, whereas changes in affective responses from pre- to post-exercise are generally homogenous and positive in nature, responses observed during exercise have been found to be heterogeneous, with some participants experiencing improvements, some reporting declines, and others demonstrating no change (Van Landuyt, Ekkekakis, Hall, & Petruzzello, 2000). Furthermore, acute exercise that is sufficiently demanding to cause participants to exceed their ventilatory threshold (i.e., essentially the marker for the lactate threshold and the point of transition to greater use of anaerobic metabolism to meet the exercise demands) results in negative affective responses (Ekkekakis & Lind, 2006). Collectively, these findings suggest there may be considerable individual variability in the affective responses to acute exercise, particularly during activity. Based on these findings, Ekkekakis (2003) proposed the dual mode model in an attempt to explain the individual variability and negative shifts in affect observed when exercise exceeds the ventilatory threshold. The model suggests that there may be systematic shifts in the influence of cognitive and physiological cues upon the affective responses as exercise intensity increases. According to the dual mode model, cognitive factors play a central role in shaping affective responses during exercise performed at a steady state. Conversely, interoceptive, physiological cues are proposed to have primacy in influencing affective responses once exercise demand surpasses the ventilatory threshold.

Exercise performed at intensities that are proximal to, yet below, the ventilatory threshold appear to result in considerable variability in affective responses (Ekkekakis, 2003; Van Landuyt et al., 2000). At this intensity, some people report positive affective responses, whereas others report declines in pleasure. The divergent responses have been proposed to be related to key cognitive and/or evaluative judgments such as self-efficacy (Ekkekakis, 2003). That is, those who have higher self-efficacy for exercise appear to be better able to tolerate the exertional demands of exercise performed at or near the lactate threshold, and consequently report more favorable affective responses. However, when exercise intensity exceeds the ventilatory threshold, affective variability decreases, with shifts toward less favorable affective responses becoming more common. Findings from this line of inquiry may have important implications for individualized exercise prescription and the development of exercise guidelines. However, although these findings are of considerable interest, evidence supporting the tenets of the dual mode model remains relatively limited. Accordingly, the veracity of this model for explaining affective responses to acute exercise warrants further investigation.

In summary, there is now a considerable body of evidence demonstrating that exercise is consistently associated with psychological benefits, including significant improvements in affect, depression, and anxiety. Although it is now well established that exercise can yield clinically relevant improvements in an array of psychological outcomes, the mechanisms underlying the beneficial effect of exercise upon psychological well-being have yet to be adequately delineated. Numerous hypotheses have been proposed in an attempt to explain the beneficial effect of exercise on psychological well-being. The majority of proposed explanations can be categorized as addressing either primarily psychological or biological mechanisms. A brief overview of the most viable and frequently cited mechanisms proposed to be responsible for the psychological beneficence of exercise is provided in the following section.

Proposed Psychological Mechanisms

The *mastery hypothesis* suggests that the psychological benefits of exercise are derived from a sense of accomplishment or increase in one's perceived capabilities that can accompany exercise participation. This perspective proposes that self-efficacy beliefs may play an important role in the psychological benefits of exercise. Self-efficacy, one's belief in his or her ability to successfully satisfy specific situational demands (Bandura, 1997), has been consistently demonstrated to be a relevant antecedent, outcome, and mediator of exercise behavior (McAuley & Blissmer, 2000). It is well established that self-efficacy is consistently correlated with exercise participation (Dishman & Buckworth, 2002; Trost, Owen, Baumann, Sallis, & Brown, 2002). However, there is also mounting evidence that affective benefits of exercise are related to self-efficacy beliefs (Focht, Knapp, Gavin, Raedeke, & Hickner, 2007; Jerome et al., 2002; McAuley, Talbot, & Martinez, 1999; Raedeke, Focht, & Scales, 2007). Notably, individuals reporting the highest self-efficacy demonstrate the most favorable psychological responses to exercise, and changes in self-efficacy are strongly related to changes in affect (Focht et al., 2007). Furthermore, findings from a limited number of studies demonstrated that experimental manipulations that successfully enhanced self-efficacy beliefs resulted in significantly improved affective responses to acute exercise (Jerome et al., 2002; McAuley et al., 1999).

The *distraction hypothesis* proposes that exercise improves psychological well-being by distracting individuals from daily worries or stressors (Raglin & Morgan, 1987). Initial support for the distraction hypothesis emanated from studies demonstrating comparable, significant reductions in state anxiety following exercise, relaxation, meditation, and quiet rest sessions (Garvin,

Koltyn, & Morgan, 1997; Raglin & Morgan, 1987). However, more recent evidence addressing the viability of the distraction hypothesis has been equivocal with some studies demonstrating that exercise results in superior improvements in select psychological responses when compared to quiet rest (Focht & Hausenblas, 2001; McAuley, Mihalko, & Bane, 1996). For example, whereas exercise and quiet rest yielded comparable reductions in state anxiety, exercise resulted in significantly greater improvements in positive affective states such as energy, engagement, and enjoyment (Focht & Hausenblas, 2001).

The *enjoyment* and *social interaction* hypotheses propose that exercise elicits psychological benefits because it is perceived as being a pleasurable activity or because it promotes interpersonal interaction, respectively (Lox et al., 2006). These explanations have considerable intuitive appeal and may, in part, account for the psychological benefits of exercise. Nonetheless, there is little empirical evidence supporting either hypothesis, and it is unlikely that either accounts entirely for improvements in psychological well-being given that: (a) exercise performed alone has been linked with improvements in psychological outcomes and (b) favorable affective responses have been observed following exercise not rated as being particularly enjoyable (Focht, 2009; Lox et al., 2006).

Proposed Biological Mechanisms

The *monoamine hypothesis* suggests that exercise-induced changes in the monoaminergic systems in the brain, similar to those observed with many contemporary psychotherapeutic medications, are responsible for the psychological benefits accompanying exercise (Dishman & Buckworth, 2002; Landers & Arent, 2007). For example, selective serotonin reuptake inhibitors (SSRIs) and monoamine oxidase inhibitors (MAOIs) work by altering the amounts of neurotransmitters such as serotonin, norepinephrine, and dopamine available in the synapses in the brain. Consistent with this therapeutic mechanism of action, exercise has been shown to result in similar effects on central monoaminergic systems (Chaouloff, 1997; Dishman, 1997). At the present time, however, direct evidence that exercise consistently produces increases in brain levels of monoamines remains sparse. The limited empirical evidence is due, in part, to the challenges associated with obtaining accurate measures of brain levels of monoamine concentrations.

The *endorphin hypothesis* is frequently cited in the popular fitness media as the primary mechanism underlying exercise-induced improvements in psychological states. However, empirical evidence supporting the endorphin hypothesis remains inconsistent. Additionally, the plausibility of endorphins having direct effects on the central nervous system is limited due to the restricted permeability of the blood–brain barrier to endorphins (Dishman & Buckworth, 2002; Landers & Arent, 2007). Thus, whereas endorphins are frequently implicated in the psychological responses to exercise, given the lack of direct effects of plasma endorphins on the brain, it is unlikely they play a primary role in the affective benefits of exercise.

There are numerous additional psychologically and biologically oriented explanations for the relationship between exercise and psychological well-being, including social support, hypo-thalamic-pituitary-adrenal axis, brain-derived neurotrophic factor, and thermogenic hypotheses. Whereas each of these proposed mechanisms remains viable, they have either received insuffi-cient study to confirm their plausibility or have received mixed empirical support at the present time. Each potential explanation warrants further inquiry to determine the extent to which it may contribute to the psychological benefits of exercise.

Although there are equivocal findings for each of the aforementioned explanations, unitary support for any single underlying mechanism is presently absent. Furthermore, the complexity of the relationship between exercise and psychological well-being makes it unlikely that any single mechanism is entirely responsible for these beneficial outcomes. Because each mechanism has unique features that can plausibly influence the psychological responses to exercise, it is reasonable to contend that the psychological beneficence of exercise is due to multiple, redundant mechanisms encompassing both biological and psychological factors. Thus, it is possible that some, or all, of the proposed mechanisms are viable and may operate, at least partially, in conjunction with each other to explain the influence of exercise upon psychological well-being.

The Challenge of Promoting Physical Activity Participation: A Role for Psychological Outcomes?

Despite considerable evidence of the physical and psychological benefits of an active lifestyle, physical activity participation rates remain disturbingly low in the United States (Blair et al., 2004; Dishman et al., 2004). Physical activity is unquestionably a complex health behavior, and numerous factors have been linked with physical activity participation. Correlates of physical activity represent a complex constellation of factors, including, but not limited to, demographic and personal, psychological, behavioral, social and cultural, environmental, and activity characteristic factors (Blair et al., 2004; Dishman & Buckworth, 2002; Dishman et al., 2004).

Psychological constructs are proposed to be integral determinants of behavior in several well-established theories of health behavior that are frequently applied to explain physical activity participation. The theory of planned behavior is one of the most commonly employed theoretical frameworks used to explain the adoption and maintenance of health behaviors (Ajzen, 1991). This conceptual framework posits that the positive and/or negative evaluation of a behavior (attitude), perceived social pressure to engage in a behavior (subjective norm), and perceived control over participation (perceived behavioral control) determine an individual's intention to engage in health behaviors. There is considerable evidence supporting the relationship between theory-of-planned-behavior constructs and exercise behavior, and strong associations between the constructs of intention and exercise, perceived behavioral control and intention, and attitude and intention have been reported in recent meta-analyses addressing the application of the theory of planned behavior in the exercise domain (Symons-Downs & Hausenblas, 2005).

Social cognitive theory proposes there are bidirectional, reciprocally deterministic relationships among the person, environment, and behavior that shape behavioral tendencies and the motivation to take action (Bandura, 1997). Self-efficacy, the primary motivational construct in social cognitive theory, is one of the strongest, most consistent correlates of physical activity behavior (McAuley & Blissmer, 2000; Trost et al., 2002). Consequently, there is considerable support for the position that one's self-efficacy beliefs serve as an integral determinant of physical activity participation.

Hedonic theories of motivation suggest that people generally engage in activities perceived as being pleasurable and avoid participating in activities that elicit feelings of displeasure (Emmons & Diener, 1986; Loewenstein & Lerner, 2003; Watson, 2002). Hence, within this perspective on motivation, affective responses play an integral role in behavioral decision making. Thus, the amount of pleasure or displeasure that one experiences during exercise may influence the likelihood that the individual subsequently adopts or maintains regular participation.

Affective responses observed early in structured exercise programs have been shown to be associated with exercise adherence (Carels, Berger, & Darby, 2006; Kwan & Bryan, in press; Williams et al., 2008). Emerging empirical evidence also demonstrates relationships between affective responses to acute exercise and the central motivational constructs identified in social cognitive theories of health behavior. For example, Focht (2009) recently observed that affective responses to a 10-minute walk were significantly related to intention to walk for exercise. Additionally, affective responses to acute exercise are significantly correlated with self-efficacy beliefs in recent findings (Focht et al., 2007; Raedeke et al., 2007). Affective responses are also proposed to shape the formation of attitude (Ajzen, 1991) and self-efficacy beliefs (Bandura, 1997), providing a conceptual link between how one feels and his or her motivation for behavior as proposed in established theories of health behavior. Thus, the psychological responses to exercise may play an important role in determining the adoption and maintenance of regular physical activity participation. The relationship observed between affective states, adherence, and established theory-based correlates of physical activity in recent research suggests that affective responses to acute exercise merit consideration in efforts to promote physical activity.

Overall Summary

Recognition of the psychological benefits of exercise continues to grow. There is now a considerable body of empirical evidence supporting the beneficial effect of physical activity and exercise on a wide range of psychological responses, including anxiety, depression, mood, and affect. These responses represent important aspects of psychological well-being and warrant further inquiry as efforts to attenuate the personal, social, and economic costs of mental health disorders in the United States continue. An important caveat must be acknowledged when considering the relationship between exercise and psychological well-being. Although exercise is linked with clinically meaningful improvements in a wide array of psychological responses, it would be imprudent for exercise to be advocated as a substitute for other well-established and efficacious treatment strategies. However, exercise clearly has benefits for improving psychological well-being, and focused efforts to determine how exercise and physical activity can be most effectively integrated into comprehensive approaches to the prevention and treatment of mental health disorders would be particularly informative.

Exercise-related improvements in these outcomes may also favorably influence motivation to adopt and maintain regular physical activity participation. Accordingly, further investigation of the extent to which improvements in psychological well-being may aid in efforts of physical activity promotion and obesity prevention is also of great public health importance. Taken collectively, findings from the extant research provide compelling support for the psychological beneficence of exercise and reinforce the notion that a healthy mind does indeed reside within a healthy body.

References

Ajzen, I. (1991). The theory of planned behavior. *Organizational Behavior and Human Decision Processes, 50,* 179–211.

Arent, S. M., Landers, D. M., Matt, K. S., & Etnier, J. L. (2005). Dose-response and mechanistic issues in the resistance training and affect relationship. *Journal of Sport and Exercise Psychology, 27,* 92–110.

Babyak, M., Blumenthal, J. A., Herman, P., Khatri, M., Doraiswamy, P. M., Moore, K., Craighead, W. E., Baldewicz, T. T., & Krishnan, K. R. (2000). Exercise treatment for major depression: Maintenance of therapeutic benefit at 10 months. *Psychosomatic Medicine, 62,* 633–638.

Bandura, A. (1997). *Self-efficacy: The exercise of control.* New York: Freeman.

Bartholomew, J. B., & Linder, D. E. (1998). State anxiety following resistance exercise: The role of gender and exercise intensity. *Journal of Behavioral Medicine, 21,* 205–219.

Berger, B. G., & Motl, R. W. (2000). Exercise and mood: A selective review and synthesis of research employing the Profile of Mood States. *Journal of Applied Sport Psychology, 12,* 69–92.

Berger, B. G., & Tobar, D. A. (2007). Physical activity and quality of life: Key considerations. In G. Tennenbaum & R. C. Eklund (Eds.), *Handbook of sport psychology* (pp. 598–620). Hoboken, NJ: John Wiley & Sons.

Blair, S. N., LaMonte, M. J., & Nichamon, M. Z. (2004). The evolution of physical activity recommendations: How much is enough? *American Journal of Clinical Nutrition, 79,* 913S–920S.

Blumenthal, J. A., Babyak, M. A., Moore, W. E., Craighead, W. E., Herman, S., Khatri, P., Waugh, R., Napolitano, M. A., Forman, L. M., Appelbaum, M., Doraiswamy, P. M., & Krishnan, K. R. (1999). Effects of exercise training on older patients with major depression. *Archives of Internal Medicine, 159,* 2349–2356.

Bouchard, C. (2001). *Physical activity and obesity.* Champaign, IL: Human Kinetics.

Brenes, G. A., Williamson, J. D., Messier, S. P., Rejeski, W. J., Pahor, M., Ip, E., & Penninx, B. (2007). Treatment of minor depression in older adults: a pilot study comparing sertraline and exercise. *Aging and Mental Health, 11,* 61–68.

Broocks, A., Bandelow, B., Pekrun, G., George, A., Meyer, T., Bartmann, U., Hillmer-Vogel, U., & Ruther, E. (1998). Comparison of aerobic exercise, clomipramine, and placebo in the treatment of panic disorder. *American Journal of Psychiatry, 155,* 603–609.

Carels, R. A., Berger, B. G., & Darby, L. (2006). The association between mood states and physical activity in post-menopausal, obese, sedentary women. *Journal of Aging and Physical Activity, 14,* 12–28.

Caspersen, C. J. (1989). Physical activity epidemiology: Concepts, methods, and applications to exercise science. *Exercise and Sport Sciences Reviews, 17,* 423–473.

Chaouloff, F. (1997). The serotonin hypothesis. In W. P. Morgan (Ed.), *Physical activity and mental health* (pp. 179–198). Washington, DC: Taylor and Francis.

Craft, L. L., & Landers, D. M. (1998). The effect of exercise on clinical depression and depression resulting from mental illness: A meta-analysis. *Journal of Sport and Exercise Psychology, 20,* 339–357.

Dishman, R. K. (1997). The norepinephrine hypothesis. In W. P. Morgan (Ed.), *Physical activity and mental health* (pp. 199–212). Washington, DC: Taylor and Francis.

Dishman, R. K., & Buckworth, J. (2002). *Exercise psychology.* Champaign, IL: Human Kinetics.

Dishman, R. K., Washburn, R. A., & Heath, G. W. (2004). *Physical activity epidemiology.* Champaign, IL: Human Kinetics.

Dunn, A. L., Trivedi, M. H., Kampert, J. B., Clark, C. G., & Chambliss, H. O. (2005). Exercise treatment for depression: Efficacy and dose response. *American Journal of Preventive Medicine, 28,* 1–8.

Ekkekakis, P. (2003). Pleasure and displeasure from the body: Perspectives from exercise. *Cognition and Emotion, 17,* 213–239.

Ekkekakis, P. (2008). Affective circumplex redux: The discussion on its utility as measurement framework in exercise psychology continues. *International Review of Sport and Exercise Psychology, 1,* 139–159.

Ekkekakis, P., & Acevedo, E. (2007). *The psychobiology of exercise.* Champaign, IL: Human Kinetics.

Ekkekakis, P., & Lind, E. (2006). Exercise does not feel the same when you are overweight: The impact of self-selected and imposed intensity on affect and exertion. *International Journal of Obesity, 30,* 652–660.

Ekkekakis, P., & Petruzzello, S. J. (1999). Acute aerobic exercise and affect: Current status, problems, and prospects regarding dose-response. *Sports Medicine, 28,* 337–374.

Ekkekakis, P., & Petruzzello, S. J. (2001). Analysis of the affect measurement conundrum in exercise psychology: II. A conceptual and methodological critique of the Exercise-Induced Feeling Inventory. *Psychology of Sport and Exercise, 2,* 1–26.

Emmons, R. A., & Diener, E. (1986). A goal-affect analysis of everyday situational choices. *Journal of Research in Personality, 20,* 309–326.

Focht, B. C. (2002). Pre-exercise anxiety and the anxiolytic responses to acute bouts of self-selected and prescribed intensity resistance exercise. *Journal of Sports Medicine and Physical Fitness, 42,* 217–223.

Focht, B. C. (2009). Brief walks in outdoor and laboratory environments: Effects on affective responses, enjoyment, and intentions to walk for exercise. *Research Quarterly in Exercise and Sport, 80,* 611–620.

Focht, B. C., & Arent, S. M. (2008). Psychological responses to acute resistance exercise: Current status, contemporary considerations, and future research directions. In J. Giebling & M. Frohlich (Eds.), *Current results of strength training research* (pp. 89–103). Cuvillier Verlag: Gottingen.

Focht, B. C., & Hausenblas, H. A. (2001). Influence of quiet rest and acute aerobic exercise performed in a naturalistic environment on selected psychological responses. *Journal of Sport and Exercise Psychology, 23,* 108–121.

Focht, B. C., Knapp, D. J., Gavin, T. P., Raedeke, T. D., & Hickner, R. C. (2007). Affective and self-efficacy responses to acute aerobic exercise in sedentary older and younger adults. *Journal of Aging and Physical Activity, 15,* 123–138.

Focht, B. C., & Koltyn, K. F. (1999). Influences of resistance exercise of different intensities on state anxiety and blood pressure. *Medicine & Science in Sports & Exercise, 31*(3), 456–463. doi:10.1097/00005768-199903000-00016

Focht, B. C., Koltyn, K. F., & Bouchard, L. J. (2000). State anxiety and blood pressure responses following different resistance exercise sessions. *International Journal of Sport Psychology, 31*(3), 376–390.

Focht, B. C., Rejeski, W. J., & Rejeski, A. F. (2005). Treating obesity in patients with knee osteoarthritis. *Journal of Musculoskeletal Medicine, 22,* 491–502.

Freemont, J., & Craighead, L. W. (1987). Aerobic exercise and cognitive therapy in the treatment of dysphoric moods. *Cognitive Therapy and Research, 112,* 241–251.

Garvin, A. W., Koltyn, K. F., & Morgan, W. P. (1997). Influence of acute physical activity and relaxation on state anxiety and blood lactate in untrained college males. *International Journal of Sports Medicine, 18,* 470–476.

Gauvin, L., & Rejeski, W. J. (2001). Disentangling substance from rhetoric: A rebuttal to Ekkekakis & Petruzzello. *Psychology of Sport and Exercise, 2,* 73–88.

Griest, J. H., Klein, M. H., Eishens, R. R., Faris, J., Gurman, J. S., & Morgan, W. P. (1979). Running as treatment for depression. *Comprehensive Psychiatry, 20,* 41–54.

James, W. (1899). *Talks to teachers on psychology: And to students on some of life's ideals.* New York: H. Holt.

Jerome, G. J., Marquez, D. X., McAuley, E., Canaklisova, S., Snook, E., & Vickers, M. (2002). Self-efficacy effects on feeling states in women. *International Journal of Behavioral Medicine, 9,* 139–154.

Kessler, R. C., McGonagle, K. A., Zhao, S., Nelson, C. B., Hughes, M., Eshlemen, S., Wittchen, H., & Kendler, K. (1994). Lifetime and 12-month prevalence of DSM-III-R psychiatric disorders in the United States: Results from the National Comorbidity Survey. *Archives of General Psychiatry, 51,* 8–19.

Kwan, B. M., & Bryan, A. D. (in press). Affective response to exercise as a component of exercise motivation: Attitudes, norms, self-efficacy, and temporal stability of intentions. *Psychology of Sport and Exercise.*

Landers, D. M., & Arent, S. M. (2007). Physical activity and mental health. In G. Tennenbaum & R. C. Eklund (Eds.), *Handbook of sport psychology* (pp. 469–491). Hoboken, NJ: John Wiley & Sons.

Lawlor, D. A., & Hopker, S. W. (2001). The effectiveness of exercise as an intervention in the management of depression: A systematic review and meta-regression analysis of randomized controlled trials. *British Medical Journal, 322,* 1–8.

Loewenstein, G., & Lerner, J. S. (2003). The role of affect in decision-making. In R. J. Davidson, K. R. Scherer, & H. H. Goldsmith (Eds.), *Handbook of affective science* (pp. 619–642.) New York: Oxford University Press.

Lox, C. L., Martin Ginis, K. A., & Petruzzello, S. J. (2006). *Psychology of exercise: Integrating theory and practice.* Scottsdale, AZ: Holcomb Hathaway.

Martinsen, E. W., Hoffart, A., & Solberg, O. (1989). Comparing aerobic with nonaerobic forms of exercise in the treatment of clinical depression: A randomized trial. *Comprehensive Psychiatry, 30,* 324–331.

McAuley, E., & Blissmer, B. (2000). Self-efficacy determinants and consequences of physical activity. *Exercise and Sport Sciences Reviews, 28,* 85–88.

McAuley, E., Mihalko, S. L., & Bane, S. (1996). Acute exercise and anxiety reduction: Does the environment matter? *Journal of Sport and Exercise Psychology, 18,* 408–419.

McAuley, E., Talbot, H. M., & Martinez, S. (1999). Manipulating self-efficacy in the exercise environment in women: Influence on affective responses. *Health Psychology, 18,* 288–294.

Mutrie, N. (2000). The relationship between physical activity and clinically-defined depression. In S. J. H. Biddle, K. R. Fox, & S. H. Boutcher (Eds.), *Physical activity and psychological well-being* (pp. 46–62). London: Routledge.

Netz, Y. (2007). Physical activity and three dimensions of psychological functioning in advanced age: Cognition, affect, and self-perception. In G. Tennenbaum & R. C. Eklund (Eds.), *Handbook of sport psychology* (pp. 492–508). Hoboken, NJ: John Wiley & Sons.

North, T. C., McCullagh, P., & Tran, Z. V. (1990). Effect of exercise on depression. *Exercise and Sport Science Reviews, 18,* 379–415.

O'Connor, P. J. (1997). Overtraining and staleness. In W. P. Morgan (Ed.), *Physical activity and mental health* (pp. 145–160). Washington, DC: Taylor and Francis.

O'Connor, P. J., Raglin, J. S., & Martinsen, E. W. (2000). Physical activity, anxiety, and anxiety disorders. *International Journal of Sport Psychology, 31,* 136–155.

O'Connor, P. J., Smith, J. C., & Morgan, W. P. (2000). Physical activity does not provoke panic attacks in patients with panic disorder: A review of the evidence. *Anxiety, Stress, and Coping, 13,* 333–353.

Paffenbarger, R. S., Lee, I. M., & Leung, R. (1994). Physical activity and personal characteristics associated with depression and suicide in American college men. *Acta Psychiatrica Scandinavia, 257,* 16–22.

Petruzzello, S. J., Landers, D. M., Hatfield, B. D., Kubitz, K. A., & Salazar, W. (1991). A meta-analysis of the anxiety-reducing effects of acute and chronic exercise: Outcomes and mechanisms. *Sports Medicine, 11,* 143–182.

Pitts, F. J., & McClure, J. J. (1969). Lactate metabolism in anxiety neurosis. *New England Journal of Medicine, 277,* 1329–1336.

Raedeke, T., Focht, B. C., & Scales, D. (2007). Social environmental factors and psychological responses to acute exercise for socially physique anxious females. *Psychology of Sport and Exercise, 8,* 463–476.

Raglin, J. S. (1997). The anxiolytic effects of physical activity. In W. P. Morgan (Ed.), *Physical activity and mental health* (pp. 107–126). Washington, DC: Taylor and Francis.

Raglin, J. S., & Morgan, W. P. (1987). Influence of exercise and quiet rest on state anxiety and blood pressure. *Medicine and Science in Sports and Exercise, 19,* 456–463.

Rejeski, W. J., & Mihalko, S. L. (2001). Physical activity and quality of life in older adults. *Journals of Gerontology, 56A,* 23–35.

Symons-Downs, D., & Hausenblas, H. A. (2005). The theories of reasoned action and planned behavior applied to exercise: A meta-analytic update. *Journal of Physical Activity and Health, 2,* 76–97.

Trost, S. G., Owen, N., Bauman, A. E., Sallis, J. F., & Brown, W. (2002). Correlated of adults participation in physical activity: Review and update. *Medicine and Science in Sports and Exercise, 34,* 1996–2001.

Van Landuyt, L. M., Ekkekakis, P., Hall, E. E., & Petruzzello, S. J. (2000). Throwing the mountains into the lakes: On the perils of nomothetic conceptions of the exercise-affect relationship. *Journal of Sport and Exercise Psychology, 22,* 208–234.

Watson, D. (2002). Positive affectivity. In C. R. Snyder & S. J. Lopez (Eds.), *Handbook of positive psychology* (pp. 106–119). New York: Oxford University Press.

Williams, D. M., Dunsiger, S., Ciccoli, J. T., Lewis, B. A., Albrecht, A. E., & Marcus, B. H. (2008). Acute affective response to a moderate-intensity exercise stimulus predicts physical activity participation 6 and 12 months later. *Psychology of Sport and Exercise, 9,* 231–245.

Wing, R. R. (1999). Physical activity in the treatment of adulthood overweight and obesity: Current evidence and research issues. *Medicine and Science in Sports and Exercise, 31,* S547–S542.

8 | FINANCIAL WELLNESS

Daniel Gutierrez, Patrick Mullen,
Catherine Griffith, & Christopher Christmas

Zig Ziglar once described money as "not being the most important thing in life but being close to oxygen on the 'gotta have it scale.'" Most likely, as a college student, you can identify with this sentiment. Most attend college with the intention of bettering their lives, but soon after enrollment, they begin to see the various fees and other expenses that tend to weigh down their ambitions and increase their stress levels (Hornak, Farrell, & Jackson, 2010). At the very least, financial worries become one more thing to add to the list of the *many* concerns for the college student, and causes excessive worries that negatively influence wellness. It becomes difficult to focus on class work, or study for midterms, if you find yourself scared that you will not be able to pay rent this month or feel frustrated by the harassing calls from bill collectors. Conversely, being financially well helps individuals avoid these unnecessary stressors and be prepared for life's unexpected events, and serves to increase one's overall wellness.

Maintaining financial wellness does not mean you have to be rich or that you will never have a financial worry. That would be like saying that maintaining physical wellness means you must be an Olympic runner and never catch a cold. In fact, financial satisfaction is not associated with a specific amount of money, and a specific amount of money may make one person feel financially satisfied, while someone else, given the same amount, is left feeling financially stressed (Rutherford & Fox, 2010). Therefore, financial wellness is less about perfection and more about living to your fullest potential. For instance, how would life be different if you did not have to worry about money? Would you be closer to your goals? Would you be able to focus more on school or work? A study conducted by Nelson, Lust, Story, and Ehlinger (2008) reported that students with credit card debt over $1000 were more likely to overeat unhealthy foods, watch excessive amounts of television, and misuse drugs and alcohol. Moreover, college students who are financially strained are more likely to drop out of school (Joo, Durband, & Grable, 2008), and have to work multiple jobs, which usually affects their academic performance (Roberts et al., 2000). Therefore, staying financially well can help you make healthy choices, such as staying in school and keeping a healthy diet; and financial wellness offers you the freedom to focus on things you value, such as school and your future career.

The goal of this chapter is to provide you with some strategies and resources that will help you become financially well. To this aim, we use the following definition of a financially well person:

> The financially well person develops a healthy budget managing both income and expenditures. They develop a discipline of saving to prepare for short-term, long-term, and emergency expenses. They manage credit cards and other consumer credit usage responsibly and develop the skills to manage resources. (Student Wellness Center, Office of Student Life, Ohio State University)

In essence, financially well students are better able to overcome the financial pressures that may come later in life because they know how to handle money and avoid making bad financial decisions. So, how does one become financially well? According to the definition just noted, financial wellness comes from learning how to budget effectively, manage credit wisely, and find overall effective strategies for managing your money. In the next couple of sections, we will expand on this definition and outline how to practice these behaviors. In addition, throughout this chapter we will provide you with some tips and strategies for getting financially well, and at the end of the chapter we will provide resources to help you get back on track, if you have already run into some trouble with finances.

FINANCIAL BUDGETING

One of the first steps you will take toward financial wellness involves budgeting. Have you ever wondered where all your money goes or how you spent that much that fast? It comes down to budgeting. A budget is a calculated plan for effectively using your money. A budget helps you get the most out of every penny. More specifically, a budget determines the *how, what,* and *when* of financial planning. The next section presents and discusses some important information pertaining to budgeting.

KEYS TO BUDGETING

When looking at budgeting, it is important to consider some basics. First, budgeting is personal to you. Each individual has different needs, and thus everyone budgets differently. How George Clooney allocates his funds is going to be much different when compared to the funds allocation of a middle-class family. As such, how you budget your own finances will vary from the methods of peers or family who are facing different life circumstances. Thus, when deciding on how to budget, consider the various lifestyle choices you have and make decisions that are congruent with your own personal preferences.

Next, keep personal budgets simple and make them easy to follow. Making an overly complicated budget will only cause stress and mistakes. "Keep it simple stupid," or *KISS,* is a design principle developed by the U.S. Navy and represents the idea that most things work best when you avoid complexity. Take this same advice when it comes to your budget. When making decisions regarding how you plan to spend money, choose plans that are simple in their design. This allows for ease during implementation. Avoid budget plans that are complex and difficult to enforce. Keeping your budget simple will take away the pressure of following a complex budget.

Last, budgets should be flexible to changing life situations. As you progress through college and into adulthood, life will change, so be prepared to ebb and flow with it. Being flexible allows you to adjust and modify the budget in the case of unforeseen problems or life changes. Flexibility means that you develop a budget that is prepared to change based on unexpected needs or life events (e.g., car breaks down, you or a family member gets chronically ill). Hence, creating some cushion room for these unexpected issues will allow you to stick to your budget even through these difficult times.

In summary, when planning your budget, be sure to consider: (a) your individual needs, (b) keeping it simple, and (c) building in flexibility. These principles may seem overly simple or obvious, but keeping them in mind will help the budget-making process go much more smoothly and be less frustrating. Oftentimes, beginning budgeters overlook these ideas, which results in them not being able to stick to the budgets they have created. You can avoid this experience by being thoughtful in planning your budget.

THE BUDGETING PROCESS

Now that we have an understanding of budgeting basics, let us discuss the budget-planning process. Budgeting your finances can seem intimidating. Therefore, we have broken down the process into four steps: Identify your goals, track your spending, develop your budget, and adjust the budget to accommodate changes in finances. We unpack each of these ideas in the following sections.

Step One: Identify Your Goals

Before you can create a budget, you have to develop your personal goals. Life goals help to steer you in the right direction, help you to evaluate your progress, and give you something to look forward to. Your goals can develop during early adulthood or younger and will probably continue into retirement. When setting goals, it is important to keep in mind the need to be flexible as you progress through different life stages. That is, your financial goals should be different as a college student than when you are in a job or retired. Goals are a crucial component to developing a budget that meets your individual needs.

It is important to consider both short-term and long-term goals when planning. Short-term goals are focused events that will occur within weeks, months, or a year. For example, if a goal is to go on vacation to Cancun for spring break, it would be considered short term. Long-term goals are plans that will result in an event occurring a year or longer from the initial planning. An example of long-term goal is developing a retirement account or a major investment in the stock market. In addition to short- and long-term goals, another type of goal is the enabling goal. When someone establishes an enabling goal, his or her intent is to aid the fulfillment of a long-term goal. Enabling goals are small short-term goals that are steps to achieving the long-term goal. For instance, if your long-term goal is to work as a mental health counselor, a shorter-term goal may be to graduate with a degree in psychology, and an enabling goal would be to attend and participate in class each semester.

Now, it's time for you to create your own goals based on your individual lifestyle and choices. When thinking of personal goals, take some time and write down your initial thoughts about the goals you have. Initially, just write as many ideas as you can develop. No idea is a bad idea. Once you have developed a comprehensive list of goals, start to prioritize the goals by level of importance to you, personally. After reflecting on the most important goals, eliminate some goals that are not as important or are unrealistic. When you have a list of realistic goals, assign deadline (e.g., I will get my bachelor's degree in psychology by May 2015). Some of the goals may be short term and some long term. Nevertheless, develop an idea of when you want to achieve them. Then, identify the amount of money you will need to accomplish the listed goals. Writing out and developing your goals will help you identify how much money you realistically need. Similar to a New Year's resolution, personal goals help individuals to identify specific and realistic objectives to obtain within a specific timeline.

Tracking Your Spending

Now that you have goals and a realistic direction in mind, the next step in the budgeting process is to track your spending. People typically make the best decisions when they have the most information about the situation. This process may take time, but the effort will result in an informed decision. In budgeting, it is important to identify how you spend before you start to budget future spending. By tracking your current spending, you can identify the areas where you spend the most money and identify ways to be more efficient in your spending.

There are many ways to track your spending. Some modern ways include the use of apps such as *Spending Tracker* and *Spending Log* for the iPhone/iPad or *Expense Manager* or *AndroMoney* for Android devices. These apps include comprehensive ways in which you can log and review your spending. Another way to monitor spending is to utilize Microsoft Word or Excel programs to create a living log that can track your spending. A simple Internet search using keywords such as *Excel* or *Word* and *spending log* will produce some examples of such resources. In addition, you might want to create your own spending log in Excel or Word and then customize it to your lifestyle. Although these forms of logs require more time to create and maintain, they provide an efficient method to log your spending. Last, a potentially simpler alternative to log spending is to create a spending diary using a binder or notebook. This form of a spending log may be a preference for some people because it is easy to modify and can be taken anywhere.

When using a spending log, one must be mindful of what the log measures. Specifically, be sure to include the following measurement items: (a) categories of spending (e.g., rent, Internet/cable, groceries), (b) the amount you spend per time duration, and (c) an appropriate time measure (e.g., measure by day, week, or month). Inherent in the use of a spending log is that you will develop your own preference for how to measure your spending. Additionally, if you use an app, it will have a measurement system already in place. No matter which form of spending log you use, it is an important step in the budgeting process.

Create a Budget

Up until now, you have identified your goals and your spending habits. The next step involves creating the budget. Before doing so, you first need to factor in your spending habits, needs, and wants. *Needs* includes the minimum requirements for you to live a healthy lifestyle. For example, you need food to eat, books for class, healthcare, and a roof over your head (rent). Without these items, you may not be able to be successful no matter how much money you have. *Wants* are the things you want or enjoy doing. That is, they are the luxuries of life. Wants are not life sustaining, and include iPods, eating out, going to the movies, and new clothing, to name a few. You may consider listing out the things you are regularly spending money on and identifying which of these expenditures are wants and which are needs. Be sure to identify which items you actually need and which you *could* give up if you needed to cut back. Examining your wants and needs will aid in the process of writing out your budget.

Once you have a clear goal in mind, you have a grasp on your current spending, and you have identified your wants and needs, you are ready to begin budgeting. First, identify your sources of income. This includes scholarships, any type of employment (e.g., part time or full time), family support, and student loans. Then, identify your yearly expenses. Yearly expenses may include tuition, room and board, and books. In addition to yearly expenses, look at your fixed expenses, the expenses that are the same month by month. Your fixed expenses may include rent, a car payment, and insurance. When creating your budget, the fixed expenses stay the same unless an unexpected change in the item or service occurs. Next, you will want to outline expected variable expenses, the expenses that change each month. Things to include in variable expenses are utilities, food, entertainment, and transportation. You can identify your variable expenses by examining your spending log and noting which items you typically spend money on. This process helps you to gain a comprehensive view of your income and spending habits.

When developing your budget, we recommend the use of the rule of conservatism. The *rule of conservatism* states that you should underestimate the amount of income and overestimate the cost of expenses. Following this rule will allow you to set a clear boundary of how much you are able to spend. Ideally, this rule will help you save money, but at the very least you are not spending more than you are making. As we noted, everyone's budget is individually customized. However, there are a few general rules in money management that you may find helpful. One rule of thumb is the *10-10-80 rule*. This rule states that you should give 10 percent of your income to a charity or your faith community, 10 percent should go into savings, and you should live on the other 80 percent. The focus on giving and saving as the first priorities in this plan has been praised by many financial advisors and spiritual leaders and probably by older generations as well. If you do a Google search on this rule, you will get over 800,000 hits and will find several variations as well. Some critics are now saying that the 10 percent savings is not enough and that retirement savings alone should be in the 10 to 15 percent range. Another rule of thumb is to have an emergency fund. This fund can be as low as $1,000 while you are working to pay off debts, but the goal would be to have about three months of expenses saved up in the event of an emergency. That kind of savings can provide tremendous peace of mind, which would contribute to financial wellness.

After constructing your budget and making some decisions about money management, you can begin to assess your financial wellness. Specifically, you should investigate if you are bringing in more that you are spending. Ideally, you will be bringing in more income than you are spending, which will give you some extra money to save or use in an emergency. In addition, any time you spend more than you make, you are spending future income. A search of the Internet using keywords such as "budgeting template" can produce some publicly available Excel and Word templates for budgeting. In addition, several personal finance apps exist for mobile devices that may be useful in the budgeting process. For example *iReconcile* and *Expenditure* are both available for purchase through iTunes, and *MoneyWise* is available for Android users. Creating a budget can be challenging and exciting at the same time. After you have built the initial template of your budget, you will also need to be able to make adjustments in your budget, goals, and spending habits as you develop your personal finances. The following section talks about this process.

Adjusting the Budget

As M. Scott Peck said, "Life is complex. Each one of us must take his own path through life." Your budget reflects your life and its many complexities. Hence, you can expect changes and adjustments, especially if you are just starting out. In college, how you spend your money may change throughout those years. While in college, expect to review your budget on a regular basis, preferably monthly. In doing so, compare your budget with those of previous months and monitor for trends and patterns in the changes you have noticed. Most likely, your planned expenses and income will not match the actual income and expenses. Nonetheless, you can use this experience to reflect on your budget plan and revise as needed.

When reviewing and adjusting your budget, reflect on the changes and differences. To aid in the reflection process, you can ask yourself some questions: How has this one-time expense affected my budget? Is there a need to adjust my budget based on this new information? How do my goals or priorities fit within the current budget, and do I need to change them? Am I being conservative or copious in my spending, and should I take steps to change this? As time and experience accumulate, your ability to develop and maintain a budget that is efficient and appropriate for your lifestyle will develop. Nevertheless, it is important to be a critical inspector of your budget to assure that you are preparing yourself a sound foundation of financial security.

CONQUERING CREDIT

Now that we have an understanding of budgeting and managing our income and expenses, we need to talk about the healthy use of credit. The financially well person must know how to wield credit wisely. Credit can be helpful, at times, but just like anything else, the unhealthy use of credit could have a major impact on your life. In the following sections we discuss how to conquer credit before credit takes ownership of you. Specifically, we focus on how to select and manage a credit card, how to care for your credit score, and how to make smart decisions about student loans. We begin by discussing credit cards.

Credit Cards

Many companies attempt to lure students into signing up for a new credit card by offering free items, such as gift cards and other small prizes. Are the high interest rates and annual fees really worth a new hoodie or a flash drive? Savvy consumers (and consumers who want to be financially well) don't take on such big commitments on impulse—they take the time to research various offers before signing on the dotted line. According to the Federal Reserve (2010), the average annual percentage rate (APR) for credit cards is approximately 14.5 percent. However, many companies out there are clamoring for your business, so the offers can get competitive if you are willing to do a little digging first. For example, some credit card companies will offer a 0 percent APR for 6 to 12 months, zero annual fees, and points for every dollar you spend that can be redeemed for rewards such as an iTunes gift code or airline miles. However, take note: it is crucial that you always read *all* of the terms of your credit agreement. Now, with the Fair Credit Reporting Act, seeing what you're really getting yourself into is easier than ever, and companies have to clearly inform you if that attractive 0 percent APR shoots up to a much-less-reasonable 18 percent after six months. Nevertheless, that is still no excuse not to read the fine print. It can seem like an overwhelming amount of information to wade through, but it is ultimately worth the time it takes in order to avoid a bad situation. Pay special attention to the APR, annual fee (if any), grace period (the amount of time before monthly interest begins), and penalty fees for things such as paying your balance late.

More important, resist the urge to buy items you cannot actually afford! Paying for something on credit may *feel* like you're getting it for free, but it's often the case that you're actually paying much more for that item than if you had taken the time to save up first. Consider that sweater you are interested in, for example. At $40, you might say to yourself that credit is the ideal option because you do not have the cash for it right now; however, if you do not pay it off right away,

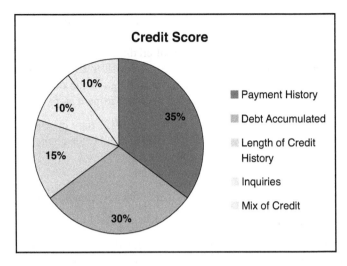

FIGURE 8.1   Factors in Determining Credit Score

and stick with only the minimum payments, you could ultimately end up paying double for it, depending on your interest rate.

You might be wondering, then, with all of these possible pitfalls, why get a credit card at all? Well, responsible credit use can in fact be very helpful in building your credit score. A credit score is the number that tells folks like landlords, car dealers, and banks that you're financially responsible and that you can be trusted enough to stick to a contract and pay what you owe. In fact, even schools and potential employers at times check on your credit score. The argument could be made that having credit cards is actually somewhat of a necessity, nowadays. However, you must use them sensibly. Remember, the converse is also true: getting a bad credit score by missing payments and accumulating debt can limit the places you will be able to rent, the loans you'll be able to get for school or starting a business, and the larger assets you'll be able to acquire, such as a car or home.

Five factors are used to determine your credit score (Figure 8.1):

- *Payment History (35 percent).* This is the most important factor, and reflects how good you have been in the past at paying off your debt. If you repeatedly miss making your payments on time, your score is going to reflect that.
- *Debt Accumulated (30 percent).* This measurement is simply the amount of unpaid debt you have compared to the maximum that you have available to you. For example, if you owe $250 on your credit card that has a limit of $1,000, then you have accumulated 25 percent of what is available to you. The lower this percentage is the better, but a good rule of thumb is to keep your debt-to-limit ratio under 50 percent.
- *Length of Time as a Credit User (15 percent).* The longer you have had a single line of credit the better—this is why folks over 30 typically have much better credit scores.
- *Inquiries (10 percent).* This reflects the number of times you have authorized someone to check your credit report (typically through credit card applications, renting an apartment, or nongovernmental student loans). Every time you apply for a credit card and the creditor

checks your report, it hurts your credit score slightly. Therefore, you should avoid applying for credit repeatedly if you keep being denied.

- *Mix of Credit (10 percent)*. Customers with a wider variety of credit lines (e.g., car loan, house loan, and a credit card) are actually viewed as being a lower risk to those lending you money. Having multiple credit cards, however, does not count. A "good" mix involves having a mortgage, car loans, student loans, major credit cards, and department store cards.

You will also want to take care that you avoid fraud. According to a 2012 study by Javelin Strategy & Research, 18- to 24-year-olds take nearly twice as long to detect fraud when compared to other age groups; young people, therefore, are especially vulnerable.

According to Klein (2010), common schemes include the following:

- *phishing*, in which e-mails direct a victim to fraudulent sites that mimic respectable entities, including, for example, banks and government organizations;
- *SMiShing*, in which text messages bait a victim to download malicious spyware;
- *pharming*, in which malicious code on computers sends victims to fraudulent websites; and
- *keylogging*, in which hidden software monitors victims' keystrokes to collect passwords.

You should also be careful of even simpler methods of fraud. For instance, someone could ask you to write your personal information on a fake application form. You may think that you are signing up with a legitimate company, but in reality, you are giving your name, birthday, and Social Security number—the key ingredients of identity theft—to someone with malicious intent. Therefore, you should be extremely careful of which websites you visit and whom you give your personal information to.

In summary, here are some strategies for being financially well with credit cards:

- *Do your research*. Avoid frauds and find a card with a reasonable APR (12 percent or under) and no annual fee. Bonus points for starting with a modest limit ($1,000 limit *or less*) to avoid the temptation of taking on a pile of debt.
- *Spend smart*. Only buy things with your card that you know you can pay off immediately, thereby avoiding having to pay monthly interest charges. This is what shows responsibility and subsequently builds a better credit score.
- *Keep track of your credit*. Check in online to make sure you do not miss a payment and are well below your spending limit. Also, review your itemized purchases regularly to make sure no one has used your card without your authorization. You can also request your credit report free once a year from each of the three reporting bureaus (Equifax, Experian, and TransUnion) by visiting www.annualcreditreport.com. This will list any credit account and/ or loans you have and their balances, how regularly you make your payments, and if any action has been taken against you because of unpaid bills. Always scan your report for any fraudulent activity, such as the opening of an account that you did not actually authorize. Signing up with a company to track your credit score more regularly is also an option, but keep in mind that several companies that advertise this service for free will eventually charge a fee after the free grace period.

Remember, how you manage your credit now can greatly affect your prospects later on. In fact, your credit score is your most important number in your financial life! Just as your SAT or ACT scores helped to determine whether or not you were able to attend college, your credit score can help determine many of the opportunities you have financially. Spend wisely, and remember to pay off the balance of each card *on time and in full* each month.

Student Loans

We have spent some time addressing how to avoid excessive credit card debt, but what about other types of debt that are practically a necessity for college students? Odds are, if you are enrolled in some form of postsecondary education, you have already or are soon planning on taking out student loans. There are a number of other ways to pay for college of course, such as grants, scholarships, savings, or a job. It is highly recommended that you exhaust all of these options first and treat student loans as a last resort. Given the rising cost of higher education, however, it is likely that your expenses will still necessitate taking on some debt. Recent reports indicate that two-thirds of students who earned a bachelor's degree in 2011 had student loan debt, with an average of $26,600 per borrower (Institute for College Access and Success, 2012). If you are in that category, here are the two primary loans types you will want to consider:

1. *Federal Loans.* These types of loans are subject to oversight and regulation by the federal government and have many benefits, such as fixed interest rates and income-based repayment plans. In order to be eligible for them, you will need to fill out the Free Application for Federal Student Aid (FAFSA) by your state's priority deadline. Types of federal loans include the following:
   - Direct subsidized loans, where the U.S. Department of Education is the lender and pays the interest while you are in school (a good thing). These loans are for students who can demonstrate financial need via the FAFSA.
   - Direct unsubsidized loans, where the U.S. Department of Education is the lender but you are responsible for paying the interest during your time in school. You still have the option to defer payments until graduation, but the interest will accrue (accumulate) and be capitalized (that is, your interest will be added to the principal amount of your loan). You do not need to demonstrate financial need in order to take advantage of unsubsidized loans.
   - Federal Perkins loans, which are low-interest loans for students who can demonstrate exceptional financial need.
   - Federal family education loans (FFELs), where private lenders make loans backed by the federal government.

2. *Private Loans.* These are loans made by any nonfederal lender, such as a bank, credit union, state agency, or school, and are generally a more inconvenient and expensive option in the long run, for the following reasons:
   - Unlike federal loans, many private loans require payments while you are still in school.
   - Private student loans can have variable interest rates, meaning that they can start out being reasonable (say, 5 percent) but then spike at any point (some upwards of 18 percent). A variable rate may substantially increase the total amount you eventually repay.
   - Private loans are always unsubsidized, so no one else pays the interest but you.
   - Do you remember when we said your credit score is important? Your credit score will affect the loan amount and the interest rate offered by a private lender. Private loans will be difficult to obtain if you do not already have an established credit record.
   - Payment options will be stricter, with fewer available options than federal loans if life circumstances make it so that you have difficulty repaying.

We hope we have made our case that you will want to take advantage of federal loans as much as possible before resorting to private loans, but for more detailed information visit www.studentaid.ed.gov. Nevertheless, whichever route you decide on, you will want to think about what type of job you will likely have after you graduate and subsequently what you will be able to afford to pay back. Your lender will need to provide you with a repayment schedule that outlines what your monthly payments will be, for how long you will make payments, and how much you will ultimately be paying based on accumulated interest, so review that document carefully and decide accordingly.

Also, keep in mind that just as with credit cards, there are frauds involving student aid. Unscrupulous companies will use a variety of tactics in order to convince you to pay for services that are already free or that you do not actually need. Take the FAFSA, for example. It is free to fill out via www.fafsa.gov, but hundreds of companies will gladly take your money to prepare it on your behalf, stressing how "impossibly complicated" it is, and how they are the "only ones who can help you through the process and find all the aid for which you are eligible." Although the FAFSA can potentially be time consuming depending on your financial situation, the application site is very user-friendly, and you can always enlist the help of your school advisor or financial aid office to help complete it, without paying a dime. Similarly, several websites charge for their scholarship listings, but you are much better off accessing the free scholarship search at www.studentaid.ed.gov/scholarship to get all of the same results. The most amusing claims, perhaps, are those companies that describe how if you use their services, "you're guaranteed to get at least $5,500 in student aid for college, or we'll give you your money back!" The trick here is that the majority of students are already eligible for a minimum of $5,500 in unsubsidized student loans by virtue of filling out the FAFSA. Finally, we hope you never fall for the old "you've qualified for our scholarship, and all we need now is your bank account information to deposit the funds" scheme. A legitimate company would never ask for such personal information like this (or your Social Security number, credit card information, mother's maiden name, etc.), so run, and do not walk, away from these requests. Better yet, report these scams to the Federal Trade Commission at www.ftc.gov/scholarshipscams.

In general, here are some things the Federal Trade Commission (2008) suggests you look out for and some advice when it comes to loan frauds:

- Beware of private lenders that use names, seals, logos, or other representations similar to those of government agencies to mislead you into assuming that they are affiliated with the federal government and its student loan programs.
- If you have received an email advertisement, mailer, or any other solicitation to borrow money, know that it did not come from the U.S. Department of Education, which will never spam you in this way.
- Do not let promotions or incentives such as gift cards, credit cards, and sweepstakes prizes divert you from assessing whether the key terms of the loan are reasonable.
- Do not give out personal information unless you know exactly whom you are dealing with. Private student lenders typically ask for your Social Security number, saying they need it to help determine your eligibility. However, because scam artists who purport to be private student lenders can misuse this information, it is critical to provide it or other personal information only if you have confidence in the private student lender with whom you are dealing.
- Finally, you can check out the record of accomplishment of particular private student lenders with your state's attorney general (www.naag.org), your local consumer protection agency (www.consumeraction.gov), and the Better Business Bureau (www.bbb.org).

At the end of the day, your goal should be to be as informed a consumer as possible when it comes to student aid, and to have a good understanding of your options prior to entering any long-term contracts. A college education is an investment in your future; it can be expensive, but with a little research and planning, you can limit the amount your debt will cost you.

FINANCIAL RECOVERY AND MONEY MANAGEMENT

Finally, we want to discuss the process of financial recovery. For many of us, the previous information may be coming too late in our financial journeys. In this section, we discuss how to take steps toward financial recovery. Financial recovery is the pathway back to stability after a financial crisis or financial ruin has occurred. Many people have found themselves in financial ruin for a number of reasons. Common reasons include the loss of a job, health problems and medical treatments, significant consumer debt or student loan debt, living beyond your means, and risky investments. According to a recent report, 43.9 percent of all U.S. households are only one financial setback away from poverty (CFED, 2013). This means that nearly half of all U.S. households do not have enough savings to last for three months at the poverty level in the event of a job loss, health crisis, or other financial blow. People in that situation are going to have a very difficult time recovering if a financial misfortune comes their way. Recently, with historically high unemployment and foreclosure rates, financial crises have been happening all around us. Most of us probably know someone significantly affected by financial losses. Fortunately, whatever the reasons may be for financial ruin, recovery is possible.

It is important to note that recovery is almost never a rapid process. Imagine you collapse and are rushed to the hospital. The doctor has diagnosed you with high blood pressure, diabetes, and morbid obesity. The doctor may prescribe lifestyle changes including healthier foods, exercise three or more times a week, and portion control at your meals. Based on your lifestyle, up to that point, the changes you would need to make may be dramatic; however, the results of improved health and weight loss will take time. After all, it was years of bad habits in diet, exercise, and other health decisions that led to the collapse. Likewise, it is often poor financial habits over time that contribute to a financial collapse. Although the actual event that triggers a financial collapse, such as a job loss or health problem, may not be preventable, there are habits that you can build to be able to weather the financial storms that come your way.

Getting a Financial Physical

If you want to be proactive in financial recovery *before* a collapse occurs, you need to go for a check-up. There are several ways that you can get a snapshot of your financial health. One easy way is by going online and taking a survey. For example, on www.sixwise.com you can fill out a survey called *What Is the State of Your Financial Health?* At the conclusion, you get a score and a brief description of your current financial state. Another website, https://www.debtinfocus .org/oaktrustcu/DataWizard.aspx, takes you through a few steps to calculate income, debt, and expenses and gives you recommendations based on the data you enter. You can take a more comprehensive path and fill out a multipage financial assessment form that covers assets and liabilities and income and expenses. One example of an assessment form can be found at www.pwcgov.org/government/dept/vce/documents/10318.pdf, along with an instruction sheet located at www.pwcgov.org/government/dept/vce/documents/10319.pdf. You can also do something as simple as asking yourself the following questions about your finances.

1. Do you have credit card debt?
2. Do pay off all of your credit cards in full each month?
3. Do you have a car loan or other debt (apart from student loans)?
4. Do you make more income than you spend each month?
5. Do you have a negative attitude toward credit?
6. Do you have health insurance?

7. Has your income remained flat or gone down within the last year?
8. Do you have a solid plan to increase your income within the next year?
9. Do you feel "unlucky" in your current financial state?
10. Do you make financial plans for a few years or more?

To calculate your score, give yourself one point for a "Yes" on the even questions and one point for a "No" on the odd questions. Next, subtract one point for a "Yes" on the odd questions and a "No" on the even questions. The higher your score, the better your financial health. If your score is below a zero, then you have habits that will make it difficult for you to recover from a financial collapse if you haven't already had one.

Other forms of assessment include talking with a financial planner, coach, or counselor or beginning a program of financial education. Some universities offer credit counseling or other financial counseling services at no cost or low cost to students, and most universities will offer workshops or some other form of financial education to students. Whether it is talking one on one about your situation or going to a workshop, you will usually begin with an assessment. One such program is *Financial Literacy 101,* which is an online program offered by several universities (https://www.financialliteracy101.org/index.cfm). The first step in that program is a survey that evaluates financial knowledge, attitudes, and behaviors. One free website, www.smarteys.com, helps you create a *Real-Life Summary*, which will then direct you to services based on the data you have provided. Interestingly, students who struggled to find their way after graduating from college created smarteys.com. So whether you choose to take an online assessment, begin a program of financial literacy, or talk to a professional who can give you direction, it's important to begin by "getting a physical" to assess your current situation.

Financial Resources and Advice

There is no shortage of financial advice available, from books, to seminars, to blogs, to radio and TV shows. Keeping that in mind, please note that you will find significantly different opinions depending on whose advice you choose. Beware of the get-rich schemes and "financial secrets" that many will try to sell to you. As you consider financial advice, look for a balanced and proven approach. For example, one popular system of getting financially healthy is *Financial Peace University*, a program designed by Dave Ramsey. Ramsey has a daily radio show and a host of financial books, tools, and information available about getting out of debt and building wealth without any of the "secrets" and proprietary strategies that are so common with many financial seminars and books. Clark Howard is another TV and radio personality who focuses on financial management and advice. He approaches finances as a consumer expert. On his show and his website, he offers tips about how to "save money, spend less, and not get ripped off." There are more books and websites than we could possibly begin to explore in this book. Just remember that financial wellness and financial recovery are not magical processes. They come with building healthy money habits. As you weigh financial advice, remember to investigate the quality of the financial habits recommended.

Summary

In summary, being financially well will help you avoid unnecessary stress and potential health concerns, and reach your goals. The steps to financial wellness are not magical. Financially well people develop a healthy budget and develop strategies for managing money and credit wisely, by making informed decisions and sticking to their budgets. In addition, if your financial wellness is already under attack, there are several resources and strategies to help you get back on track. Finally, financial wellness is not a get-rich-quick scheme, and it does not happen overnight. Becoming financially well takes time and effort, and is an ongoing process. However, the risks and efforts are highly outweighed by the benefits.

References

Corporation for Enterprise Development (2013) http://cfed.org/

Federal Reserve. (2010, May). *G.19 report on consumer credit*. Retrieved from http://www.federalreserve.gov/releases/g19/Current/

Federal Trade Commission. (2008, June). Student loans: Avoiding deceptive offers. Retrieved from http://www.consumer.ftc.gov/articles/0160-student-loans

Hornak, A. M., Farell, P. L., & Jackson, N. J. (2010). Making it (or not) on a dime in college: Implications for practice. *Journal of College Student Development, 51*, 481–495.

Institute for College Access and Success. (2012, October). Student debt and the class of 2011. Retrieved from http://projectonstudentdebt.org/files/pub/classof2011.pdf

Javelin Strategy & Research. (2012, February). 2012 identity fraud report: Social media and mobile forming the new fraud frontier. Retrieved from http://itsecurity.und.edu/2012%20Identity%20Fraud%20Report%20Brochure.pdf

Joo, S., Durband, D. B., & Grable, J. (2009). The academic impact of financial stress on college students. *Journal of College Student Retention, 10*, 287–305.

Klein, A. (2010, March 17). 18- to 24-year-olds most at risk for ID theft, survey finds. *The Washington Post*, p. B01.

Nelson, M. C., Lust, K., Story, M., & Ehlinger, E. (2008). Credit card debt, stress, and key health risk behaviors among college students. *American Journal of Health Promotion 22*, 400–407.

Roberts, R., Golding, J., Towell, T., Reid, S., Woodford, S., Vetere, A., & Weinreb, I. (2000). Mental and physical health in students: The role of economic circumstances. *British Journal of Health Psychology. 5*, 289–297.

Rutherford, L. G., & Fox, W. S. (2010). Financial wellness of young adults age 18–30. *Family and Consumer Sciences Research Journal, 38*, 468–484.

9 PREVENTATIVE SELF-CARE: BENEFITS OF MODERN MEDICINE

Maria Elliot

Eating a vegetarian diet, walking (exercising)
every day, and meditating is considered radical.
Allowing someone to slice your chest open and
graft your leg veins in your heart is considered
normal and conservative.

DEAN ORNISH, CARDIOLOGIST

SELF-CARE: DEFINED

Quality of life is a concept hard to measure, but one that wellness-oriented individuals work to help their clients achieve. Quality of life reflects a general sense of happiness and satisfaction with one's life and environment. It encompasses all aspects of life, including health, recreation, culture, rights, values, beliefs, aspirations, and the conditions that support a life containing these elements (Office of Disease Prevention and Health Promotion, 2008). Health-related quality of life reflects a personal sense of physical and mental health and the ability to react to factors in the physical and social environments. A basic concept in both the mental health and medical fields is that the individual has control over this aspect. Self-care is the individual's ability to take responsibility for his or her own wellness through self-care and safety habits that are preventive in nature (Myers, Witmer, & Sweeney, 1997). We will discuss three elements of self-care: (1) habits we learn in order to protect ourselves from injury, disease, or death; (2) Healthcare, which includes periodic medical check-ups that may prevent a disease or enable one to get early treatment; and (3) avoiding harmful substances, both those that we might ingest and toxic substances in the environment (Witmer, 1997). Understanding of preventative self-care and participation in such behaviors and services is a crucial element in wellness.

SELF-CARE: THEN AND NOW

It seems obvious to understand and believe in the value of quality of life and self-care. Especially because we live in one of the wealthiest nations in the world, individuals in the United States must be able to obtain this health-related quality of life due to our advanced medical care system, knowledge, and access to services. You can pick up any magazine or turn on any television station and feel overwhelmed by the amount of resources related to wellness, health, and disease management that are available to individuals within the United States. Yet why is it that the leading causes of death in the United States are all preventable based on lifestyle and early detection? How can individuals in the wealthiest and most medically fortunate nation in the world be killing themselves? Why can we not live longer, more highly qualitative lives, and why are health-oriented individuals doing nothing about it?

It seems appropriate to start by briefly examining what has been done throughout history to stop the occurrence and spread of disease. Societies throughout history share many similarities with societies today, and we can learn from their wisdom and implementation of knowledge. At the beginning of the 1900s, infectious diseases ran rampant in the United States and worldwide and topped the leading causes of death. Societies responded with certain practices and behaviors to prevent the spread of such diseases. Yet the implementation of public health standards, policies, and practices began much earlier than the 20th century. Box 9.1 briefly outlines the development of prevention and treatment throughout history.

Today in the United States, it appears that recognition of the causes of disease and preventative self-care is needed more than ever. Recent sources attribute two-thirds of all deaths to lifestyle choices that contribute to preventable deaths (e.g., heart disease, cancer, stroke, injuries, HIV infection, low birth weight, alcohol and drug problems, and inadequate immunization) (Witmer, 1996). These

---

BOX 9.1   Historical Overview of Prevention and Treatment

Dawn of History	Shamans diagnose, treat, and in some cases prevent the spread of disease, believed to be malevolent forces, to provide spiritual and physical healing.
Ancient Rome	The establishment of cities creates the need for municipal water supplies and sewage systems.
Dark Ages and Medieval Period 500–1000 CE	Public health activities, such as overseeing the water supply and sewerage, street cleaning, and supervision of the markets, fell under the jurisdiction of the church and councils. Isolation of cases of leprosy represents the earliest application of public health practice still in use.
Renaissance and the Plague Period 1300s–1400s	Due to the plague and many other epidemics that devastated the population of the world, the organization of boards of health, the promulgation of a theory of contagion, and the introduction of health statistics came about.
Enlightenment and Sanitary Reform 1750–mid-19th Century	The prevalence and causation of preventable diseases became the focus of much study. As a result, sewerage, potable and plentiful water supplies, refuse disposal systems, proper ventilation of residences and places of work, supervision of public works by qualified professionals, and legislative authorization of measures to obtain these results were put forward.
Bacteriology 1870s–1880s	Louis Pasteur and Robert Koch discovered pathogenic bacteria. Sanitation became science-based, and the development of vaccines promised the prevention of many infectious diseases.

Source: Breslow & Cengage (2002).

preventable causes of death have been estimated to be responsible for 900,000 deaths annually—nearly 40 percent of the total yearly mortality in the United States (Cohen, Neumann, & Weinstein, 2008). There exists in the United States a high prevalence of people with unhealthy lifestyles and behaviors, such as insufficient exercise, being overweight, and tobacco use, which are risk factors for many of these fatal chronic diseases and disabilities (Centers for Disease Control and Prevention [CDC], 2007). Yet these unhealthy behaviors seem to continue and increase in spite of our knowledge of their damaging effects, demanding attention in the medical and counseling fields. Our nation's changing demographic will also lead to an increasing occurrence of such conditions, especially if the unhealthy behaviors continue throughout the lifespan. With an aging population and longer life expectancy comes increasing total prevalence of chronic diseases and conditions associated with aging, such as disability and limitation of activity (CDC, 2007).

Many people have begun to better understand the necessity of including preventive self-care into their routines to prevent many diseases. With the control of many infectious agents as described earlier and the increasing occurrence of unhealthy behaviors and the rising age of the population, chronic diseases top the list of leading causes of death: heart disease accounts for 31.4 percent, cancer accounts for 23.3 percent, stroke accounts for 6.9 percent, and chronic obstructive pulmonary disease (COPD) accounts for 4.7 percent (CDC, 2007; Office of Disease Prevention and Health Promotion, 2008). Box 9.2 shows how these figures have changed over the last century.

STRATEGIES FOR PROMOTING SELF-CARE

Medical research and the expertise of professionals in the field can offer much understanding of the prevalence and causes of these detrimental diseases. Because of the high cost of human life, as well as financial cost, the Office of Disease Prevention and Health Promotion, the U.S. Department of Health and Human Services, and the Centers for Disease Control and Prevention have sought out this knowledge, compiled many reviews of the literature, and propose current recommendations to begin to decrease such diseases and deaths, specifically those causing 55 percent of the deaths—heart disease and cancer.

Heart disease is the leading cause of death in the United States and is a major cause of disability. Almost 700,000 people die of heart disease in the United States each year. Heart disease is the leading cause of death for American Indians and Alaska Natives, blacks, Hispanics, and whites. For Asians and Pacific Islanders, cancer is the leading cause of death (26.1 percent); heart disease is a close second (26.0 percent). Prevention of heart disease takes the form of screening and healthy lifestyle choices. Lifestyle actions such as eating a healthy diet, getting regular physical activity, not smoking, and maintaining a healthy weight will help keep normal blood pressure levels. Professionals recommend having blood pressure checked regularly, and if it is high, to control and bring down the level with lifestyle changes and medicine. Individuals should also prevent and control high blood cholesterol, a major risk factor for heart disease. Preventing and treating high blood cholesterol includes eating a diet low in saturated fat and cholesterol and high in fiber, keeping a healthy weight, and getting regular exercise. Professionals recommend having cholesterol levels checked once every five years; if found to be high, doctors may prescribe medication as well as healthy lifestyle changes. Individuals with diabetes also have an increased risk of heart disease, but can reduce their risk through weight loss and regular physical activity. To prevent heart disease, individuals are also encouraged to not use tobacco, as such use increases the risk of high blood pressure, heart disease, and stroke. Excessive alcohol use increases the risk of

BOX 9.2   Changes in the Leading Causes of Death over the Last Century

Leading Causes of Death, 1997

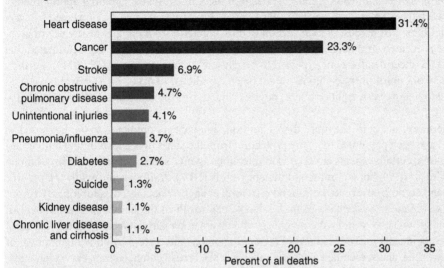

Leading Causes of Death, 1900

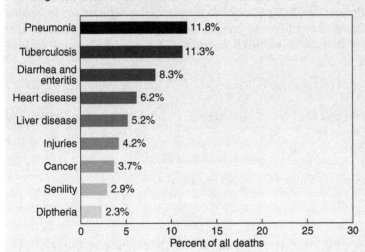

Source: Centers for Disease Control and Prevention, National Center for Health Statistics, 1997, National Vital Statistics System and unpublished data.

high blood pressure, heart attack, and stroke, and individuals who drink should do so in moderation. Finally, maintaining a healthy weight, engaging in regular physical activity, and having an overall healthy diet will aid in the prevention of heart disease (CDC, 2007).

Cancer is the second leading cause of death in the United States, claiming approximately 1,500 lives each day (American Cancer Society, 2008). Many cancers may be prevented by early detection and lifestyle choices. All cancers caused by cigarette smoking and heavy use of alcohol could be prevented completely. In 2008, the American Cancer Society (ACS) estimated that about 170,000 cancer deaths were expected to be caused by tobacco use (ACS, 2008). Further, approximately one-third of the 565,650 cancer deaths predicted to occur in 2008 were expected to be related to being overweight or obese, physical inactivity, and nutrition, and thus could also be prevented.

Furthermore, many of the more than 1 million skin cancers predicted to be diagnosed in 2008 could have been prevented by using protection from the sun's rays and avoiding indoor tanning. In addition, certain cancers are related to infectious agents, such as hepatitis B virus, human papilloma virus (HPV), human immunodeficiency virus (HIV), *Helicobacter pylori* (*H. pylori*), and others, and could be prevented through behavioral changes, vaccines, or antibiotics. Regular screening examinations by healthcare professionals can result in the detection and removal of precancerous growths, as well as the diagnosis of cancers at an early stage when they are most treatable. Screening can prevent cancers of the cervix, colon, and rectum by allowing removal of precancerous tissue, and screening can detect cancers of the breast, colon, rectum, cervix, prostate, oral cavity, and skin at early stages. For most of these cancers, early detection has been proven to reduce mortality (ACS, 2008). Professionals can help encourage decreases in rates of cancer and deaths from cancer by promoting some of these healthy lifestyles and preventive screenings.

The Partnership for Prevention (2007) has ranked the preventive services recommended by medical professionals that are most likely to prevent these top diseases in a cost-effective manner. The Partnership's recommendations highlight the need for individuals to ask medical professionals about:

- Childhood immunizations (prevent many diseases)
- Screenings:
  - Tobacco use screening and brief intervention (prevent heart disease, cancer, stroke, and other pulmonary conditions)
  - Cervical and colorectal screenings
  - Vision screenings for adults 65+ years
  - Vision screening for young children for visual impairments
  - Hypertension screenings
  - Cholesterol screenings
  - Problem drinking screenings
- Daily aspirin use in high-risk adults (prevent heart disease, heart attack, and stroke)
- Adult vaccines: influenza and pneumococcal vaccines

The U.S. Preventive Services Task Force also recommends that clinicians discuss and offer certain preventive services for the well-being of patients. These are listed in Box 9.3.

BOX 9.3   Preventative Services Recommendations for Adults and Special Populations

	Adults		Special Populations	
Recommendation	Men	Women	Pregnant Women	Children
Abdominal Aortic Aneurysm, Screening[1]	X			
Alcohol Misuse Screening and Behavioral Counseling Interventions	X	X	X	
Aspirin for the Primary Prevention of Cardiovascular Events[2]	X	X		
Bacteriuria, Screening for Asymptomatic			X	
Breast Cancer, Chemoprevention[3]		X		
Breast Cancer, Screening[4]		X		
Breast and Ovarian Cancer Susceptibility, Genetic Risk Assessment and BRCA Mutation Testing[5]		X		
Breastfeeding, Behavioral Interventions to Promote[6]		X	X	
Cervical Cancer, Screening[7]		X		
Chlamydial Infection, Screening[8]		X	X	
Colorectal Cancer, Screening[9]	X	X		
Dental Caries in Preschool Children, Prevention[10]				X
Depression, Screening[11]	X	X		
Diabetes Mellitus in Adults, Screening for Type 2[12]	X	X		
Diet, Behavioral Counseling in Primary Care to Promote Health[13]	X	X		
Gonorrhea, Screening[14]		X	X	
Gonorrhea, Prophylactic Medication[15]				X
Hepatitis B Virus Infection, Screening[16]			X	
High Blood Pressure, Screening	X	X		
HIV, Screening[17]	X	X	X	X
Iron Deficiency Anemia, Prevention[18]				X
Iron Deficiency Anemia, Screening[19]			X	
Lipid Disorders, Screening[20]	X	X		
Obesity in Adults, Screening[21]	X	X		

Osteoporosis in Postmenopausal Women, Screening[22]		X	
Rh (D) Incompatibility, Screening[23]			X
Syphilis Infection, Screening[24]	X	X	X
Tobacco Use and Tobacco-Caused Disease, Counseling to Prevent[25]	X	X	X
Visual Impairment in Children Younger than Age 5 Years, Screening[26]			X

[1]One-time screening by ultrasonography in men aged 65 to 75 who have ever smoked.

[2]Adults at increased risk for coronary heart disease.

[3]Discuss with women at high risk for breast cancer and at low risk for adverse effects of chemoprevention.

[4]Mammography every 1 to 2 years for women 40 and older.

[5]Refer women whose family history is associated with an increased risk for deleterious mutations in BRCA1 or BRCA2 genes for genetic counseling and evaluation for BRCA testing.

[6]Structured education and behavioral counseling programs.

[7]Women who have been sexually active and have a cervix.

[8]Sexually active women 25 and younger and other asymptomatic women at increased risk for infection. Asymptomatic pregnant women 25 and younger and others at increased risk.

[9]Men and women 50 and older.

[10]Prescribe oral fluoride supplementation at currently recommended doses to preschool children older than six months whose primary water source is deficient in fluoride.

[11]In clinical practices with systems to assure accurate diagnoses, effective treatment, and follow-up.

[12]Adults with hypertension or hyperlipidemia.

[13]Adults with hyperlipidemia and other known risk factors for cardiovascular and diet-related chronic disease.

[14]All sexually active women, including those who are pregnant, at increased risk for infection (that is, if they are young or have other individual or population risk factors).

[15]Prophylactic ocular topical medication for all newborns against gonococcal ophthalmia neonatorum.

[16]Pregnant women at first prenatal visit.

[17]All adolescents and adults at increased risk for HIV infection and all pregnant women.

[18]Routine iron supplementation for asymptomatic children aged 6 to 12 months who are at increased risk for iron deficiency anemia.

[19]Routine screening in asymptomatic pregnant women.

[20]Men 35 and older and women 45 and older. Younger adults with other risk factors for coronary disease. Screening for lipid disorders to include measurement of total cholesterol and high-density lipoprotein cholesterol.

[21]Intensive counseling and behavioral interventions to promote sustained weight loss for obese adults.

[22]Women 65 and older and women 60 and older at increased risk for osteoporotic fractures.

[23]Blood typing and antibody testing at first pregnancy-related visit. Repeated antibody testing for unsensitized Rh (D)-negative women at 24 to 28 weeks' gestation unless biological father is known to be Rh (D) negative.

[24]Persons at increased risk and all pregnant women.

[25]Tobacco cessation interventions for those who use tobacco. Augmented pregnancy-tailored counseling for pregnant women who smoke.

[26]To detect amblyopia, strabismus, and defects in visual acuity.

Along with preventive screenings, it appears that healthy lifestyle changes have a major effect on the occurrence of these preventable diseases and causes of death. Several recommendations have been made by the medical community and *Healthy People 2010*:

- *Increasing Physical Activity:* In 1997, only 15 percent of adults performed the recommended amount of physical activity, and 40 percent of adults engaged in no leisure-time physical activity (CDC, 2007). Women generally are less active than men at all ages, and persons with lower incomes and less education are typically not as physically active as those with higher incomes and education. African Americans and Hispanics are less physically active than whites. People with disabilities are less physically active than people without disabilities.

Regular physical activity throughout life is important for maintaining a healthy body, enhancing psychological well-being, and preventing premature death. Regular physical activity decreases the risk of death from heart disease, lowers the risk of developing diabetes, helps prevent high blood pressure, and is associated with decreasing the risk of colon cancer.

Muscle and bone strength and lean muscle increase, while body fat decreases, with physical activity. The current recommendations for preventive purposes encourage individuals recommendation is to engage in vigorous physical activity that promotes cardiorespiratory fitness three or more days per week for 20 or more minutes per occasion, and/or to engage in daily moderate physical activity for at least 30 minutes each day. Engaging in physical activity also has psychological effects, as it appears to enhance psychological well-being and reduce symptoms of depression and anxiety while improving mood (CDC, 2007).

• *Decreasing the Incidence of Obesity and Individuals Who Are Overweight*: The number of overweight children, adolescents, and adults has risen over the past four decades, with more than half of U.S. adults estimated to be overweight or obese (CDC, 2007). In 1995, the estimated cost to manage the population effects of overweight individuals was $99 billion (CDC, 2007). Obesity is especially prevalent among women with lower incomes and is more common among African American and Mexican American women than white women. Overweight and obese persons are major contributors to many preventable causes of death. Higher body weights are associated with higher death rates, as being overweight raises the risk of high blood pressure, high cholesterol, Type 2 diabetes, heart disease and stroke, gallbladder disease, arthritis, sleep disturbances and problems breathing, and certain types of cancer.

The current recommendations for preventative purposes include choosing a healthful assortment of foods that includes vegetables, fruits, whole grains, fat-free or low-fat dairy products, fish, lean meat, poultry, and beans. Individuals should choose food low in saturated fats and low in added sugars, while limiting portion size. Along with the healthy diet, individuals are encouraged to engage in at least 30 minutes of moderate physical activity most or all days of the week. Psychologically, obesity affects the individual as well. Obese individuals may suffer from social stigmatization, discrimination, and lowered self-esteem (CDC, 2007).

• *End Tobacco Use:* Cigarette smoking is the single most preventable cause of disease and death in the United States. Tobacco-related deaths number more than 430,000 per year, representing more than 5 million years of potential life lost. Smoking itself results in more U.S. deaths each year than AIDS, alcohol use, cocaine use, heroin use, homicides, suicides, motor vehicle crashes, and fires combined! It is estimated that tobacco-related diseases cost approximately $50 billion per year. Tobacco use is a major risk factor for heart disease, stroke, lung cancer, and chronic lung diseases—all of which are leading causes of death. Environmental tobacco smoking, or second-hand smoking, increases the risk of heart disease and significant lung conditions such as asthma and bronchitis. Due to these risks, the current recommendation for individuals is to cease use. There is no safe level or amount of use.

• *Decrease Substance Use:* Excessive alcohol and drug use are associated with various negative outcomes, including child and spousal abuse, sexually transmitted diseases, teen pregnancy, school failure, vehicle crashes, escalation of healthcare costs, low worker productivity, and homelessness. Long-term heavy drinking can lead to heart disease, cancer, alcohol-related liver disease, and pancreatitis. Alcohol use during pregnancy causes fetal alcohol effects, the leading cause of preventable mental retardation. Current recommendations for alcohol use are one drink per day for women and two drinks per day for men. There are not currently recommendations for drug use for individuals (CDC, 2007).

- *Obtain Immunization:* Vaccines are among the greatest public health achievements of the 20th century. Yet in 1998, only 73 percent of children received all of the vaccines recommended for universal administration. In the United States, immunization rates are significantly lower for African American and Hispanic adults than for Caucasian adults. Immunizations prevent disability and death from infectious diseases and can help control the spread of infections. Immunizations against influenza and pneumococcal disease, the sixth leading cause of death, can prevent serious illness and mortality. The current recommendations for preventative purposes are that all children born in the United States should be receiving 12 to 16 doses of vaccine by age two to be protected against 10 vaccine-preventable childhood diseases. For adults aged 65 and older, recommended immunizations include a yearly influenza vaccine and a one-time immunization against pneumococcal disease (CDC, 2007).

Summary

This chapter identifies a number of preventative self-care strategies that contribute to longevity and well-being. It is important to note that heart disease and cancer are the two leading causes of death in the United States. Early detection and lifestyle change are the keys to preventing death related to these illnesses. Additionally, numerous preventative screenings are listed in this chapter that can halt the development of serious illnesses. Included among these are regular breast examinations for women and testicular examinations for men. Several behavior recommendations are outlined for preventative self-care based on *Healthy People 2010*, including increasing physical activity, ceasing cigarette use, and decreasing alcohol consumption.

Reflection Activities

1. Review the list in Box 9.3 to find which preventative screenings you should be receiving based on your age and gender.
2. Using the behavior guidelines outlined in this chapter, reflect on areas for behavior change in your life that could contribute to longevity and well-being.
3. Think of the people in your life who experience chronic illnesses. Which of these illnesses could have been prevented by lifestyle change or early detection?

References

American Cancer Society. (2008). Facts and statistics. Retrieved from http://www.cancer.org/docroot/home/index.asp

Breslow, L., & Cengage, G. (2002). History of public health. *Encyclopedia of Public Health*. Retrieved from http://www.enotes.com/public-health-encyclopedia/history-public-health

Centers for Disease Control and Prevention. (2007). Health, United States, 2007. Retrieved from http://www.cdc.gov/nchs/hus.htm

Cohen, J., Neumann, P., & Weinstein, M. (2008). Does preventive care save money? Health economics and the presidential candidates. *The New England Journal of Medicine, 358*(7), 661–663.

Myers, J. E., Witmer, M. J., & Sweeney, T. J. (1997). The WEL workbook: A guide to assessing personal resources for wellness and developing a plan for living life more fully. Unpublished monograph.

Office of Disease Prevention and Health Promotion. (2008). *Healthy People 2010*. Retrieved from http://www .healthypeople.gov/

Partnership for Prevention. (2007). Priorities for America's health: Capitalizing on life-saving, cost-effective preventive services. Retrieved from http://www.prevent .org/images/stories/clinicalprevention/executive%20 summary.pdf

Witmer, J. M. (1996). Reaching towards wellness: A holistic model for personal growth and counseling. Unpublished monograph.

10 SPIRITUALITY AND MEANING

Todd Gibbs, M.A., L.P.C.

Spirituality exists wherever we struggle with the issue of how our lives fit into the greater cosmic scheme of things. This is true even when our questions never give way to specific answers or give rise to specific practices such as prayer or meditation. We encounter spiritual issues every time we wonder where the universe comes from, why we are here, or what happens when we die. We also become spiritual when we become moved by values such as beauty, love, or creativity that seem to reveal a meaning or power beyond our visible world. An idea or practice is "spiritual" when it reveals our personal desire to establish a felt-relationship with the deepest meanings or powers governing life.

FULLER, 2001

Before you begin to read this chapter, use the following reflection to set a frame of mind for considering spiritual wellness. Take paper and a writing utensil and complete the sentence stems in Reflection 10.1 on the next page. In this chapter, we will take a closer look at the relationship between your spirituality and your wellness. An emerging body of research indicates that religious and spiritual activities and beliefs are related to health and well-being (Hill & Pargament, 2003; Koenig, 2004; Larson & Larson, 2003). As this evidence base grows, many wellness experts are beginning to recognize the potential that spiritual and religious factors possess to change people's lives. Although it may be new to ground spirituality in scientific research, these ideas have been a part of human understanding for millennia. As you engage with the concepts presented in this chapter, try to connect them to your own experiences to see what meaning you can find for your life in these ancient and contemporary explorations of what it means to be fully human and fully alive.

Reflection 10.1

- The persons I most respect, love, or enjoy are . . .
- I am aware of a strong sense of belonging or connection when I am with . . .
- I feel energetic and alive when I am . . . .
- I have experienced a deep sense of meaning and purpose when I . . .
- The places that I find most sacred, holy, beautiful, or calming are . . .
- When I need to relax, recharge, or think deeply, I go . . .
- One experience that made me feel like I was part of something larger than myself was . . .
- I really believed my life mattered when . . .

Read through your responses to these prompts, and then try to answer the following question:

- How do you experience spirituality?

Several key points about spirituality are raised by this exercise. One important thing to note is that spiritual experiences are not separate from the lived activities that make up your life. Instead, it is critical to seek meaning and purpose in the everyday spirituality that comprises your daily routines and relationships. To look elsewhere for miracles is to miss the point that everything is miraculous (Maslow, 1972). Additionally, although spiritual experiences are a universal element of human existence, spirituality is inherently personal and developmental in nature. In other words, each person understands spirituality in a distinctive and individual manner that changes over time. Therefore, the same person is likely to define spirituality differently as he or she grows and changes over the course of his or her life (Cashwell, 2005).

SPIRITUALITY AND RELIGION

It is difficult to discuss spirituality without also considering religion. For many people, religious adherence is the site and source of their spiritual beliefs and practices. For others, there is considerable overlap between these two concepts, and therefore it can be challenging to clearly define either one. Both terms may come with a considerable amount of cultural baggage. People are often quick to make assumptions about others based upon belonging to a particular spiritual or religious group. Similarly, persons who identify as belonging to a group may assume that others who identify with the same group automatically hold the same beliefs. In both cases, any inherent assumptions or internalized biases toward spiritual or religious practice represent a form of cultural encapsulation, which may result in the exclusion of additional perspectives (Cashwell, 2010). As you engage with the concepts of spirituality and religion, try to stay aware of your values and the limits of your understanding, as well as the limitations of this text in adequately describing spirituality and religion in a few short paragraphs.

Defining Spirituality and Religion

As stated, spirituality is a difficult concept to define. Not only is it personal and developmental in nature, but it typically occurs internally. Moreover, spiritual experiences are often kept private by those who find meaning in them. Religion, by contrast, is significantly easier to define, as it is grounded in external practices that are organized by groups in an often public manner. Two

TABLE 10.1   Distinguishing Between Spirituality and Religion

Spirituality (Intrinsic Religion)	Religion (Extrinsic Religion)
• Universal/Ecumenical	• Denominational
• Internal	• External
• Affective	• Cognitive
• Spontaneous	• Ritualistic
• Private	• Public

Source: Richards & Bergin (1997).

terms that are helpful in understanding this distinction are *extrinsic religion* and *intrinsic religion*. Extrinsic religion refers to the outer forms of worship practiced by an organized assembly of individuals that often include rituals, recitation of scriptures, singing, chanting, and intercessory prayer. Intrinsic religion conceptualizes spirituality as a direct inner experience that is characteristic of an individual rather than a group. Intrinsic religion may contain such transcendent experiences as a sense of peace, inner visions, bliss, joy, awe, and wonder (Roach & Young, 2013). These experiences can be spontaneous but they may also be achieved through practices such as meditation and contemplative prayer. Table 10.1 lists the distinctions between spirituality, or intrinsic religion, and (extrinsic) religion.

Spirituality is universal and ecumenical in the sense that all human beings possess the capacity for spiritual experience, and persons who are spiritually well tend to be more open to differing experiences on the part of others. Religion is denominational because people identify and affiliate with differing traditions. Describing spirituality as affective indicates that spiritual experiences often relate to feelings and provoke emotional responses. Religion tends to evoke more cognitive language, such as the shared "beliefs" that demonstrate adherence to a particular religion. Spiritual experiences can occur without intention and arise spontaneously, whereas religious experience is centered on various forms of organized ritual. Finally, spirituality is largely private and internal, whereas religion is public, visible in community practice, readily articulated, and engaged through external relationships (Richards & Bergin, 1997).

The Relationship Between Religion and Spirituality

By using these definitions, it is clear that persons can be spiritual without being religious and religious without being spiritual (Roach & Young, 2013). Although spirituality and religion can be viewed as separate dimensions of life, the two concepts can also fit together and support spiritual wellness. Three primary categories can be used to articulate the relationship between religion and spirituality. *Hand in hand* is the category for those who experience religion and spirituality in a complementary manner. Membership in a religious community may provide opportunities for spiritual practice, may supplement individual practices, or can form the basis for spiritual life. By contrast, the *Jungian Path of Pretending* refers to those whose participation in religion is disconnected from spiritual experience. Their membership in religious communities may have more to do with avoidance of punishment or simple habit than any desire to integrate spirituality into their personal wellness. Finally, a growing category, particularly in western cultures, is to be *spiritual but not religious.* Persons who identify as such may possess a range of perspectives toward organized religion, from valuing and acceptance to disdain and contempt. Persons with this perspective may have had little prior exposure to religious organizations, or may have chosen, for whatever reason, to relinquish their beliefs (Cashwell, 2010). Therefore, while some people experience spirituality within the beliefs and practices of a religious group, and others as part of their individual practices and beliefs, still others combine individual and group practices in ways that contribute to their overall spiritual wellness.

Spirituality and Religion on College Campuses

The first major longitudinal study of spirituality among undergraduate college students supports this framework for understanding religion and spirituality. Researchers at UCLA's Higher Education Research Institute (Astin, Astin, & Lindholm, 2011) took up the question of how colleges and universities support the development of student qualities related to spirituality, such as values and beliefs, morality, emotional maturity, and self-awareness. A pilot survey was conducted in 2003 with about 3,700 college students to develop measures of these characteristics. In the fall term of 2004, a follow-up survey containing the refined content areas was completed by over 112,000 first-year students. A final survey was completed by a sample of 14,527 of these students in the spring term of 2007 as the participants were about to finish their junior year to explore any changes in spiritual and religious qualities during the first three years of undergraduate education. Analyses of the data revealed five consistent measures of spirituality and five stable measures of religiousness.

The spiritual measures are a mix of internally directed and externally directed aspects of spirituality. The first internal measure, *spiritual quest*, assesses an interest in searching for meaning and purpose, attaining inner harmony, and developing a meaningful philosophy of life. The second, *equanimity*, reflects the students' ability to feel centered and at peace, to find meaning even in challenging circumstances, and to feel good about their direction in life. The external measures focus on elements of connectedness to others and caring about or for each other. *Ethic of caring* looks at student commitment to values such as helping others, reducing suffering in the world, promoting understanding for oppressed groups, and making the world a better place. *Charitable involvement* records student activities such as community service, financial charitable contributions, and helping friends with personal problems. The final measure, *ecumenical worldview*, measures student interest in different religions and cultures, belief in the interconnectedness of life, acceptance of others, and viewing love as the root of all great religions.

The religious measures that emerged are distinct from the spiritual measures in ways that align with the distinctions between spirituality and religion put forth in this chapter. *Religious commitment* reflects whether students' religious beliefs are central to their lives. *Religious engagement* denotes student behaviors such as attending religious services, praying, and reading or studying sacred texts. *Religious/social conservatism* describes the degree of opposition to choices such as casual sex and abortion, a belief in punishment for those who do not believe in God, a commitment to proselytize, and use of prayer to seek forgiveness. The authors note that this construct could alternatively be labeled "fundamentalism." *Religious skepticism* encompasses beliefs that science will eventually explain everything, that the universe came into existence by chance, and disbelief in concepts of life after death. A final construct, *religious struggle,* describes the extent to which students felt uncertain about religious matters, had questioned or held disagreements with the beliefs of their families, or felt distant from God.

There were strong correlations among the religious dimensions, such that students with high scores in religious commitment were likely to have high scores on religious engagement and religious/social conservatism, and low scores on religious skepticism. Among the spiritual measures, spiritual quest had a positive relationship with ethic of caring and ecumenical world-view. High scorers on charitable involvement also had high scores for ethic of caring. Religious struggle stood out as a construct with only minimal relations to any other measure. Participants with high scores on religious struggle did not tend to show any particular increase or decrease in the other religious and spiritual measures.

The study indicated that undergraduate students tend to show significant growth in all of the spiritual measures during the college years, and described correlations with positive student outcomes for all of the spiritual areas with the exception of spiritual quest. Students with high scores on spiritual quest tended to have a lowered satisfaction with college and a decreased sense of psychological well-being. Alternatively, student scores for religious/social conservatism and religious engagement tend to decrease over the first three years of college. Religious commitment and religious skepticism show little evidence of change, and religious struggle tends to increase during college. However, the correlation between religious struggle and other outcomes is mixed, as students with higher scores in this area also showed higher commitment to racial understanding, but negative impacts on leadership, psychological well-being, and satisfaction with college (Astin et al., 2011).

It may be important to pause here and reflect before reading on. As you read about how other students experience spirituality and religion as undergraduates, what were the constructs that resonated with you? Consider your own involvement with religion and spirituality.

SPIRITUALITY AND WELLNESS

Comprehensive models of wellness have consistently included spirituality as a vital dimension within the conceptualization of wellness. Some models even use spirituality as the foundational

---

Reflection 10.2

Spirituality, Religion, and You

- What roles has religion played in your life?
- What role does it currently play in your life?
- How has this changed over time?
- What events or experiences have influenced these changes?
- How have these changes impacted you?

The answers to these questions may help you to determine how religion relates to your spiritual wellness. Think about whether you would like your pursuit of spiritual wellness to include religious practices and affiliations. If it has never been a part of your experience, it could be interesting to explore the social support of a religious community. Many college campuses offer opportunities for students to engage with religious practices. Alternatively, you may find that you are more drawn to cultivating intrinsic spiritual practices apart from participation in organized religion, regardless of whether religion has been part of your formational experience. Either way, there are potential benefits to your health and wellness. However, studies of religious orientation (Allport & Ross, 1967; Batson & Ventis, 1982) tend to indicate that intrinsic religion and personal spirituality are more predictive of wellness than extrinsic religion and denominational affiliations. Therefore, we will shift our focus from a distinction between religion and spirituality to a more explicit exploration of the relationship between wellness, spirituality, and intrinsic religious practices both within and apart from extrinsic religious settings.

and central element of wellness, such as the Wheel of Wellness (Witmer & Sweeney, 1992). More recently, Purdy and Dupey (2005) created a Holistic Flow Model of Spiritual Wellness that places spirituality at the center of life. Their model suggests that individuals who possess a healthy spirituality have incorporated spiritual activities into their everyday lives that strengthen and reinforce dimensions of spirit. The Holistic Flow Model organizes these activities according to thematic categories such as connectedness, a movement toward compassion, an ability to find meaning in life and to make meaning in death, and belief in an organizing force in the universe (Purdy & Dupey, 2005). Although it does not receive this level of emphasis in every model that is used for wellness, spirituality almost always appears as a key factor in articulations of human wellness. The most common wellness perspective is a view of spirituality as one of the primary dimensions for wellness. Therefore, in many models it is assigned equal importance with factors such as emotional wellness, social wellness, and physical wellness. By giving spirituality equal standing with these other dimensions of human functioning, the wellness models represent the long-standing human perspective that mind, body, and spirit are all valuable components for optimal development. Let's explore some of the research that supports the inclusion of spirituality in wellness models, bearing in mind that the literature thus far has a strong orientation toward intrinsic, individual practices.

THE EFFECTS OF SPIRITUAL PRACTICE ON WELLNESS

Practices of meditation and prayer have been the subject of more studies than any other method of engagement with spiritual wellness. Although these practices are frequently important components of spiritual life in spiritual or religious communities, they can also be adopted by nonreligious practitioners as components of spiritual wellness. Prayer and meditation have similarities in that both involve concentrated engagement with a being or a concept that is larger than oneself. By shifting one's focus from the self to the other through meditation or prayer, individual practitioners invite the possibility of *transcendence*. Transcendence literally refers to an ability to go beyond, which implies that intrinsic practices offer opportunities to move past the limitations ascribed to the self, and to realize possibilities for an expanded experience of existence. When have you encountered transcendence in your life? Your transcendent moments could range from small occurrences to peak experiences. Take some time to think of one or two times when you have, for whatever reason, been able to let go of your concerns and experienced transcendence. With those moments in mind, consider as you read how practices of meditation and prayer could also generate transcendent experiences.

Meditation

Meditation has been a spiritual practice for more than 5,000 years. Forms of meditation are associated with all of the major religions, including Christianity, Hinduism, Sikhism, Buddhism, Jainism, Islam, Taoism, Shintoism, and Judaism (Roach & Young, 2013). Although there are hundreds of varieties of meditation, there are two basic types that are typically utilized for practice: mantra-based meditation and mindfulness meditation. Practitioners of mantra-based meditation repeat a word or phrase either verbally or internally to focus the mind. Mantras are often uttered slowly at regular intervals, thus providing ongoing opportunities to call the mind back from tangents to the focus of the meditation (Singh, 1999).

There are two types of mantra meditation: unfocused meditation and focused meditation. One widespread example of an unfocused mantra-based meditation is transcendental meditation (TM).

Practitioners of TM sit for 20 minutes in a comfortable position with their eyes closed two times daily. Rather than concentrating on any particular idea, the TM practitioner repeats a predetermined mantra to help eliminate other thoughts and increase a calm sense of attending. The purpose of this practice is to allow the mind to move beyond thought patterns to a level of pure awareness. Repeated practice at maintaining this state of restful alertness is intended to help the brain function in a more coherent manner while providing a sense of relaxation and rest to the body. There is a wide base of support for TM in the research literature, with over 600 studies that have been conducted at more than 200 universities and research centers.

In addition to the unfocused approach represented by TM, there are many forms of focused meditation. A simple method that has fairly widespread use is the Jyoti, or "flame," meditation technique (Singh, 1999), which involves sitting, closing your eyes, repeating a mantra, and star- ing directly into the darkness to focus on what practitioners refer to as the third or single eye. The aim of this focused meditation is to visualize light as occurring internally, and then spreading that inner light throughout the body as a form of purification and cleansing. Once this is achieved, the Jyoti practitioner can then extend his or her visualization of this light as moving outward from the body as a form of connection with others. Unlike TM, which is practiced for 20 minutes twice daily, this focused form of meditation is often practiced at a regularly scheduled time for up to several hours per day.

Mindfulness meditation has been steadily increasing in popularity since its introduction in a Westernized form by Jon Kabat-Zinn (Kabat-Zinn, 1993). The Mindfulness Based Stress Reduc- tion (MBSR) program started in the Stress Reduction Clinic at the University of Massachusetts Medical Center in 1979. It is derived from Theravadin Buddhist practice, and involves being in the present and focusing on the breath. The mindfulness practitioner tries maintain an awareness of his or her present experience rather than attending to thoughts of the past or the future. Unlike mantra-based meditation, mindfulness meditation does not use a repetitive word or phrase. Instead, the practitioner will typically focus on his or her breath as a means of retaining a constant focus for the duration of the meditation. One of the most important aspects of mindfulness meditation is to avoid any judgments about the self, because to do so would require a loss of the ability to stay with the present moment. Self-criticism is a *metacognition*, meaning that it is a form of thinking about thinking. When you engage in self-judgment, you are having thoughts about your thoughts. By contrast, a mindfulness practitioner simply becomes aware of the thoughts that arise during meditation, accepts them, and allows them to pass so that he or she can remain focused on the present moment. MBSR has been utilized as part of a comprehensive treatment approach for many medical concerns, including chronic pain, cancer, heart disease, and anxiety disorders. It has been shown to assist in lowering blood pressure and reducing overall arousal and emotional reactivity. In addition to MBSR, elements of mindfulness meditation have been combined with the approaches of cognitive psychotherapy into a format called mindfulness-based cognitive therapy (MBCT; Segal, Williams, & Teasdale, 2013) to help facilitate treatment of major depression. In MBCT, much like MBSR, the practitioner learns first to accept unwanted thoughts instead of attempting to push them out of his or her consciousness. MBCT does not attempt to promote feelings of relaxation but rather to increase the practitioner's ability to increase acceptance of and control over automatic reactions to thoughts that would otherwise cause anxiety or depression (Segal et al., 2013).

Prayer and Religion

Prayer is an essential practice in many religious traditions. Like meditation, prayer also involves a process of listening and openness, and may also be practiced with a great deal of consistency and intention. It is generally viewed as a way to promote individual or collective well-being through a form of interaction with a higher power. This section will offer a very brief overview of common prayer practices and beliefs in some of the major global religious traditions. The traditions are sequenced according to the approximate time that they emerged as organized practices among different cultural groups.

Prayer has long been a part of Native American healing traditions (Portman & Garrett, 2006). The connection between healing practices and spirituality across many indigenous cultures acknowledges that guidance provided by representations of higher power can be experienced through prayer. Prayer is an integral part of many healing rituals that focus on practices of purification (e.g., the sweat lodge ceremony), self-reflection with a spiritual focus (e.g., the vision quest), burning herbs for cleansing purposes (e.g., smudging), and additional ceremonies, including the Sun Dance. The Blessing Way is a form of daily practice that utilizes prayer and song to promote or restore balance and harmony (Portman & Garrett, 2006).

Hinduism is the oldest known form of organized religion and the third largest religion in the world (Cashwell, 2010). Prayer is a major practice for Hindus, who pray to Brahman (God) for worldly and spiritual blessings (Roach & Young, 2013). Prayer also takes the form of asking Brahman for blessings and may include mantras that are believed to take one to higher levels of consciousness and to cure diseases (Bhaskarananda, 2002).

In Judaism, prayer is considered communication between the individual and God (Roach & Young, 2013). Communal prayer is practiced in synagogues three times each day, in the morning, afternoon, and evening, with additional services on Sabbath days, festival days, and Yom Kippur. In the Jewish faith, prayer promotes virtue and a concern for the well-being of others (Miller, 2003).

Prayer can vary across differing forms of Buddhism. Whereas Theravadin Buddhists generally do not offer prayers directly to the Buddha, other forms may do so (Roach & Young, 2013). Alternatively, they may utilize mantras. For example in Tibetan Buddhism, the repetition of the phrase, "Om Mane Padme Hum" ("The Jewel Is in the Lotus") may be repeated several hundred times per day as a form of prayer. Other forms of Buddhism may use chanting of the sacred writings called *sutras* (Gethin, 1998).

There are many forms of prayer across the diversity of Christian traditions. Christianity is the largest religion in the United States, and one of the largest religions in the entire world, with nearly one in three persons identifying as Christian (Cashwell, 2010). As a result, Christian prayer is widely represented in the Western research literature that addresses the relationship between prayer and wellness. Given the broad representation of studies in this area, Christian prayer will be addressed at length in the following section of this text on prayer and health.

Islam is the third largest religion in the United States and second largest religion in the world, with over 1.5 billion persons who identify as Muslim (Cashwell, 2010). The fundamental practices of Muslims are outlined in the Five Pillars. The second pillar of Islam is canonical prayer. The sacred text of Islam (the Qur'an, or Koran) encourages Muslims to be constant in prayer, and to this day, Muslims are required to pray five times daily (salat) while facing toward Mecca. Salat is formal ritualized prayer that is practiced at dawn, midday, mid-afternoon, sunset, and bedtime, and it may be accompanied by voluntary prayers as a way to draw closer to God and create an inner sense of harmony and peace. Friday is a special day of prayer for Muslims and includes a reading from the Qur'an, a sermon, and the ritual of prayer (salat) in the mosque (Gulevich, 2004).

This section only begins to scratch the surface of the vast diversity of major world religions. However, the intent is to represent the many varieties of prayer that occur as a result of religious adherence. Within religious traditions, prayer provides a form of connection with a higher power, or a representation of the divine. This connection can promote well-being by providing a structure to understand and cope with life events and by helping those who pray to achieve a sense of meaning and purpose, to enhance feelings of self-efficacy, and to promote perceptions and practices of connection with others (Roach & Young, 2013).

Prayer and Health

Whether prayer occurs within a religious community or in individual practice, it is considered a form of spiritual practice that is associated with health and well-being (Fry, 2000; George, Larson, Koenig, & McCullough, 2000; Hill & Pargament, 2003; Larson & Larson, 2003). Prayer can function as a means of coping with the needs, adjustments, challenges, and symptoms that are experienced as a result of physical, mental, and emotional illnesses. Persons with a range of health concerns, including advanced cancer, HIV/AIDS, chronic or serious illness, depression, and anxiety, have all cited prayer as an important component of their ability to persevere and experience healing. Research conducted on the relationship between prayer and health has found numerous positive associations. Prayer has been correlated with increased chances of longer life; improved surgical outcomes; recovery from depression and anxiety; decreased rates of suicide; lowered risk of substance abuse; an increased sense of well-being, hope, and optimism; higher rates of adherence with preventative health-related behaviors; a greater sense of meaning and purpose in life; and improved relationships, including both social support and marital satisfaction (Close, 2001; Hampton, Hollis, Lloyd, Taylor, & McMillan, 2007; Harvey & Silverman, 2007; Koenig, 2004; Larson & Larson, 2003; Maltby, Lewis, & Day, 1999).

Given the preponderance of Christianity in Western society, it follows that Christian prayer is by far the most frequent form of prayer discussed in the research literature. From this point forward, the studies discussed in this section can be considered studies of prayer within the Christian tradition. Prayer can be viewed as means of connecting or communicating directly with the sacred or divine that involves both direction and intentionality (Ladd & Spilka, 2006). Regarding direction, prayer can be oriented inward by focusing on self-examination, outward by focusing on interpersonal connections, or upward by focusing on the relationship between the human and the divine. Within each of these directional categories, Ladd and Spilka (2006) provide several theoretical factors to represent the intentionality of prayer. Intentionality factors among inward-directed prayers include examination (an evaluation of one's spiritual status) and tears (when experiencing personal turmoil). Outward prayers can include intercession (prayers on behalf of others), suffering prayer (sharing another's pain), radical prayer (assertiveness regarding others), and petitionary prayer (seeking material requests). Finally, among upward-directed prayer there are the categories of rest (prayer searching for stillness) and sacrament (prayer associated with ritual or tradition). The connectivity sought through the various forms of prayer may address each individual's particular needs for a type of spiritual structure. By utilizing a particular direction and intentionality, prayer can assist in clarifying and orienting the needs, desires, and goals of the one offering the prayer (Ladd & Spilka, 2006).

Forms of prayer are considered relevant for all age groups, but may be particularly important for elderly persons and those suffering with terminal illnesses. Among these populations, those with a deeply active prayer life are more able to maintain connections to others (Close, 2001). It is interesting to note that within this study there were variations between the type of prayer utilized by an individual and the needs addressed for spiritual well-being and physical health. For example, the participants engaged in the Augustinian tradition of personalized prayer as a way of seeking a comforting, personal relationship with God. They offered intercessory prayers, which are prayers offered for others, as a way to maintain a sense of meaning and purpose in life because it provided a sense of serving as an agent in the divine plan. Intercessory prayers also offered opportunities to stay connected to their loved ones and their communities, and the participants engaged in prayer as a means for releasing long-held negative thoughts and beliefs (Close, 2001). It is important to note that there is no single right way to pray. Forms of prayer can vary across denominational traditions, and also relate to individual differences. For example, Francis and Robbins (2008) found a significant correlation between psychological types and prayer preferences. This study supports the notion that how one prays and the importance that one assigns to prayer may relate to the potential gains achieved through prayer for the individual. The research around prayer and health is not limited to the prayers offered by patients, but also focuses on prayers offered for patients. Although there is a significant body of research that supports the beneficial relationship between prayer and health, studies of intercessory prayer do not yield unanimously encouraging results. In a recent study of over 1,000 heart bypass patients, the researchers observed that those patients who were certain that others were praying for them actually experienced more complications in their procedures and recovery (Benson et al., 2006).

Motivation for prayer is an important consideration for wellness outcomes. The motivation for prayer practices may be relatively internalized, or may be primarily based upon external factors. Four levels of motivation have been associated with prayer practices (Neyrinck, Vansteenkiste, Lens, Duriez, & Hutsebaut, 2006). Persons with an external motivation pray because of a belief that they are supposed to or because they believe others expect them to pray. When external influences are internalized, this is referred to as an *introjected regulation*. Those with this level of motivation pray to avoid feelings of guilt and shame, and want others to see them as worthy. As previously discussed, others engage in religious practices because they identify with the importance of spiritual activities. Those who identify this way engage in prayer because they find it personally meaningful and valuable, and endorse prayer as an important part of their lives. The most internalized level of motivation is an integrated approach to prayer. Individuals who possess this level of motivation pray to experience a sense of harmony and because it corresponds and connects with their goals for life and their way of being. As you might expect, persons with more internalized motivations for prayer demonstrate a greater likeliness to pray regularly. Perhaps more surprising is that internalized motivations for prayer are associated with wellness outcomes such as self-actualization, a clear sense of identity, self-esteem, and satisfaction with life (Neyrinck et al., 2006). Studies like this make it clear that meditation and prayer can yield positive results for wellness. Think about how these spiritual disciplines fit with your particular beliefs. Can you envision ways to incorporate some of the practices associated with intrinsic religion into your life as a way of increasing your spiritual wellness? Think about your openness to exploring this area of wellness as we discuss the impact of spirituality on college student outcomes.

Spirituality and College Student Populations

Astin, Astin, and Lindholm (2011) explored how measures of spirituality and religion among undergraduate students related to academic/intellectual and personal/emotional outcomes. Academic and intellectual outcomes included overall grade point average (GPA) after three years of school, motivation for further education, and a construct that they termed *intellectual self-esteem*. Intellectual self-esteem is made up of students' academic self-efficacy, writing and math abilities, intellectual self-confidence, and overall drive toward academic achievement. Personal/emotional outcomes were described as psychological well-being, self-rated leadership skills, and satisfaction with college. Compared with students from the general college population, students who showed growth in the spiritual measure of equanimity (feeling at peace and centered, finding meaning during hardship, positive view of life direction) reported a positive impact on GPA, intellectual self-esteem, psychological well-being, leadership skills, and satisfaction with college. Equanimity is the only spiritual or religious measure noted to directly improve GPA (Astin et al., 2011). Consider what you have learned about some of the health outcomes associated with spiritual disciplines. Can you see how meditation or prayer could impact equanimity as a spiritual measure? Does it follow for you that equanimity provides a means for coping such that students report higher well-being, self-esteem, satisfaction with college, leadership skills, and even increased performance in overall GPA?

Additional significant findings from the different religious and spiritual measures revealed that growth on the measure of spiritual quest (attaining inner harmony, becoming a more loving person, searching for meaning and purpose in life) also has a positive impact on intellectual self-esteem. However, it also has a negative impact on psychological well-being and satisfaction with college. The authors suggest that engaging in such a search may result in a sense of frustration or an increased awareness of the problems of the world. It may be necessary to balance work within your spiritual quest with the equanimity necessary to accommodate the challenges required to seek out this type of personal development. Students who experience growth in ethic of caring and ecumenical worldview (concerns with helping others and identifying with the global community) tend to carry increased aspirations to achieve advanced degrees. By contrast, growth in religious engagement (attending services, praying, reading sacred texts) decreases student satisfaction with college and the likelihood that students will pursue advanced degrees. Similarly, students who report higher scores for religious struggle also report lower satisfaction with college, decreased growth in leadership skills, and diminished psychological well-being (Astin et al., 2011).

This large-scale study raises some provocative questions about spirituality and wellness among college student populations. However, it is not the only body of research to examine spirituality among college students. Several studies have noted a positive relationship between spirituality and self-esteem (Hayman et al., 2011; Payne, Bergin, Bielema, & Jenkins, 1991; Reinert & Bloomingdale, 1999). Spirituality has also been shown to help moderate the effects of depression and anxiety, and the impact of stress on self-esteem (Hayman et al., 2011; Young, Cashwell, & Shcherbakova, 2000). The growing body of research on spirituality among college student populations largely supports the positive impact of spirituality on well-being, stress, self-esteem, and achievement. Spiritual wellness is therefore not a separate, detached, or optional dimension of human functioning. Instead, spiritual wellness has a direct impact on overall functioning, and can play a beneficial role in your growth, development, and achievement over the course of your time in college.

EXPLORING YOUR SPIRITUAL WELLNESS

Given the potential for personal benefits from increased engagement with spirituality, it is important to consider ways that you can begin to identify what spiritual wellness may mean for you. However, it is not possible to predict levels of health or wellness by simply considering whether someone is a religious or spiritual person (Roach & Young, 2013). Religion and spirituality are complex constructs that involve intellectual, emotional, behavioral, interpersonal, and physiological dimensions. Fortunately, an emerging body of research has begun to identify the spiritual concepts and measures that are more related to health and well-being. Studies have demonstrated that some of the key factors for spiritual wellness include perceived closeness to God, the degree to which spirituality and/or religion are orienting and motivating forces for one's life, the strength of religious support systems, and the degree to which one experiences religious struggles (Hill & Pargament, 2003).

Problematic Spirituality

It is possible to use spiritual and religious practices as a way to avoid acknowledging or dealing with painful psychological experiences or other personal, interpersonal, or emotional concerns. Rather than addressing the real issue, some people use religious terms or spiritual language to explain away their distress. When this occurs, it is termed *spiritual bypass*. Spiritual bypass can result in many difficulties, including suppression of painful or unacceptable emotions, idealization of one's own spirituality as superior to that of others, relinquishing personal responsibility of control for outcomes to external or divine sources, blind faith in spiritual leaders, and social withdrawal and isolation (Cashwell, Bentley, & Yarborough, 2007). Spiritual bypass is one clear example of ways that religious or spiritual commitments and practices can be helpful in some contexts, but may also have the potential to be harmful for wellness in some particular settings or when these disciplines begin to limit other forms of healthy functioning.

Another example of possible problems arising due to spirituality can come during periods of religious struggle. The process of searching through and questioning spiritual and religious beliefs is a necessary component of growth and development. However, normal developmental transitions or traumatic events may trigger uncertainty regarding previously held spiritual or religious beliefs. The resulting religious struggles can play a role in limiting growth in college student populations (Astin et al., 2011). In the midst of suffering, it is difficult to make sense out of painful life experiences, and individuals often look for someone or something to blame. Therefore, anger is often directed toward God for allowing difficult life experiences (Roach & Young, 2013). Research suggests that spiritual struggles represent a critical decision point for many people. The choices that are made regarding these struggles can lead in the direction of health and wellness, but can also result in increased distress and dissatisfaction. Hill and Pargament (2003) suggest that the degree to which individuals are able to resolve spiritual struggles plays a key role in this decision-making process. Furthermore, the attitude toward suffering and the ability to construct meaning during difficult experiences is central to concepts of equanimity and well-being (Astin et al., 2011; Frankl, 1969). The ability to find meaning in challenging life circumstances and thereby reconnect with the sacred can be central to restoring faith and resolving spiritual and religious struggles (Roach & Young, 2013).

Beginning a Spiritual Practice

Cashwell (2005) offers a list of recommendations for individuals who are considering development of a spiritual practice. It is important to determine your personal goals for initiating this practice. This is true for all areas of wellness, and your ability to set meaningful, realistic, and achievable goals will facilitate your ability to maintain this practice over time. Not all spiritual and religious practices are meaningful or effective for every person. Take the time to learn about a variety of spiritual practices, and choose items that appeal or attract your interest. You may wish to select practices that align with your individual belief systems, or to broaden your understanding by moving beyond your comfort zone to explore spiritual or religious traditions that are new for you. Either way, you should feel confident that the practice you have selected will be likely to facilitate movement toward your stated goals. Once you have selected a practice, approach it with discipline. Set time aside each week for this practice and make it part of your regular routine. Consider implementing the practice within a community that is supportive of the practice. Engaging in spiritual practices may produce strong emotional reactions as you grow more competent over time. A supportive community of persons who have shared similar experiences can help to normalize your reactions and help you integrate them into your ongoing development of spiritual wellness (Cashwell, 2005). It may be beneficial to explore the resources available on your college campus. Many university counseling centers offer different forms of mindfulness training for individuals and groups. College campuses often provide opportunities to attend meetings with religious student groups or university-affiliated interfaith organizations. All of these resources provide opportunities to engage with spiritual practices, and your engagement can have a positive impact on your wellness and your college satisfaction, achievement, and success. Additionally, as you explore the areas of spirituality and religion, you may find an emerging sense of meaning and purpose for your life.

MEANING AND PURPOSE

Nearly all of the researchers and authors who have studied and written about spirituality and wellness incorporate a sense of meaning and purpose in life as a primary component of what they mean by spirituality (Chandler, Holden & Kolander, 1992; Hettler, 1980; Myers, Sweeney & Witmer, 2000; Sweeney & Witmer, 1991; Zimpfer, 1992). Consider the factors that contribute to the spirituality measures from the survey of college undergraduates conducted by Astin, Astin, and Lindholm (2011). The spiritual quest measure assesses interest in searching for meaning and purpose in life. Equanimity looks for the ability to find meaning in times of hardship and to feel good about life's direction. The ethic of caring measure involves helping others and improving the world by reducing pain and suffering. Charitable involvement involves community service, and ecumenical worldview sees all life as interconnected. Taken as a whole, it is easy to see how meaning and purpose can flow forth from spiritual practices. Regardless of its source, meaning can play an equally important role in supporting individual well-being.

The Benefits of Meaning

In the book *Man's Search for Meaning,* Victor Frankl described his experience as a Jewish prisoner of war in a Nazi concentration camp. As a trained psychiatrist, he observed the lives and attitudes of his fellow prisoners, and asserted that despite the atrocities that they all endured, the prisoners who fought despair and maintained a sense of meaning and purpose in their lives were more likely to survive (Frankl, 1963). His observations and subsequent work in the mental health field following World War II provided evidence of the interaction between meaning and purpose in life, human well-being, and the ability to cope with catastrophic stressors. Savolaine and Granello (2002) indicated that health and wellness are impacted by a strong sense of meaning and purpose in life in several ways. First, a sense of meaning and purpose in life can foster the development of a strong personal identity. When individuals live their lives according to these principles, it supports self-esteem. For instance, if you value helping others, you may gain an increased sense of meaning and purpose by engaging in service activities such as volunteering at local food banks or tutoring students from less privileged neighborhoods in after-school programs. These acts of service foster self-approval, increase a sense of identity as a caring and helpful person, and subsequently boost self-esteem and wellness. Second, a strong sense of meaning and purpose can lead to improved interpersonal functioning and social interactions. Meaning and purpose can lead to involvement with other individuals or groups sharing similar ideals, and thereby promote strong social connections. A third way that meaning can impact wellness is by helping to overcome the existential despair or sense of emptiness experienced by many college students. A sense of purpose provides a steady direction for involvement that reduces perceptions of meaninglessness. Finally, a strong sense of meaning and purpose in life can provide a sense of coherence. *Coherence* refers to the ability to make sense of life experiences and stressful events. Therefore, the coherence provided by a strong sense of meaning and purpose improves the spiritual measure of equanimity, which has a strong relationship with positive outcomes for college students (Astin et al., 2011). Contemporary understandings of the sense of meaning and purpose are prominent in the research literature. The following sections present a brief review of some of the dominant perspectives from research on meaning. These ideas can provide a sense of scope for the way that these studies have defined meaning and purpose, and serve as sources of understanding for our exploration of spirituality, meaning, and wellness.

Broaden and Build

Folkman and Moskowitz (2000) assert that a sense of meaning can not only aid in reducing stress but also represents a powerful coping technique on its own. Positive emotions arise as individuals assign positive meanings to life events. The presence of these positive emotions over time provides a number of significant physiological benefits and moderates the impact of long-term stressful situations, or strains. According to the "Broaden and Build Model of Positive Emotions" (Fredrickson, 2001), when negative emotions arise from a problematic situation, they restrict thought processes and constrict plans of action regarding resolution of the situation. Positive emotions counteract the physical effect of negative emotions, and instead of limiting responses they encourage and empower people to broaden their search for solutions. Therefore, the ability to find personal meaning in challenging circumstances results in the presence of positive emotions that moderate the effects of stress and widen the variety of potential responses for resolution, thereby reducing symptoms of depression, anxiety, and anger (Schwarzer & Knoll, 2003). A sense of meaning thereby contributes to wellness by facilitating stress reduction and generating new and more creative or adaptive ways of resolving problematic situations or personal challenges.

Coherence

Antonovsky (1979) proposed the concept of a *salutogen* as the opposite of a pathogen. Whereas pathogens cause disease, salutogens promote wellness. One of the salutogens that Antonovsky discussed was called *sense of coherence* (SOC). SOC is comprised of three psychological constructs: comprehensibility, manageability, and meaningfulness. *Comprehensibility* occurs when an individual can make sense of the world instead of viewing life as an endless sequence of random events. *Manageability* refers to the belief that one has the resources to adapt, cope, and survive with the circumstances that one must face or endure in life. The central component of *meaningfulness* refers simply to the feeling that life makes sense. Meaningfulness is related to a person's ability to believe that he or she can make choices that will lead to desirable or preferred outcomes. In this sense, meaningfulness is the opposite of helplessness. Antonovsky (1979) suggested that SOC was related to positive factors, including an individual's immune functioning. This is due to the fact that a person who has a high SOC interacts with factors that produce stress in a different manner than a person with a low SOC. The individual with a high SOC is better able to think about stressors in a manner that promotes understanding and makes meaning out of difficult situations. As a result, persons with a high SOC can manage these stressors well enough to achieve reasonable outcomes. Therefore, over time, persons with a strong SOC come to view sources of potential distress as challenges rather than threats. When stressors are reframed in this manner, it reduces the degree of physiological response and improves immune functioning, thus contributing to increased levels of personal well-being (Young, 2013).

Hardiness

Existentialism has had a significant impact on the fields of psychology and mental health. As an existential psychotherapist, Yalom (1980) suggests that human problems are ultimately forms of conflict that arise when individuals confront the primary concerns of life, such as death, freedom, isolation, and meaninglessness. Each person must construct his or her own meaning for life, and this construction must be both adaptable and firm enough to support the challenges that life will bring (Yalom, 1980). Existentialist philosophies thus provide the perspective that a sense of meaning is the central cause of thought and action (Maddi, 1998). When individuals possess an effective and courageous sense of meaning, it can influence how they view and respond to the world. This courageous sense of meaning is termed *hardiness*. Hardiness was identified as an important dimension of personality in individuals who demonstrated a resistance to heart disease. Upon exploration, their resistance to stress was primarily based upon their particular worldview (Kobasa, 1979). Hardiness as a construct is made up of three interwoven beliefs about the world referred to as commitment, control, and challenge (Maddi & Kobasa, 1984). *Commitment* involves a belief that individuals engage actively with the world rather than embracing beliefs that result in feelings of alienation. *Control* is a belief that struggle and hard work are inevitable and valuable components of human experience, and that through our labor we can realize our power to influence the outcomes of our lives. *Challenge* is similarly related to stress and discomfort. Those who lack this belief desire comfort and security and view any obstacles to these goals as forms of hardship. Persons who hold the belief associated with challenge instead view barriers and stress-inducing events as opportunities to learn better coping skills. Taken together, these three beliefs provide a sense of meaning and a worldview that results in an overarching perspective that helps individuals to navigate their life challenges and struggles without impairing their personal wellness and optimal functioning (Young, 2013).

DEVELOPING A SENSE OF MEANING

There are two perspectives regarding the development of meaning in life: the outcome-oriented perspective and the process-oriented perspective (King, 2004). Outcome perspectives view meaning as coming from achieving desired goals or accomplishments such as loving relationships, financial security, or success in your selected career path. A process perspective on meaning in life offers very different rewards. This perspective provides an understanding of how one's life experiences are significant and meaningful and can change over time in ways that better support your perspective at various points in your life. For the purposes of wellness, we will focus on a process-oriented perspective regarding meaning in life, and in this section, we turn to an application of the research around meaning and wellness to help you strengthen your sense of meaning and purpose.

A Meta-Model for Meaning

As we begin, consider the following four questions that are related to the sentence stems that began this chapter:

1. When, or with whom, do you feel a strong sense of belonging?
2. When, or during what activities, do you feel a strong sense of competence?
3. When have you felt a high degree of self-awareness or understanding?
4. How do each of these experiences relate to your sense of meaning in life?

King (2004) proposed a model made up of three fundamental ways that people establish meaning across the lifespan: belonging, doing, and understanding oneself and the world. *Belonging* refers to the interpersonal relationships that form one's life. *Doing* addresses the activities that provide opportunities for meaningful engagement. *Understanding* involves the development of greater levels of self-awareness and comprehension of how others function as well. The model proposes that each individual forms a personal sense of meaning in distinctively different ways that are shaped by cultural values and the opportunities and constraints of one's environment. Therefore, there is no one correct or proper way to develop a sense of meaning. Instead, your purpose is a product of your experiences in relating to others, learning new skills, and reflecting on how these dimensions construct your identity and your way of being in the world. Additionally, these structures that impact meaning in life can change over time as the individual develops. It is likely that your sense of belonging, competency, and self-awareness has changed since your childhood. It follows that your sense of meaning and purpose would therefore shift to adapt to the changing circumstances of your own development and growth. This model relates to wellness most directly through its principle of commitment to meaning in life. Because this is a process-oriented model, its primary focus is on intrinsic goals rather than extrinsic outcomes or achievements. In research conducted with college student populations, intrinsic goals for affiliation with others, helping others and improving the state of the world, and becoming more fully self-actualized were related to higher levels of wellness, whereas an orientation toward extrinsic goals (e.g., attractiveness, wealth, popularity) was related to lower well-being (Kasser & Ryan, 1996). However, the model suggests that one must not only possess these intrinsic aspirations for belonging, doing, and understanding, but must also have a strong level of commitment to these goals to give life meaning. King (2004) suggests that "meaning in everyday life derives from active engagements or commitments to goals that help people feel connected, mobilize their activities and efforts, and contribute to their understanding of themselves and their world" (p. 78). College provides an exemplary opportunity to explore how these areas apply to your life as you form new relationships, engage in new learning through coursework and student life activities, and develop new levels of self-awareness and personal identity through your experiences on your campus. It is important to be both intentional and reflective. Choose relationships and opportunities that possess the possibility for enhancing your commitment to your intrinsic goals. As you engage with these different experiences, make time to think about how they fit with your aspirations for the life that you desire.

Reflect on Questions About Meaning

Frankl (1969) suggested that every experience provides an opportunity to find meaning. When faced with difficulty or challenge, individuals find the motivation to make meaning out of their circumstances. This can be accomplished through taking action, or by developing attitudes that promote understanding. Even when one cannot change the outcomes of a situation, it is still possible to decide how one will interpret the situation (Lukas, 2000). Therefore, it is important to consider how you make meaning of your experiences. Take a moment to identify a problematic situation that you have encountered in your past. It is simple to recount the facts, and even the feelings, associated with that experience, but deeper reflection can be realized by thinking about the meaning that you made from that experience. For instance, many children are not allowed to express negative emotions within their families. Although they are able to recount their parents' responses, and the subsequent shame or isolation that they felt as a result of these responses, on a deeper level, it is likely that they are internalizing meaning from these experiences (e.g., "If I show my emotions, others will reject me"). It can be difficult to identify the meanings that you have made from your experiences. Fortunately, college students are afforded many opportunities for support in identifying internalized meaning that has been made from experiences. Most college campuses have counseling centers that provide services to students, and new programs in health and wellness coaching are becoming common features in student affairs. You may find it beneficial to consult with a licensed therapist to process past or current experiences in the context of an empathetic relationship.

Finding Your Vocation

Buechner (1990) described vocation as the intersection between an individual's deep gladness and the deep needs of the world. The word *vocation* is derived from the Latin word *vocare,* which refers to a calling. Although the word is traditionally associated with religious commitments, *vocation* is frequently used among career-oriented individuals to refer to identification of a career track that provides a sense of spiritual fulfillment through achieving meaning and purpose through one's work. The concept of vocation makes it evident that meaning and wellness are connected to one's life work (de Klerk, 2005). There are a multitude of dimensions that shape your career, and a variety of perspectives you can take to help develop your overall plan to achieve the career you desire. In the midst of what may become competing preferences that seem difficult to integrate and

---

Reflection 10.3

Using the Future to Plan for the Present

To accomplish this task, you will need to use your imagination. Place yourself in the future with the assumption that you have lived a satisfying, fulfilling life. Now, in your later years, you are taking a moment to reflect on all that has transpired. As best as you are able right now, write your answers to the following questions from the assumption that you have realized the life you desired for yourself:

- Who are the most important people in your life now? How much time do you spend with them? How often does this take place?
- How affluent are you? What has determined your earning potential? How have you used your financial assets?
- What have been the most meaningful experiences of your life? What have you valued the most? How have these opportunities shaped who you are as a person?
- What do you want to be said about you when you die? If you could write your own eulogy, what would you want it to say?

Once you have written out your answers to these questions, read through your ideas and note anything that seems to relate to your career plan. For instance, if you have imagined that your children are the most important people in your life, and the experiences that you value most have related to them, what does that tell you about your career? It could mean that you want to find work that allows you flexible hours to spend time with your family, but it could also suggest that you are willing to work extra hours to earn money to provide the opportunities that you most value for your children. When you consider the activities you find to be most meaningful, does it seem likely that your job will provide you with that sense of purpose, or does your work instead offer enough resources that you can seek out a sense of fulfillment through your personal activities apart from the workplace? Perhaps most important, what kind of person do you hope to become, and how will your career impact and shape this personal development? Use your vision of your preferred future as a lens for considering the options you have right now to plan a career path that will help you realize the goals of meaning and purpose in your life.

prioritize, it could be helpful to pause one more time to reflect on the core of your drive toward whatever career path seems most enticing right now.

CONCLUSION AND SUMMARY

Spirituality is a core dimension of human life that has provided an important source of wellness, meaning, and purpose for millennia. Spirituality is difficult to define because it is at once developmental and individualized. Religion often overlaps with spirituality and can play an important role in promoting spiritual wellness for many people. Broad-based research among college student populations has generated evidence-based measures of spirituality and religion that correspond with academic, intellectual, personal, and emotional outcomes. Spirituality is a fundamental construct in most wellness models, and a bulk of the research on spiritual wellness has explored the benefits of intrinsic spiritual practices. Spiritual practices can be problematic, but can also serve as important sources of meaning and purpose. An extensive body of research supports wellness benefits associated with meaning and purpose, including increased ability to cope with stress and improved health. Meaning is grounded in practices of belonging, doing, and understanding, and, much like spirituality, is both distinct for each individual and developmental in nature. Meaning can be cultivated through work with a helping professional, through reflective practices, and through identifying a career trajectory that supports ongoing sources for making meaning throughout the lifespan. Spirituality, meaning, and purpose are integral dimensions of personal wellness and sources of improved functioning, and intentional development of spiritual practices can support a satisfying and meaningful life.

References

Allport, G. W., & Ross, J. M. (1967). Personal religious orientation and prejudice. *Journal of Personality and Social Psychology, 5*(4), 432–443.

Antonovsky, A. (1979). *Health, stress and coping: New perspectives on mental and physical well-being.* San Francisco, CA: Jossey-Bass.

Astin, A. W., Astin, H. S., & Lindholm, J. A. (2011). *Cultivating the spirit: How college can enhance students' inner lives.* San Francisco, CA: Jossey-Bass.

Batson, C. D., & Ventis, W. L. (1982). *The religious experience: A social-psychological perspective.* New York: Oxford University Press.

Benson, H. , Dusek, J. A., Sherwood, J. B. , Lam, Pl, Bethea, C. F., Carpenter, W., Levitsky, S., Hill, P. C., Clem, D. W., Jr., Jain, M. K., Kopecky, S. L., Mueller, P.S., Marek, D. Rollins, S., & Hibbert, P. L. (2006). Study of the therapeutic effects of intercessory prayer (STEP) in cardiac bypass patients: A multicenter randomized trial of uncertainty and certainty of receiving intercessory prayer. *American Heart Journal, 15,* 934–942.

Bhaskarananda, S. (2002). *The essentials of Hinduism: A comprehensive overview of the world's oldest religion* (2nd ed.). Seattle, WA: Viveka Press.

Buechner, F. (1990). *Wishful thinking: A theological abc.* San Francisco, CA: Harper & Row.

Cashwell, C. S. (2005). Spirituality and wellness. In J. E. Myers & T. J. Sweeney (Eds.),*Counseling for wellness: Theory, research, and practice* (pp. 197–205). Alexandria, VA: American Counseling Association.

Cashwell, C. S. (2010). Spiritual diversity. In D. G. Hays & B. T. Erford (Eds.), *Developing multicultural counseling competence: A systems approach* (pp. 367–387). Upper Saddle River, NJ: Pearson.

Cashwell, C. S., Bentley, P. B., & Yarborough, J. P. (2007). The only way out is through: The peril of spiritual bypass. *Counseling and Values, 51*(1), 139–148.

Chandler, C. K., Holden, J. M., & Kolander, C. A. (1992). Counseling for spiritual wellness: Theory and practice. *Journal of Counseling and Development, 71*(2), 168–175.

Close, R. E. (2001). The role of prayer in the health concerns of elderly Christians. *Journal of Religious Gerontology, 13*(2), 35–44.

de Klerk, J. J. (2005). Spirituality, meaning in life and work wellness: A research agenda. *International Journal of Organizational Analysis, 13*(1), 64–88.

Folkman, S., & Moskowitz, T. J. (2000). Positive affect and the other side of coping. *American Psychologist, 55*(6), 647–654.

Francis, L. J., & Robbins, M. (2008). Psychological type and prayer preferences: A study among Anglican clergy in the United Kingdom. *Mental Health, Religion, & Culture, 11*(1), 67–84.

Frankl, V. (1963). *Man's search for meaning.* Boston, MA: Beacon Press.

Frankl, V. (1969). *The will to meaning: Foundations and applications of logotherapy.* New York: New American Library.

Fredrickson, B. L. (2001). The role of positive emotions in positive psychology: The broaden-and-build theory of positive emotions. *American Psychologist, 56*(3), 218–226.

Fry, P. S. (2000). Religious involvement, spirituality, and personal meaning for life: Existential predictors of psychological wellbeing in community residing and institutional care elders. *Aging & Mental Health, 4*(4), 375–387.

Fuller, R. C. (2001). *Spiritual but not religious: Understanding unchurched America.* New York: Oxford University Press.

George, L. K., Larson, D. B., Koenig, H. G., & McCullough, M. E. (2000). Spirituality and health: What we know, what we need to know. *Journal of Social and Clinical Psychology, 19*(1), 102–116.

Gethin, R. (1998). *The foundations of Buddhism.* New York: Oxford University Press.

Gulevich, T. (2004). *Understanding Islam and Muslim traditions: An introduction to the religious practices, celebrations, festivals, observances, beliefs, folklore, customs, and calendar system of the world's Muslim communities, including an overview of Islamic history and geography.* Detroit, MI: Omnigraphics.

Hampton, D. M., Hollis, D. E., Lloyd, D. A., Taylor, J., & McMillian, S. C. (2007). Spiritual needs of persons with advanced cancer. *American Journal of Hospice & Palliative Care, 24*(1), 42–48.

Harvey, I. S., & Silverman, M. (2007). The role of spirituality in the self-management of chronic illness among older African and Whites. *Journal of Cross-Cultural Gerontology, 22*(2), 205–220.

Hayman, J. W., Kurpius, S. R., Befort, C., Nicpon, M. F., Hull-Blanks, E., Sollenberger, S., & Huser, L. (2007). Spirituality among college freshmen: Relationships to self-esteem, body image, and stress. *Counseling and Values, 52*(1), 55–70.

Hettler, B (1980). Wellness promotion on a university campus. *Family and Community Health, 3*(1), 77–95.

Hill, P. C., & Pargament, K. I. (2003). Advances in the conceptualization and measurement of religion and spirituality: Implications for physical and mental health research. *American Psychologist, 58*(1), 64–74.

Kabat-Zinn, J. (1993). Mindfulness meditation: Health benefits of an ancient Buddhist practice. In D. Goleman & J. Gurin (Eds.), *Mind/Body Medicine* (pp. 259–275). New York: Consumer Reports Books.

Kasser, T., & Ryan, R. M. (1996). Further examining the American dream: Differential correlates of intrinsic and extrinsic goals. *Personality and Social Psychology Bulletin, 22*(3), 280–287.

King, G. A. (2004). The meaning of life experiences: Application of a meta-model to rehabilitation sciences and services. *American Journal of Orthopsychiatry, 74*(1), 72–88.

Kobasa, S. C. (1979). Stressful life events, personality, and health: An inquiry into hardiness. *Journal of Social Psychology, 37*(1), 1–11.

Koenig, H. G. (2004). Religion, spirituality, and medicine: Research findings and implications for clinical practice. *Southern Medical Association, 97*(12), 1194–1200.

Ladd, K., & Spilka, B. (2006). Inward, outward, upward prayer: Scale reliability and validation. *Journal for the Scientific Study of Religion, 45*(2), 233–251.

Larson, D. B., & Larson, S. S. (2003). Spirituality's potential relevance to physical and emotional health: A brief review of quantitative research. *Journal of Psychology and Theology, 31*(1), 37–51.

Lukas, E. (2000). *Logotherapy textbook: Meaning-centered psychotherapy.* Saratoga, CA: Institute of Logotherapy Press.

Maddi, S. R. (1998). Creating meaning through making decisions. In P. T. P. Wong & P. S. Fry (Eds.), *The human quest for meaning: A handbook of psychological research and clinical applications* (pp. 1–26). Mahwah, NJ: Lawrence Erlbaum.

Maddi, S. R., & Kobasa, S. C. (1984). *The hardy executive: Health under stress.* Homewood, IL: Dow-Jones-Irwin.

Maltby, J., Lewis, C. A., & Day, L. (1999). Religious orientation and psychological well-being: The role of the frequency of personal prayer. *British Journal of Health Psychology, 4*(4), 363–378.

Maslow, A. H. (1972). *The farther reaches of human nature.* New York: Viking.

Miller, G. (2003). *Incorporating spirituality in counseling and psychotherapy: Theory and technique.* New York: Wiley.

Myers, J. E., Sweeney, T. J., & Witmer, J. M. (2000). The wheel of wellness counseling for wellness: A holistic model for treatment planning. *Journal of Counseling & Development, 78*(3), 251–266.

Neyrinck, B., Vansteenkiste, M., Lens, W., Duriez, B., & Hustebaut D. (2006). Cognitive, affective, and behavioral correlates of internalization of regulations for religious activities. *Motivation & Emotion, 30*(4), 323–334.

Payne, I. R., Bergin, A. E., Bielema, K. A., & Jenkins, P. H. (1991). Review of religion and mental health: Prevention and the enhancement of psychosocial functioning. *Prevention in Human Services, 9*(2), 11–40.

Portman, T. A. A., & Garrett, M. T. (2006). Native American healing traditions. *International Journal of Disability, Development and Education, 53*(4), 453–469.

Purdy, M., & Dupey, P. (2005). Holistic flow model of spiritual wellness. *Counseling and Values, 49*(2), 95–106.

Reinert, D. F., & Bloomingdale, J. R. (1999). Spiritual maturity and mental health: Implications for counseling. *Counseling and Values, 43*(3), 211–223.

Richards, P. S., & Bergin, A. E. (1997). *A spiritual strategy for counseling and psychotherapy.* Washington, DC: American Psychological Association.

Roach, L., & Young, M. (2013). Spirituality: Benefits of belief. In P. F. Granello (Ed.), *Wellness counseling* (pp. 157–174). Boston: Pearson.

Rogers, C. R. (1980). *A way of being.* Boston: Houghton Mifflin.

Savolaine, J., & Granello, P. F. (2002). The function of meaning in individual well-being. *Journal of Humanistic Counseling, Education, and Development, 41*(2), 178–189.

Schwarzer, R., & Knoll, N. (2003). Positive coping: Mastering demands and searching for meaning. In J. Lopez & C. R. Snyder (Eds.), *Positive psychological assessment: A handbook of models and measures* (pp. 393–410). Washington, DC: American Psychological Association.

Segal, Z. V., Williams, J. M. G., & Teasdale, J. D. (2013). *Mindfulness-based cognitive therapy for depression.* New York: Guilford Press.

Singh, R. (1999). *Inner and outer peace through meditation.* Boston: Element.

Sweeney, T. J., & Witmer, M. J. (1991). Beyond social interest: Striving toward optimum health and wellness. *Individual Psychology, 47*(40), 527–540.

Witmer, M. J., & Sweeney, T. J. (1992). A holistic model for wellness and prevention over the life span. *Journal of Counseling and Development, 71*(2), 140–148.

Yalom, I. D. (1980). *Existential psychotherapy.* New York: Basic Books.

Young, J. S., Cashwell, C. S., & Shcherbakova, J. (2000). The moderating relationship of spirituality on negative life events and psychological adjustment. *Counseling and Values, 45*(1), 49–57.

Young, M. E. (2013). Meaning and wellness: Purpose for living. In P. F. Granello (Ed.), *Wellness counseling* (pp. 148–156). Boston: Pearson.

Zimpfer, D. G. (1992). Psychosocial treatment of life-threatening disease: A wellness model. *Journal of Counseling and Development, 71*(2), 203–209.

CULTURAL AND ENVIRONMENTAL ASPECTS OF WELLNESS

Adam Clevenger

Look around you. What is it that you see? Are you sitting in a classroom? Are you reading from home? Are you working online at a café? Are you in the city? Are you in a rural environment? Who are the people around you? Friends? Colleagues? Students? What does the environment look like aesthetically? Are there windows? What type of lighting is overhead? Is it a clinical environment, or are you in a warm, comfortable setting? If you are eating, where did your food come from? Really—where did it come from? Was the food shipped to you cross-country, or was it grown locally? What do you hear? Is there music playing? What are the discussions being had around you?

As interest continues to grow around the topic of wellness, so too does the interest regarding the cultural and environmental effects on wellness. *How do contextual influences affect the way that we live our lives?* This question has provoked an increase in research and discussion among scholars, political junkies, doctors of medicine, parents, clergy members, and many others throughout time. *How does the interplay between our individual actions and the environmental responses that we receive in return affect the other dimensions of wellness?*

The relationship between the environment and our health is not a new concept; theorists in ancient Greece postulated that a person's total well-being is always influenced by "environmental factors, living habits or lifestyles, climate, topography of the land, and the quality of air, water and food" available to the individual (Yadavendu, 2001, p. 2785). With the increased understanding of medicine as it relates to curing illness in our more recent history, focus was averted from environmental interactions to a total biological conceptualization of health. The "cause" of any particular ailment was strictly defined as a problem within the person rather than a manifestation of problems within the environment; thus, rather than looking for solutions within the environmental context, a "cure" for the ailment was thought to require scientific treatment and medicine (Yadavendu, 2001). The discourse surrounding wellness in Western society has slowly begun to evolve so that we now discuss and define *wellness* as a multidimensional state that accounts for much more than a person's physical and biological experience. The World Health Organization has now changed its definition of *health* from a physical state to an all-encompassing health status that integrates both mental and social health concerns.

Today, the cultural and environmental understanding of health and wellness is considered the "second paradigm" within medical discourse, being that this approach directly conflicts with the biological understanding of health (Yadavendu, 2001, p. 2788); however, the impact of cultural and environmental factors in healthcare and wellness continues to garner much attention as research continues to show significant correlations between external events and environmental characteristics and our internal states. *High-level wellness* is a term that has been used to address the outcomes of a positive relationship with the environment. In order for a person to achieve high-level wellness, a person must learn to maintain a reciprocal, stable relationship with the environment in which both the individual and the environment can continue to grow together. This type of wellness increases a person's ability to adapt to unexpected events that occur in any given context and manage the resulting consequences within the environment (Ureda & Yates, 2005). As we begin to discuss the environmental and cultural effects on wellness, the questions presented earlier should prompt you to consider important elements of your environment that likely have been shown to have consequential effects on your functioning.

As you may have guessed, there is growing evidence suggesting that contact with your natural environment has a very positive impact on your physical and mental health. Reese and Myers (2012), for instance, report that contact with nature (e.g., trees, mountains, animals) has been associated with stress reduction; a decrease in symptoms related to attention-deficit/hyperactivity disorder (ADHD), depression, and anxiety; decreased recovery time from illnesses; increases in concentration; improvements in academic performance; and greater positive outlooks on life. In addition, environmental characteristics such as high-rise living, graffiti, and exposure to noise have been associated with lower levels of wellness (Guite, Clark, & Ackrill, 2006). Specifically, Guite and colleagues (2006) identified several factors that were especially associated with lower wellness: high levels of noise in a person's neighborhood, the feeling of being overcrowded at home, dissatisfaction with the amount of green space and access to public facilities, and the fear of crime in a person's neighborhood.

Another study that addressed the effects of environmental characteristics on individual wellness presented similar outcomes. Kuo and Sullivan (2001a) interviewed people living in an apartment complex in inner-city Chicago and found that reports of aggression and violence were highest among people who were living in the apartments with outside views of concrete and asphalt. When asked about conflicts with their partners, residents living in apartments that did not have views of outside green spaces (e.g., parks, gardens, etc.) reported higher levels of psychological aggression, mild aggression, and severe violence when compared to those residents who had views of green space from their apartment windows. In a separate study, residents living in complexes surrounded by more green space reported less total crime, fewer property crimes, and fewer violent crimes compared to residents living in complexes with less access to green space. Within both of these studies, all of the participating residents were found to be similar in multiple demographic categories (age, education, socioeconomic, drug use, etc.). These studies underscore the idea that external physical stimuli can be very influential in a person's wellness outcomes; the majority of this chapter, however, will focus on the effects of nonphysical external stimuli.

THE ECOLOGICAL APPROACH TO WELLNESS

Defining Culture

While engaging in the topic of environment and culture, it is important that we define what those abstract concepts entail beyond the physical domain as they relate to wellness. Before we begin that conversation, take a moment to consider the following questions, and refer back to your answers as you read this chapter. By reflecting on examples from your own life, you will be able to better conceptualize the themes and ideas presented later in this chapter.

Reflection 11.1

Define your culture. In what ways do you think some of these environmental and cultural factors have shaped and influenced your personal wellness?

In what region of the United States were you born? (If you were born outside of the United States, in what country were you born?)

What year were you born?

What was the political environment like in the country at that time?

What was your family's socioeconomic status? What did this mean for your access to resources such as food, healthcare, education, and so on?

Is there a law banning smoking in public places where you live?

How has your world changed since you were born? (How has your environment been affected by changes in the use of technology? How have values and beliefs shifted or evolved since you were a child?)

Where are you most productive? What is it about that particular setting that makes it a positive environment?

Culture and Environment

The perception that a person's culture and environment can impact his or well-being is known as the *ecological view of wellness*. The ecological view of wellness encompasses the belief that wellness cannot be considered on a solely biological basis because a person's health is interdependent on his or her physical and symbolic environment (Kirsten, van der Walt, & Viljoen, 2009). *Ecology* is a term that was linked to human development and wellness by Urie Bronfenbrenner in his 1979 publication of the ecological model of human development. Bronfenbrenner used this term to describe the mutual relationship between a developing person and his or her environment (Bronfenbrenner, 1995, pp. 612–613). Bronfenbrenner's ecological model expresses the view that behavior must be analyzed and understood as a consequence of the combination between personal characteristics and characteristics of the environment. Personal characteristics are considered to be biological and psychological traits such as personality and heritage. The environmental contextual characteristics are the physical, social, and cultural elements found in our direct environments (e.g., within our families, schools, and neighborhoods), as well as the characteristics that are found in the broader structural and historical context of society (e.g., the era in which one was born, and the political and economic environment). This underlying premise—that people do not exist in a vacuum and that they are affected by what is happening around them—is the main premise spurred by Bronfenbrenner's ideas (Moen, 1995).

Apart from the ecological model of development just described, traditional theoretical models of wellness have not traditionally included external stimuli within the understanding of wellness; the impact that these factors have on wellness has often been overlooked. However, Kirsten and colleagues (2009) developed a model relating directly to wellness that helps break down and illustrate the environmental components that impact a person's well-being. Within the model, they first defined people as "bio-psycho-spiritual units," underscoring the internal psychological, social, and spiritual mechanisms that affect wellness. However, they then included and defined the "ecological context" and the "metaphysical context" in their model as influential factors that impact a person's well-functioning.

Throughout this chapter, *ecological* will continue to be used as an encompassing term for all of the environmental effects—including the metaphysical. Within this model, however, the ecological context is strictly defined as the physical environment—both living and nonliving characteristics—that may include social, natural, human-made, and community/societal (e.g., political, economic, health, educational, security, juridical) factors. Environmental factors also play an extremely important role in "the development of well functioning, integrated norm and moral systems" (Magnusson, 1995, p. 34). The suggested meaning of the previous statement draws upon the idea that our experience with the environment and the culture in which we live has a profound impact on the ways we learn about who we are and what is important. The metaphysical context addresses this environmental impact. The metaphysical encompasses the symbolic and abstract characteristics of the environment that may include personalized viewpoints and beliefs, religious beliefs, and cultural influences. This model helps to expand our understanding of context and illustrates how the environmental impact on wellness can occur even outside of our awareness. According to Kirsten et al. (2009), this model is considered a "holistic eco-systemic model" of wellness. In this interpretation, the authors are relying on a systemic view of wellness in which a person is thought to be an integrated system of individual parts that rely on one another to maintain a balanced and healthy state of being; although the individual components (i.e., psychological, environmental, spiritual) can be well understood when separated, they can never exist independently from one another.

Magnusson (1995) proposes that one of the main roles of the environment in our functioning is to serve as a "source of information" for people—a playbook that provides immediate feedback concerning ways to move about safely and successfully in relation to others (p. 35). This understanding of a person's relation to the environment—in addition to awareness of how people can impact their environments—proposes an understanding of human–environment interaction as that of an intertwined, or symbiotic, relationship. Within wellness discourse, human beings and the environment are not considered to be separate distinct entities but instead are viewed as interacting with one another in a purposeful way. The context of any given situation or event will have broad consequences for the outcome of the event. Magnusson (1995) expands on this idea by discussing how direct person–environment interactions that occur on a small-scale level and perhaps for only a brief moment also simultaneously occur within broader society so that greater physical, social, and cultural elements of society are also affecting these interactions. The perceived meaning behind any particular interaction (i.e., what an individual tells him- or herself about the experience—either positive or negative) will not only be affected by current events but also by past circumstances and a person's background (Rutter, Champion, Quinton, Maughan, & Pickles, 1995, p. 61). To underscore the main idea of human–environment interaction: the environment presses upon people just as people press upon their environments. One does not affect an individual more than the other—both of these processes happen simultaneously throughout space and time.

Although we can have a devastating impact on our environment, the focus of this chapter will be placed on the environmental forces that act upon us as people. Again, environment will extend past the natural environment to encompass the metaphysical environment as well. Magnusson (1995) suggests that core elements of the environment that may have an effect on a person would include "social welfare, politics, culture, education, the causes and treatment of mental illness, criminal behavior and alcohol and drug abuse" (pp. 21–22). Rutter et al. (1995) also composed a list of possible ways that environments can affect people. This list is not meant to be exhaustive and instead is meant to demonstrate how simple cultural and environmental factors influence our overall wellness.

GEOGRAPHY   There have been many studies documenting neighborhood effects (i.e., differences in life circumstances caused by where a person lives) and crime rates. Most of these studies have focused on the predisposition to a life of crime among individuals growing up in certain neighborhoods; however, it can also be assumed that if a person is living in an area with greater reported crime, that individual is more likely to become the victim of a crime by experiencing a mugging or other violent act, vandalism, and burglary (Rutter et al., 1995). Other considerations regarding geography may include the political environment existing within a certain geographical landscape and the effects of living in a war zone; access to clean air, running water, and working electricity; and weather effects on wellness such as the chances of experiencing hurricanes, droughts, and forest fires. *How might these factors play out for people and affect the ways in which they live their lives?*

OCCUPATION   There is documented evidence that supports differences among occupations when assessing for job security and stress levels (Rutter et al., 1995). Other ways to consider the effects of a person's occupation on his or her wellness might include the level of prestige assigned to a particular job he or she holds (e.g., Does the occupation come with a high level of respect from community members? How is this occupation received by the parents of a romantic partner?); the environment in which the person works (e.g., Does the individual work in an environment that is dirty and overcrowded, or does the person work in a luxurious high-rise office that is spacious and quiet?); the number of hours one is expected to work, the amount of time a person is able to "take off," and the time of day a person is expected to work (e.g., Does the person work the night shift?).

INCOME   A person's level of income has consequential effects on securing housing and clean clothing, level of debt, and the ability to feed oneself and one's family. However, living in poverty has many consequences for a person's health and wellness that extend past basic needs; other ways poverty may affect a person's wellness may include the limited access a person has to community resources and higher education. Income is also likely to determine the amount of cultural experiences one has (e.g., travel, concerts, restaurants); these types of experiences can shape the ways we view the world and serve as another socialization tool that can affect wellness behavior.

PAST EXPERIENCES   Later life experiences are often associated with and affected by past experiences. Teenage pregnancy, for example, has been associated with less economic success and has been shown to be likely to decrease the chances of experiencing a stable marriage (Rutter et al., 1995). Other past experiences that may have an effect on someone's current life experiences and overall wellness include homelessness, experiencing the death of a parent or a partner, experiences with war, national tragedy, and time in prison.

ETHNICITY   Although we have made great strides to alleviate the disparities among ethnic and cultural groups in society, racial discrimination is still very prevalent and is likely to have important consequences for a person's wellness. This issue, in particular, will be discussed later in this chapter at greater length.

FAMILY   The size of a person's family and the number of family members with which he or she remains in contact is likely to have an effect on a person's wellness. Similarly, the number of people in a person's family who are physically or mentally ill or socially deviant will likely increase the stressors experienced by an individual. Family conflict, poor parenting practices, and substance abuse in the home are other examples of familial stressors that could arise (Rutter et al., 1995).

SOCIAL NETWORK   In the same regard as family considerations, the size and makeup of a person's social network that extends outside of the family will play a role in a person's wellness. Although strong social networks can be a source of stress relief and support, the larger someone's social network, the more likely he or she will be asked to help others handle their own encounters with stress and difficulties (Rutter et al., 1995).

PERSONAL   An individual's personal characteristics will have a major influence on interpersonal exchanges and interactions with the environment. For example, the effects of experiencing mental illness may increase chances of interpersonal difficulty, unemployment, becoming a victim of discrimination or crime, and other stress-provoking incidents. Physical disabilities are likely to play a role in person–environment interactions, as well as personality traits that allow for a person to more aptly engage with other members of society rather than struggling to "fit in."

The environment will act differently upon people, and the resulting outcomes and influences will differ depending on individual characteristics. This is especially true when considering specific significant events such as the birth of a child, marriage to a partner, and graduation ceremonies. Sometimes these events can occur as a random opportunity, such as a chance meeting with one's future partner, or these events can be the consequence of a person's "readiness" for certain actions, such as taking a new job or moving out of one's childhood home (Magnusson, 1995, p. 36). The effects of specific occurrences like those discussed previously are not often immediately clear; however, these events are likely to have a profound impact on a person's life course and development, and inadvertently and advertently on his or her wellness.

Prilleltensky (2008) has attributed the achievement of total wellness to the "simultaneous, balanced, and contextually sensitive satisfaction of personal, relational, and collective needs" (p. 122). By utilizing the term *contextually sensitive*, Prilleltensky is noting once again that the power and influence of the context in which one operates can often have a dramatic effect on a person.

UNDERSTANDING IMPACTS OF ENVIRONMENTAL AND CULTURAL STRUCTURE

Systemic Approach

The ecological approach to understanding wellness can be further understood from a systems perspective. Ureda and Yates (2005) define a *system* as "any structured entity comprised of components sufficiently interrelated and interdependent so as to form a whole" (p. 8). In the same way that a makeup of cells and organs is labeled as a system, families, peer groups, businesses, schools, and countries are also systems. The system has many purposes, but one of the first principles of a system is to maintain stability and equilibrium within the environment in which it exists. To do this, the system most often has to work with other systems within the environmental context in order to satisfy needs for survival (Ureda & Yates, 2005).

When thinking about individuals who form a system as a group (e.g., families, peer groups, etc.), it is important to remember that individuals will comprise several different types of group systems that create the larger societal system; in other words, systems are hierarchically interrelated based on their individual complexity. We can talk about this hierarchy in terms of subsystems and suprasystems. *Subsystems* are the smaller groups that create the *suprasystem*, or the larger group. For example, communities are subsystems of state and national suprasystems; a family is a subsystem of the overall community, or the suprasystem. A single individual can also be considered a subsystem of his or her immediate family, or the suprasystem. Therefore, a family could be comprised of four individual subsystems (e.g., mom, dad, brother, sister). Families could also be considered in terms of generation: the children and parents make up two individual subsystems, and the overall nuclear family comprises the suprasystem (Ureda & Yates, 2005).

What happens when a system's relationship to another similar system has the same level of complexity (e.g., two high schools that exist within the same school district, or the suprasystem)? These types of relationships that exist at the same level of complexity are called *horizontal relationships*. *Vertical relationships* are the relationships that exist between the subsystem and the suprasystem. The environmental context in which a system operates is considered to be anything that exists outside the boundaries of that system (Ureda & Yates, 2005).

Urie Bronfenbrenner's breakdown of social systems can be outlined as follows (Bronfenbrenner, 1994):

Microsystem: "activities, social roles, and interpersonal relations" experienced in direct contact (e.g., family, school, peer group, and workplace) (p. 39).

Mesosystem: two or more microsystems that are working together (e.g., school and workplace, home and workplace, etc.) (p. 40).

Exosystem: contains "the linkages and processes" between two or more microsystems, with at least one microsystem not containing the individual but that still has an indirect influence on the development and/or wellness of that individual (e.g., neighborhoods and communities, parents' work environment, etc.) (p. 40).

Macrosystem: "overarching culture and/or subculture" that references "belief systems, bodies of knowledge, material resources, customs, life-styles, opportunity structures, hazards, and life course options that are embedded in each of these broader systems" (p. 40).

Chronosystem: time, "changes over the life course in family structure, socioeconomic status, employment, place of residence, or the degree of hecticness and ability in everyday life" (e.g., the Great Depression, divorce, 9/11, historical events that affect development across the lifespan, etc.); it is the system that influences the ways the other systems are affected by an era or an event (p. 40).

The systems perspective of society relates to wellness because the perspective shows how different parts of society have overlapping effects on the others. Although people exist within their immediate microsystems, they are simultaneously impacted by what is going on around them within the mesosystem, exosystem, macrosystem, and chronosystem (Figure 11.1).

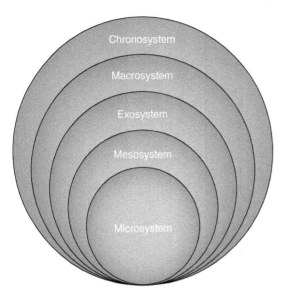

FIGURE 11.1 Systems Perspective

Maslow's Hierarchy of Needs

Quality of life is a term that is often discussed when addressing developmental wellness; a person is thought to have a higher quality of life when wellness factors are appreciated and addressed in his or her life. One of the most prominent theories concerning quality-of-life research is based on Maslow's 1970 hierarchical theory of human motivation, most commonly referred to as *Maslow's hierarchy of needs* (Gratton, 1980; Hagerty, 1999). You may have heard of Maslow's hierarchy; the basic theory addresses the effects of needs fulfillment on an individual's quality of life. Maslow hypothesized that human beings' complete functioning is centered on the continuous attempt to fulfill basic needs in order to one day reach one's greatest potential. To illustrate his theory, Maslow organized a hierarchical structure that placed the most basic human needs required for success at the bottom of the scale and placed the higher-order needs at the top of the scale. The core theoretical principle that Maslow discussed was the fixed sequence of the hierarchical structure; he stated that a person is only able to obtain higher-order satisfaction once the more crucial needs are met (Hagerty, 1999). In other words, until lower-order needs are met, an individual will place more value and importance on fulfilling the more basic needs before working to fulfill needs that come after the basic necessities. Personal growth is assumed to occur as more needs are fulfilled; when a person is unable to obtain lower-order needs, a person is likely to experience psychological and behavioral consequences (Gratton, 1980).

Maslow organized this hierarchical system into biological needs and psychological needs (Gratton, 1980). The following five categories were identified (*organized from greater-priority needs at the bottom to lesser-priority needs at the top*):

> Physiological—food, drink, shelter, warmth/clothing, sleep, sex
>
> Safety—limited violence and chaos

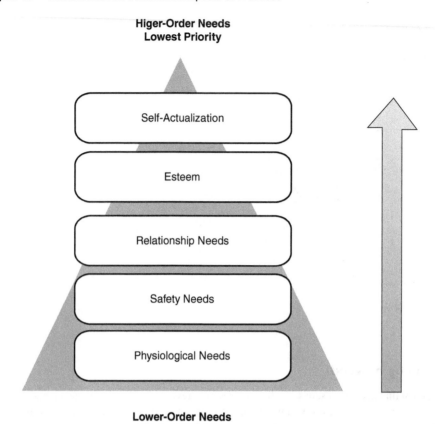

Higer-Order Needs
Lowest Priority

Self-Actualization

Esteem

Relationship Needs

Safety Needs

Physiological Needs

Lower-Order Needs
Highest Priority

FIGURE 11.2 Maslow's Hierarchy of Needs
Source: Adapted from Hagerty (1999) and Gratton (1980).

Belongingness and love—friends, family, community

Esteem—confidence, status, believing one has inherent value

Self-actualization—the point at which individuals have maximized all of their talents and are living at their best and fullest potential (Hagerty, 1999)

Figure 11.2 depicts this hierarchy.

This process has most often been used to address individual development within an environment; however, the theory has also been used to address how nations develop and improve the quality of life for their citizens (Hagerty, 1999). In other words, the hierarchy can be understood in relation to subsystems and suprasystems.

For example, in an effort to understand how cultural and environmental factors affect a person's functioning and subsequently quality of life, Gratton (1980) sought to assess how socioeconomic status (SES) affects the perceived importance of specific needs. By comparing subjects from different social classes (lower class, working class, middle class), this author found that social class was a greater predictor of "need importance" than either sex or age. Specifically, the author found that needs of belonging and esteem were more important to the working-class group, whereas belonging and physiological needs were more important to the lower-class group. This outcome suggests that lower SES can have a negative effect on someone's ability to fulfill higher-order needs such as those for esteem and self-actualization. Gratton (1980) identifies possible environmental and cultural factors that may influence someone's developmental process and growth, such as lack of community support and differences in childrearing practices. The finding that a cultural identity factor such as SES can influence a person's growth and development in obtaining higher-order needs is significant because it also supports the validity of the environmental and cultural impact on wellness.

POWER AND WELLNESS

Power is an essential component in maintaining wellness and can help further explain systemic and structural issues, needs fulfillment, and the overall ability to attain wellness (Prilleltensky, 2008). Although power may not first come to mind when considering the interplay between persons and their environments, power currents are often subtle and not easy to detect; many times, without knowing it, our basic functioning can become a product of how much power we are allocated in our living environment. Power impacts "our human experience, our understanding of it, our definition of it, and our attempts to change it" (Prilleltensky, 2008, p. 117). Prilleltensky (2008, p. 119) presents the following guidelines for understanding power in society:

1. Power refers to the capacity and opportunity to fulfill or obstruct personal, relational, or collective needs.
2. Power has psychological and political sources, manifestations, and consequences.
3. We can distinguish among power to strive for wellness, power to oppress, and power to resist oppression and strive for liberation.
4. Power can be overt or covert, subtle or blatant, hidden or exposed.
5. The exercise of power can apply to self, others, and collectives.
6. Power affords people multiple identities as individuals seeking wellness, engaging in oppression, or resisting domination.
7. Whereas people may be oppressed in one context at a particular time and place, they may act as oppressors at another time and place.
8. Due to structural factors such as social class, gender, ability, and race, people may enjoy differential levels of power.
9. Degrees of power are also affected by personal and social constructs such as beauty, intelligence, and assertiveness, constructs that enjoy variable status within different cultures.
10. The exercise of power can reflect varying degrees of awareness with respect to the impact of one's actions.

Access to power is based on the interaction between environmental and cultural dynamics. The ability to change one's access to power is completely dependent on personal variables as well as structural elements found throughout society that either promote or inhibit available options for people when working toward wellness. This internalization process of societal barriers is not necessarily noticeable but is often subtle so that we are unaware that our choices are affected by societal barriers (Prilleltensky, 2008). As similarly stated earlier in this chapter, Prilleltensky (2008) defined the attainment of wellness as the process of meeting one's personal, collective, and relational needs. Prilleltensky contends that these three domains of wellness must remain in balance and that each must be considered in order to prevent difficulties in the other domains of wellness. He states that increased attention to individual needs "is often at the expense of social values such as justice, fairness, and equality; resulting in poorly equipped communities" (Prilleltensky, 2008, p. 123). Similarly, increased attention to the collective needs will often result in "a lack of opportunities for growth, conformity, and denial of autonomy" (Prilleltensky, 2008, p. 123). Because personal and collective needs are often in conflict, a person's relational needs are of utmost importance when striving for wellness. Prilleltensky (2008) states that "respect for diversity and collaboration and democratic participation" becomes essential in striving for wellness (p. 122). Pulling from human development theory, he further contends that wellness cannot be attained without the following health-promoting factors: "political freedoms, economic facilities, social opportunities, transparency guarantee, and protective security" (p. 124). Prilleltensky is clear when he states that there is a very strong connection between socioeconomic, cultural, and contextual factors on the outcomes of wellness across the lifespan (p. 125). He argues that wellness can only be attained by tending to the structural elements of society; he states "a culture that emphasizes individualism and blames victims for their misfortune is bound to fix people and not structures" (p. 126). This ecological definition of wellness and the association with access to power can be applied to a number of social concerns that affect a person's wellness. For the purposes of this chapter, we will focus on the following: poverty and neighborhood effects, and gender socialization.

POVERTY AND NEIGHBORHOOD EFFECTS

There has been a growing interest in recent years on the impact of poverty on individual persons, neighborhoods, and communities—especially on developmental effects in childhood and adolescence (Osterling, 2007; Sampson, Morenoff, & Gannon-Rowley, 2002). As discussed earlier in this chapter, socioeconomic status (SES) is critical in obtaining resources and opportunities for wellness. SES can also be a major inhibiting factor toward attaining wellness (Grzywacz & Marks, 2001, p. 204). One way that the contextual factors of SES are discussed in regard to wellness is by looking at the neighborhood effects on the outcomes of a person's life. By using the term *neighborhood effects*, the underlying suggestion aligns with the message of this chapter: the neighborhood (environment/context) in which we grow up will have a lasting effect on our wellness.

In this case, neighborhoods can be viewed as "ecological units" within the suprasystem of the larger community—a "collection of both people and institutions occupying a spatially defined area influenced by ecological, cultural, and sometimes political forces" (Sampson et al., 2002, p. 445). Neighborhood poverty is continually associated with "unemployment, crime, health problems, child maltreatment, low educational achievement, and mental, physical, behavioral, and educational problems—especially among children and youth" (Osterling, 2007, p. 124). Concentrated poverty has also been linked to teenage pregnancy, increased rates of high school dropout, and adolescent delinquency (Sampson et al., 2002). In addition, lower SES has been linked to lower levels of physical activity. Grzywacz and Marks (2001) have reported that "older adults, women, blacks, and individuals of lower socioeconomic status are consistently found to exercise less regularly and are more likely to be completely sedentary than younger adults, men, whites, and higher socioeconomic status individuals" (pp. 202–203). All of these findings that are directly correlated to poverty and SES can be considered risk factors for lower levels of wellness. When considering the wellness of individuals living in poor communities, we can draw conclusions based on the vast base of research that residents in these communities will have a much more difficult time reaching high-level wellness than individuals from more affluent communities because of the differences in contextual impact.

One ecological explanation for this disparity in wellness outcomes for populations of different SES is based on access to higher levels of education and available leisure time. Grzywacz and Marks (2001) have suggested that higher levels of education improve people's overall knowledge of the benefits of healthy behaviors and that available leisure time increases people's ability to perform such behaviors. Exercise, for one, is likely to be inconsequential when families are trying to meet basic needs and care for their children. It is important to remember, too, that we have begun placing a value on "health" in the United States, and thus gym memberships cost money and health-promoting brands are typically more expensive. Research has shown that barriers to exercise may also be caused by contextual elements of the neighborhood such as lower levels of street lighting and neighborhood safety (Grzywacz & Marks, 2001). The ability to exercise outside is not always possible in neighborhoods with high crime rates where jogging may serve as a possible risk to safety. Also, isolated neighborhoods with high rates of poverty may only have easy access to corner stores that do not offer nutritious options based on a balanced meal plan—fast food and foods with a high sugar count found in gas stations may be the quickest and easiest available option for some people living in these neighborhoods.

Grzywacz and Marks (2001) investigated the family, work, and community microsystems within the environment in order to better understand how environmental effects might influence wellness. Higher levels of emotional support in the family and increased levels of decision-making abilities in the workplace were associated with "more regular, vigorous exercise" (p. 212). Neighborhood safety was also found to be a major component that affected exercise—the more an individual perceived his or her neighborhood to be safe, the more likely he or she was to exercise. Research suggests that urban areas are far more likely to include high-poverty neighborhoods compared to suburban areas, and that the impoverished neighborhoods are much more likely to be populated by families of color (especially African American and Latino/Latina residents) (Osterling, 2007). The researchers suggested that this particular component accounts for disparities among racial minorities in exercise, as African Americans are less likely to report living in a safe neighborhood compared to other groups. Grzywacz and Marsk (2001) reported that their results are supportive of an ecological perspective, or the important role of environmental context in behavior and development.

Social capital, or the number of social networks and resources that function to help individuals thrive, is often thought to be another major factor in neighborhood effects on community well-being. A lack of social capital is thought to increase socioeconomic disadvantage because community residents do not have access to the benefits that arise from social connections (Osterling, 2007). Social capital theory most often focuses on the connection between the individual and the neighborhood in which he or she lives; however, most research focused on this phenomenon has not typically included an investigation of the neighborhood context—the economic, political, and related power dynamics that play into the effects of social capital (Osterling, 2007). This missing link would explain why many disadvantaged communities supply strong social support networks but fail to increase economic standing among the residents; without supportive environmental factors around power, individuals do not have the resources to change their circumstances (Osterling, 2007).

Noguera (2003) identifies several characteristics that can be attributed to poverty and neighborhood that can have a detrimental effect on a person's wellness attainment: a "lack of access to healthcare, adequate nutrition, and decent housing, growing up poor and in a single-parent household, being exposed to substance abuse at a young age, and living in a crime-ridden neighborhood" have been found to increase risk behavior (pp. 437–438). Specifically, when discussing the unsuccessful academic performance of many young black men, Noguera suggests that a cultural change must occur to eliminate some of the neighborhood effects exacerbated within a "culture of poverty" to help increase academic performance among black males (p. 439). Noguera states that in order to better understand wellness outcomes (specifically around education), we must begin to understand how messages concerning race, class, and gender intersect and affect wellness outcomes. Within the next section of this chapter, we will move past SES and begin to identify some of the ways that race and gender may serve as cultural factors that affect a person's wellness.

Reflection 11.2

Before moving on, read the following statements to better understand cultural differences that may exist and affect a person's wellness based on social class and SES.

Consider the following statements and answer with yes or no.

Could you survive in poverty?

   I know which churches and sections of town have the best rummage sales.

   I know which rummage sales have "bag sales" and when.

   I know which grocery stores' garbage bins can be accessed for thrown-away food.

   I know how to get someone out of jail.

   I know how to physically fight and defend myself physically.

   I know how to get a gun, even if I have a police record.

   I know how to keep my clothes from being stolen at the Laundromat.

   I know what problems to look for in a used car.

   I know how to live without access to a checking account.

   I know how to use a knife as scissors.

   I can entertain a group of friends with my personality and my stories.

   I know what to do when I don't have money to pay the bills.

   I know how to move my family in half a day.

   I know how to get and use food stamps or an electronic card for benefits.

   I know where the free medical clinics are.

   I am very good at trading and bartering.

   I can get by without a car.

Could you survive in middle class?

   Either I knew someone close to me or I was enrolled myself in Little League, piano lessons, soccer, etc.

   I know how to properly set a table.

   I know which stores are most likely to carry the clothing brands my family wears.

   I know the best name brands in clothing.

   I know how to order in a nice restaurant.

   I know how to use a credit card, checking account, and savings account, and I understand an annuity. I understand term life insurance, disability insurance, and 20/80 medical insurance policies, as well as house insurance, flood insurance, and replacement insurance.

I talk to my children about going to college, and/or my parents talked with me about going to college.

I know how to get one of the best interest rates on my new-car loan.

I understand the difference among the principal, interest, and escrow statements on a house payment.

My parents were able to help me with my homework and did not hesitate to call the school if they needed additional information.

I know how to decorate the house for the different holidays.

I know how to order from online shops.

I know how to use the different tools in the garage.

I repair items in my house almost immediately when they break, or I know a repair service and call it.

Source: Adapted from Payne (2003).

GENDER SOCIALIZATION AND MASCULINITY ISSUES

Gender socialization is another example of how environmental and cultural influences can affect a person's wellness. The association between cultural messages and women's well-being has been of major interest to scholars and the general public since the early 1990s when a mass production of research and literature was published in the United States primarily concerning girls' educational disadvantages in the classroom (Weaver-Hightower, 2003). This increasing concern is not unjustified; women across the globe experience varying degrees of social, cultural, political, and economic disadvantages when compared to men (Weaver-Hightower, 2003). Issues related to sexual health, achievement, body image, and general self-worth have all been largely addressed in the literature covering girls' wellness, and this focus has profoundly impacted the knowledge base we have concerning environmental and cultural issues facing girls today. However, this concentration has arguably placed boys at an ironic disadvantage when compared to girls; until recently, boys' issues have remained largely unexamined.

In an effort to reveal the sexual health issues that are currently facing boys in sub-Saharan Africa, one author illustrates this research disparity within the social science community by referring to men as "the forgotten fifty percent" (Varga, 2001). In recent years, greater attention has been given to men's health and wellness research due to this observed disparity. Weaver-Hightower (2003) refers to this societal shift in focus as the "boy turn." The *boy turn* refers to the increased rates of research in areas concerning the contextual and structural influences on men's wellness. Today, more than ever, men are met with pressure to behave in ways that contradict the traditional male gender roles in society (Good, Thomson, & Brathwaite, 2005). Expectations for fathers, husbands, and neighbors, as well as expectations for men in the workplace, are increasingly centered around interpersonal and relational skills that have not been traditionally valued in men's gender performances. Perhaps due to these changing cultural messages around gender-role expectations, there has been growing interest in what some observers are calling a global "masculinity crisis." This phenomenon is associated with the observed rates of increased depression, drug use, suicide, teen sex, academic failure, and violence among men (Weaver-Hightower, 2003). Similar to the previous emphasis on education with girls, an abundance of new research has focused on boys' underachievement in schools. Changing cultural messages about what it means to be a man have led to a cultural shift that has changed the way we perceive education; some have argued that education is now viewed as a feminine institution that is not "manly" enough for boys to completely embrace (Noguera, 2003). *How might men's wellness outcomes be affected by social and cultural value influences?*

To begin understanding this effect, we must first start to understand the process of gender socialization. Gender-role development is thought to be one of the most important developmental tasks during adolescence. In the past, psychological and sociological adjustment was linked to one's ability to develop and perform the traditional and valued behaviors and interests associated with one's biological sex (Massad, 1981). Common belief among gender researchers now rejects the idea that adjustment requires adopting traditional gender roles; rather, adjustment is now thought to hinge on how positive aspects of both the masculine and the feminine gender roles are incorporated and utilized among each individual, no matter the sex assigned at birth (Barrett & White, 2002). Both sex roles have positive and negative traits. Women are traditionally associated with more expressive traits. Masculine traits that are traditionally valued in Western culture are assertiveness, independence, and competitiveness. These positive characteristics are thought to be strong indicators of resilience among those who exemplify these attributes. Men who express these desirable traits of masculinity are thought to be better adjusted and report experiencing reduced symptoms of depression and anxiety. The less socially desirable masculine traits (e.g., hostility and overconfidence) are associated with negative externalizing behaviors such as "problematic" alcohol use (Barrett & White, 2002).

When addressing the environmental and cultural effects on gender, it is important to understand the differentiation between biological sex and gender. This is a fundamental distinction when addressing social issues related to masculinity. Biological sex (e.g., male or female) is a fixed trait; gender changes over space and time because gender is socially constructed. The traditional social construction of masculinity generally requires emotional avoidance and restriction, independence, competitiveness, total avoidance of anything that could be labeled as feminine, homophobic feelings and actions, and physical and sexual aggressiveness (Good et al., 2005). The core of masculine expression is thought to be this emphasis on men's relation to the feminine; in order to express masculinity, a man must completely deviate from anything nonmasculine. This may manifest itself in men's dress, behavior, beliefs, choice of career, interests, hobbies, and social relationships. This construction of "manhood" greatly limits the options men have to move about in the world. As women are granted more access and the acceptable roles for women continue to expand outside of motherhood and domestic responsibilities, men experience less and less terrain where they are able to safely live out their lives in ways that are solely deemed "manly." The inability to find this niche often leads to feelings of vulnerability that have been associated with more aggressive attempts to exert oneself in the world as a man (Kierski & Blazina, 2009).

When referring to the related literature, issues associated with this type of masculinity conflict are endless. For one, men are found to be at greater risk of externalizing disorders such as alcohol and substance abuse (Barrett & White, 2002). Kierski and Blazina (2009) have discussed correlations between traditional gender roles and learning problems, detachment and trust issues, long-term problems following divorce, increased acts of physical violence, and higher suicide levels. In general, men also experience more injuries—both lethal and nonlethal—due to higher rates of vehicle collisions and accidents (Brooks, 2010).

Brooks (2001) discusses how patriarchal societies often celebrate and encourage violence and aggression among men. Violence is typically seen as a way to command power over other men and is many times viewed as a heroic or chivalrous act when "protecting" women. Similarly, sex is often seen as a way of performing masculinity. Traditional men often use the number of sexual partners to allude to their masculine prowess. Viewing sex as a form of conquest over another makes it difficult to associate sex with real emotion and can then lead to overt sexual issues and dysfunction among men (Brooks, 2001). Good et al. (2005) discuss the perpetration of physical and sexual violence by men, reporting that men perpetrate 95 percent of all reported violent crimes in the United States. This includes murder, sexual assault, the majority of violence among juveniles, and hate crimes. Men also experience high rates of sexual victimization; however, due to the expectations that men are "tough" and can protect themselves, it is believed that rates of victimization among men are extremely underreported because men do not want to be viewed as weak. Men are also less likely to seek help; although men are at an increased risk for mental health issues, the cultural message that men should not ask for help decreases the likelihood that men will seek counseling or another form of guidance or assistance (Good et al., 2005).

The intersection of other social identities with gender (e.g., race/ethnicity, religion, heritage, sexual orientation, disability status, region of origin, etc.) will have an effect on a person's gender performance (Good et al., 2005). In addition to advancing women's issues, the feminist movement has had a profound impact on expanding the notion of what masculinity can look like so that our society is now making room for different interpretations of masculinity performances, as well (Kahn, 2011). Perhaps we are moving further from the idea that there is one way of being a man. Unfortunately, many diverse types of masculine portrayals are still characterized as very negative. Black masculinity, specifically, is often depicted as "overly physical, out of control, prone to violence, driven by instinct, and hypersexual" (Ferber, 2007, p. 20). Conceptualizations of race and gender are best understood in relationship to one another, given that the cultural construction of gender is significant to understanding racism (Ferber, 2007). This concept can be best understood by referring to social identity theory.

Social identity theory (SIT) states that sociopolitical identities and a person's self-concept are heavily influenced by membership in specific social groups. In order to increase self-esteem and maintain power and control, people have a tendency to evaluate the groups to which they belong (in-groups) more positively than the groups that they do not identify with (out-groups). As a result, in-group biases occur that encourage prejudice and rationalization of discriminatory behavior. The more someone identifies with a particular social identity group, the more likely he or she is to endorse feelings of superiority and difference toward the other group identities. In regard to gender and race, SIT is thought to affect masculine performance by keeping other men "in check." Name-calling and the feminization of other men are common ways that men and boys try to keep one another "in check." Inferior status is ascribed to boys who do not, or cannot, uphold traditional masculine norms in behavior, beliefs, and image. This inferiority creates an inherent hierarchy and a mode of competition among men ("who is the most manly?") as subgroups of men begin to compete for power. Often, cultural and racial differences among men become a way of competing for power. However, environmental and cultural barriers repeatedly prevent black men and boys from engaging with and upholding, or performing, traditional masculine expectations (e.g., obtaining high-status jobs) that most often are assigned to white men due to racialized messages that black men are inferior to white men. Men often oppress one another for access to power and privilege (Good et al., 2005; Sherriff, 2007).

Review of the literature indicates that African American males, specifically, are in serious jeopardy within the "masculinity crisis." African American males face the highest rates of "incarceration, conviction, and arrest" (Noguera, 2003, p. 432); a third of all black men between 18 and 39 years of age "can expect to be jailed, imprisoned, paroled, or on probation at some point in their lives" (Ferber, 2007, p. 13). Black men are the least likely to be hired for employment and the most likely to be unemployed. Black males are also the most likely to be suspended and expelled from school, and the least likely to enroll in college. More than any other group, they are more likely to be labeled with a learning disability, more likely to be found in special education classrooms, and less likely to be in honors and advanced placement courses in school settings (Noguera, 2003, p. 432). Compared to white males, specifically, black males have higher rates of mental disorders, poverty, morbidity, and drug and alcohol abuse (Gause, 2005).

A common theme within the literature regarding black males is the significance of the "cool pose." The cool pose is meant to project confidence and strength and often hides insecurity and fears (Gause, 2005). More directly, the cool pose has been linked to fear of feeling vulnerable to racism (Liu, 2005). Gause (2005) suggests that the cool pose will be reflected in the adolescent male's "physical posture, style of clothing, dialect, walking style, greeting behaviors, and overall demeanor" (p. 21). The cool pose has also been interpreted as a way of obtaining power, especially over other men, "by stylizing their bodies over space and time" so that they are able to "reflect their uniqueness and provoke fear in others" (Gause, 2005, p. 19).

These issues associated with masculinity and race are not of biological origin; men are not born with an increased risk of alcoholism and a passion for physical violence, just as African American men are not biologically inhibited from competing academically. These health and wellness factors are greatly influenced by racist and sexist social and political forces that fulfill a "need" in society. As discussed earlier in this chapter, this need is often the access to and control of power over other people; racist and sexist attitudes and beliefs ensure that one group has power over another. Our wellness is greatly influenced by what we were taught to believe about ourselves, what we were taught to believe about others, and how we learned to operate and survive (both literally and metaphorically) in our overall environment. The cases of racial and gender performances discussed previously exemplify how these factors can influence a person's wellness.

Reflection 11.3

To consider other ways gender roles are exemplified in society, reflect on the following questions and consider how these socialization processes may affect wellness.

Growing up, how were the household chores divided? Were the responsibilities of your mother the same as the responsibilities for your father?

What are a man's responsibilities to his family? What are a woman's responsibilities to her family? Are men/women able to carry out the responsibilities of the other gender if needed?

Are there differences between the expectations for sons and daughters?

Are there careers that you were taught are more masculine or more feminine?

How is a woman expected to act in public?

How is a man expected to act in public?

What things can either men or women do that the other cannot do? Why is this so?

How are men and women expected to dress? Is the same level of divergence in dress afforded to both genders?

Is it okay for men to cry?

What are people's reactions to women who show aggression? What are people's reactions to women in power?

Is it common for women and men to take part in sporting activities? Do they take part in the same types of sporting activities?

When a woman and a man are together, who does most of the talking? What makes you think so?

Can a man and a woman be only friends?

Do men/men friendships differ from women/men or women/women friendships? If so, how?

Who is regarded as the head of the family?

Whom do the children go to for emotional support? For financial support?

What habits are deemed as appropriate for women but not for men?

What behaviors are deemed as appropriate for men but inappropriate for women?

What jobs are deemed as appropriate for men but inappropriate for women?

Integrating Factors Toward Higher-Level Wellness

All of the information within this chapter briefly highlights how contextual elements of our lives may have an effect on our health. You may be wondering, *What now? What can I do now to work toward the environmental and cultural dimension of wellness? How do I become environmentally and culturally well?* This is hard to say. So many of the ideas presented thus far are so abstract that it is hard to decipher what characteristics are actually causal factors in a person's wellness. There is some research suggesting that integrated cultural identities help people to cope with negative life circumstances. Specifically, Spurgeon and Myers (2010) discussed positive racial identity development as a possible factor that may help increase resilience and improve overall wellness attainment; this factor has been previously supported in research regarding positive development among minority individuals. Surprisingly, Spurgeon and Myers (2010) did not find this same association between wellness and racial identity in their study with African American male college students; still, they suggested that further attention should be given to racial identity development and wellness despite these results and suggested further research that would account for the "complexity" of wellness among African American males in this regard (p. 538). Along these same lines, and related to power dynamics, high rates of social inequality have been associated with low levels of economic growth, as well as negative social consequences such as poorer health outcomes (Wisman, 2011). In the United States, Wisman (2011) reports that "states with higher levels of inequality typically have more severe social problems" (p. 878).

Environmental identity development has also been suggested as a tool for increasing overall environmental and cultural wellness. One group of researchers discusses the positive outcomes of incorporating nature into your self-conceptualization (Reese & Myers, 2012, p. 402). Reese and Myers (2012) state that strong environmental identities are associated with strong beliefs about environmental protection as well as the desire to spend more time in nature; due to the positive effects of nature on wellness discussed earlier in this chapter, they suggest that this experience naturally increases wellness outcomes. Furthermore, relating to the natural environment has been associated with "positive affect, autonomy, personal growth, purpose in life, and self-acceptance" (Reese & Myers, 2012, p. 402). Other studies centered on environmental identity have suggested that this type of pull and relatedness to nature increases the connections that people feel to the social environment. Research has shown that time spent outside has increased research participants' acts of generosity, and increased a sense of community and feelings of inclusivity in participants (Reese & Myers, 2012).

This chapter was meant to engage the reader in a reflective process that hopefully helped to increase awareness and knowledge surrounding issues pertaining to the context of culture and environment and how these two factors can impact the wellness outcomes for different individuals.

Although some of these ideas are abstract and may still be somewhat difficult to integrate into your existing knowledge of wellness and health, it is important to remain open to the underlying concept that the environment will have an effect on you, just as you have an effect on your environment.

Reflection 11.4

Consider the ways you may have an effect on your environment.
Read each statement carefully and respond with yes, no, or sometimes.

I consciously conserve energy (electricity, heat, light, and water, etc.) in my place of residence.

I practice recycling.

I am committed to cleaning up the environment.

I consciously try to conserve fuel energy and to lessen the pollution in the atmosphere.

I do not litter.

I volunteer my time for environmental projects.

I purchase recycled items when possible, even if they cost more.

I feel very strongly about doing my part to preserve the environment.

Source: Adapted from the online Environmental Wellness Assessment available at http://www.definitionofwellness.com.

Although the previous statements do not summate all of the ways in which a person can affect the environment, they hopefully challenge you to consider the ways in which you may be currently having an effect on your surroundings. In regard to the impact the environment has on you, branch out and familiarize yourself with other cultures and other ways of living in the world. Engage with people who have different beliefs and values than you do, and talk with people to understand the way they make sense of the world. Not only will this awareness greatly impact other areas of your wellness (e.g., social, mental, intellectual, etc.), but it will help you to understand the ways in which you have been socialized in the world. In doing so, you may unknowingly uncover barriers, taught beliefs, and negative coping strategies that may currently be preventing you from reaching your highest potential.

References

Barrett, A. E., & White, H. R. (2002). Trajectories of gender role orientations in adolescence and early adulthood: A prospective study of the mental health effects of masculinity and femininity. *Journal of Health and Social Behavior*, *43*(4), 451–468.

Bronfenbrenner, U. (1994). Ecological models of human development. In *International encyclopedia of education*, (Vol. 3, 2nd ed.). Oxford: Elsevier. Reprinted in: Gauvain, M., & Cole, M. (Eds.). (1993). *Readings on the development of children* (2nd ed., pp. 37–43). New York: Freeman.

Bronfenbrenner, U. (1995). The bioecological model from a life course perspective: Reflections of a participant observer. In P. Moen, G. H. Elder, Jr., & K. Luscher (Eds.), *Examining lives in context* (pp. 599–618). Washington, DC: American Psychological Association.

Brooks, J. T. (2010). *The relationship between life balance and work stress in corporate executives. Dissertation Abstracts.* Published by BiblioLabsII, 2011.

Environmental wellness assessment. *Definition of Wellness.* Retrieved from http://www.definitionofwellness.com/dimensions-of-wellness/environmental-wellness.html

Ferber, A. L. (2007). The construction of black masculinity: White supremacy now and then. *Journal of Sport & Social Issues, 31*(1), 11–24.

Gause, C. P. (2005). The ghetto sophisticates: Performing black masculinity, saving lost souls and serving as leaders of the new school. *Taboo: The Journal of Culture and Education, 9*(1), 17–31.

Good, G. E., Thomson, D. A., & Brathwaite, A. D. (2005). Men and therapy: Critical concepts, theoretical frameworks, and research recommendations. *Journal of Clinical Psychology, 61*(6), 699–711.

Gratton, L. C. (1980). Analysis of Maslow's need hierarchy with three social class groups. *Social Indicators Research, 7*(1/4), 463–476.

Grzywacz, J. G., & Marks, N. F. (2001). Social inequalities and exercise during adulthood: Toward an ecological perspective. *Journal of Health and Social Behavior, 42*(2), 202–220.

Guite, H. F., Clark, C., & Ackrill, G. (2006). The impact of the physical and urban environment on mental well-being. *The Royal Institute of Public Health, 120*, 1117–1126.

Hagerty, M. R. (1999). Testing Maslow's hierarchy of needs: National quality-of-life across time. *Social Indicators Research, 46*(3), 249–271.

Kahn, J. (2011). Feminist therapy for men: Challenging assumptions and moving forward. *Women and Therapy, 34*, 59–76.

Kierski, W., & Blazina, C. (2009). The male fear of the feminine and its effects on counseling and psychotherapy. *The Journal of Men's Studies, 17*(2), 155–172.

Kirsten, T. G. J. C., van der Walt, H. J. L., & Viljoen, C. T. (2009). Health, well-being and wellness: An anthropological eco-systemic approach. *Health SA Gesondheid, 14*(1), art. #407.

Kuo, F. E., & Sullivan, W. C. (2001a). Aggression and violence in the inner city: Effects of environment via mental fatigue. *Environment & Behavior*, Special Issue, *33*(4), 543–571.

Kuo, F. E., & Sullivan, W. C. (2001b). Environment and crime in the inner city: Does vegetation reduce crime? *Environment & Behavior, 33*(3), 343–367.

Liu, W. M. (2005). The study of men and masculinity as an important multicultural competency consideration. *Journal of Clinical Psychology, 61*(6), 685–697.

Magnusson, D. (1995). Individual development: A holistic, integrated model. In P. Moen, G. H. Elder, Jr., & K. Luscher (Eds.), *Examining lives in context* (pp. 19–60). Washington, DC: American Psychological Association.

Massad, C. M. (1981). Sex role identity and adjustment during adolescence. *Child Development, 52*(4), 1290–1298.

Moen, P. (1995). Introduction. In P. Moen, G. H. Elder, Jr., & K. Luscher (Eds.), *Examining lives in context* (pp. 1–11). Washington, DC: American Psychological Association.

Noguera, P. A. (2003). The trouble with black boys: The role and influence of environmental and cultural factors on the academic performance of African American males. *Urban Education, 38*(4), 431–459.

Osterling, K. L. (2007). Social capital and neighborhood poverty: Toward an ecologically-grounded model of neighborhood effects. *Journal of Human Behavior in the Social Environment, 16*(1/2), 123–147.

Payne, R. (2003). *A framework for understanding poverty* (3rd ed.). Highlands, TX: aha! Process, Inc.

Prilleltensky, I. (2008). The role of power in wellness, oppression, and liberation: The promise of psychopolitical validity. *Journal of Community Psychology, 36*(2), 1167–1136.

Reese, R. F., & Myers, J. E. (2012). Ecowellness: The missing factor in holistic wellness models. *Journal of Counseling & Development, 90*, 400–406.

Rutter, M., Champion, L., Quinton, D., Maughan, B., & Pickles, A. (1995). Understanding individual differences in environmental-risk exposure. In P. Moen, G. H. Elder, Jr., & K. Luscher (Eds.), *Examining lives in context* (pp. 61–93). Washington, DC: American Psychological Association.

Sampson, R. J., Morenoff, J. D., & Gannon-Rowley, T. "Neighborhood effects": Social processes and new directions in research. *Annual Review of Sociology, 28*, 443–478.

Sherriff, N. (2007). Peer group cultures and social identity: An integrated approach to understanding masculinities. *British Educational Research Journal, 33*(3), 349–370.

Spurgeon, L. S., & Myers, J. E. (2010). African American males: Relationships among racial identity, college type, and wellness. *Journal of Black Studies, 40*(4), 527–543.

Ureda, J., & Yates, S. (2005). A systems view of health promotion. *Journal of Health and Human Services Administration, 28*(1), 5–38.

Varga, C. A. (2001). The forgotten fifty per cent: A review of sexual and reproductive health research and programs focused on boys and young men in sub-Saharan Africa. *African Journal of Reproductive Health, 5*(3), 175–195.

Weaver-Hightower, M. (2003). The "boy turn" in research on gender and education. *Review of Education Research, 73*(4), 471–498.

Wisman, J. D. (2011). Inequality, social respectability, political power, and environmental devastation. *Journal of Economic Issues, 45*(4), 877–900.

Yadavendu, V. K. (2001). Social construction of health: Changing paradigms. *Economic and Political Weekly, 36*(29), 2784–2795.

12 | SOCIAL RELATIONSHIPS: HOW TO INCREASE YOUR SOCIAL CAPITAL AND SUCCESS

Gerald A. Juhnke

Come to our breakfast, we'll come to your fire.

GOLD BEACH OREGON VOLUNTEER FIRE
DEPARTMENT T-SHIRTS (PUTNAM, 2000, P. 21)

Congratulations! You completed high school and entered the university. You likely are in your freshman or sophomore year. The world is exciting, and you are living an adventure. Young adults with similar goals, ambitions, and enthusiasm surround you. This is a time of great exploration and learning. Interestingly, the people you have met and will meet in college directly and indirectly influence your professional and personal trajectories. They also affect your personal levels of happiness, life satisfaction, and contentment. I know this to be true, because others and I have lived it. Existing literature appears to support our perceptions as well (Beilmann & Realo, 2012; Carolan, 2012; Coleman, 1988; Ghamari, 2012; Kim & Schnieder, 2005; Raza, Hashmi, Zeeshan & Shaikh, 2011; Wells, Seifert, Padgett, Park, & Umbach, 2011). Social relationships increase social capital and success. This chapter will provide a brief overview of social relationships and social capital. It will describe the importance of social relationships and how relationships within your milieu harm or benefit you. Additionally, the chapter will describe ways of assessing and escaping toxic social relationships. The chapter will then provide three key means to establish social relationships. The chapter's conclusion includes three reflection activities. Each reflection activity was designed to further personalize your reading experience and help the chapter become even more meaningful to you.

The chapter also contains actual personal and client stories. The names of the actual persons were changed and sufficient details were altered to ensure complete client confidentiality and anonymity. However, the essence and spirit of each story remains true to the actual experience.

SOCIAL RELATIONSHIPS AND SOCIAL CAPITAL

Social Relationships

For the purposes of this chapter, the term *social relationships* refers to your relationships and social interactions with others. These include favorable and unfavorable relationships, as well as indifferent relationships. Favorable relationships often begin when recurrent social interactions with the same person and common interests intersect. My favorable relationship with Steve is a prime example. He and I originally met in our office elevator. During our first elevator interaction, little more than social pleasantries were exchanged:

Steve (standing next to the elevator keypad): "What floor?"

Jerry: "Four."

Steve: "That's where I am going. Hopefully, we can make it an express and ride to the fourth floor with no stops."

Jerry: "Sounds good to me."

Steve: "I'm with economic development. Are you going to economic development?"

Jerry: "No, I'm a professor in counseling. My office is 4.310 on the fourth floor."

Steve: "Nice to meet you. My name is Steve."

Jerry: "Good to meet you, Steve. I'm Jerry. Have a good day."

Steve: "You too."

Let's discuss this brief but very important first communication interaction. First, without encountering one another, Steve and I could not have had this social interaction, and we could not develop a favorable social relationship. In other words, if our paths had not somehow crossed, we never could have met. If, for example, Steve and I worked in different office buildings, and we never encountered one another, we might never know the other person existed. Second, this was the first of many pleasant elevator encounters with Steve. If I had only encountered Steve on this single occasion and never again, we could not have an ongoing social relationship. That's the thing about relationships: They need to be reoccurring. If we do not interact with some type of regularity, the relationship stagnates and ends. Third, communication occurred. Had Steve and I entered the elevator and simply watched the digital floor numbers flash above the closed elevator door without Steve communicating, I likely would not have paid attention to Steve. Finally, it should be noted that neither Steve nor I insulted or offended one another. Can you imagine what would have happened if I entered the elevator, and Steve and I would have immediately exchanged insults?

Steve: "You are the ugliest person I have ever seen! Your nose is gigantic!"

Jerry: "Pardon me?"

Steve: "There is no pardon for you. You are just butt-ugly. You smell too. Don't you ever take baths?"

Jerry: "You are rude. Shut up and push the fourth-floor button. Never mind, I will push the fourth-floor button. Given your ill-mannered behaviors, you probably wouldn't know how to push the fourth-floor button without insulting me."

Such an interchange likely would ensure that neither Steve nor I would ride the elevator together again. In fact, if such insults were bantered back and forth, the next time I saw Cynical-Steve waiting for the elevator, I purposefully would take the stairs. I would not want to re-experience Cynical-Steve's crassness. As a matter of fact, I would likely point him out to my other social relationships and warn them about the curmudgeon down the hall. Thus, this fictitious interchange between Cynical-Steve and me demonstrates the importance of friendly and socially appropriate communications.

Returning to my true story about Steve and our favorable relationship, we had frequent positive elevator interactions. Over time, we learned more about one another and identified common experiences and interests. I learned Steve had two sons. His boys were about the same ages as my son. All three boys played high school football. Based upon this commonality, as well as the commonality of working in the same building, and our almost daily elevator rides, Steve and I had lunch. During lunch, we identified even more commonalities, and we enjoyed each other's humor, stories, and conversations. Although we did not become what some might label "best friends forever," we forged a very favorable relationship. We ride the elevator to the fourth floor at least a couple times each week, and we meet for lunch a couple of times a month. Clearly, my interactions with Steve demonstrate how a favorable relationship develops and what a favorable relationship is.

Unfavorable relationships, on the other hand, can take many forms. My personal and professional experiences suggest that most unfavorable relationships originally commence as somewhat favorable or at least indifferent relationships. Please allow me to reflect on one of my college experiences in an effort to clarify my position. In the late 1970s, I attended a large university of nearly 44,000 students. My roommate, Arnold, and I lived in one of the largest campus dorms. He was from a distant state. It was Thanksgiving break. I invited Arnold to Thanksgiving dinner at my parents' home. Arnold had a crush on one of the young women in our dorm. Her name was Barbara. She needed a ride home and did not want to wait for her parents to pick her up. Arnold volunteered us to drive Barbara home while on the way to my parents' house. Barbara's home was located in an affluent suburb of a major city. The ride in my rusting, red, 1975 Camaro was uneventful. Arnold told stories and attempted to engage Barbara in conversation. She was polite and pleasant, but certainly uninterested in Arnold's friendship. Barbara merely wanted a quick and free ride home.

Once we arrived at Barbara's home, we parked behind the mammoth home's 14-foot-tall wrought-iron gates. Arnold exited the car and extracted Barbara's three oversized Gucci tourist bags from the tiny Camaro trunk. They had barely fit in the trunk, and it clearly was an effort for Arnold to dislodge them. Barbara offered no assistance as Arnold and I toted the heavy leather bags and placed them neatly in the home's foyer. Barbara's mother abruptly entered the foyer from a back room. She clearly had been drinking and had an intimidating scowl on her face. She scolded Barbara for riding home with us and allowing us inside her home. As Barbara's mother put it, she was aghast that her daughter had come home in a "rusty, old car with such hooligans." I laughed, because I had never heard someone actually use the term *hooligan* in a sentence and because I knew neither Arnold nor I were troublemakers. I certainly thought Barbara's mother was joking. She was not. Arnold, still trying to score brownie points, complimented Barbara's mother regarding a jade necklace she was wearing. Barbara's mother arrogantly dismissed Arnold's compliment and quipped, "I am surprised a boy like you knows what fine jade looks like." Arnold's response was immediate, "Heck yeah! The toilets in my house are made of that [crap]." Barbara's mother became enraged. Her face turned red, and the veins under her skin bulged. She began yelling at Arnold. Barbara quickly hustled us out the front door, and scolded Arnold for his immaturity. I snickered and gave Arnold a high-five. We quickly got in my car and drove to my parents with a story of a lifetime. Arnold and I had a great Thanksgiving break. I thought the event was over and all was well. Regretfully, I was wrong.

When we returned to campus a few days later, Barbara had described the incident to her friends and roommates far differently than I remembered. Despite Arnold's attempts to be pleasant to Barbara and her friends, the relationship clearly qualified as unfavorable. Arnold's desired relationship with Barbara was never realized. There was little he could do except apologize for his nasty response to Barbara's mother. Arnold's apology was never accepted. Instead, Barbara and her friends ridiculed and jeered Arnold whenever they saw him.

The following semester, I was shocked to find that Barbara and I were in the same small-class experience. The class was comprised of eight or so students. The only remaining seat upon my tardy arrival was next to Barbara. I greeted Barbara with a smile and sat down next to her. She responded by calling me "jerk" and storming out of the classroom. The class laughed, and the professor made some quip about "young love." My association as Arnold's roommate guaranteed an unfavorable relationship. Later attempts at conversation with Barbara in the classroom were met with frigid contempt. Unfavorable relationships are like that. Despite one's best intentions, the situation often mushrooms and gets out of hand. Left unaddressed, these relationships seldom become favorable.

As a college student, you undoubtedly have many social relationships. You likely have a favorable relationship with your roommate and enjoy rooming with him or her. You may have the same major and may even attend some of the same classes. If your social relationship is favorable, you might regularly eat together, attend concerts together, visit each other's parents' homes, or go on spring breaks together. Additionally, you likely have other favorable social relationships with people who live in your residence hall or apartment complex, or attend classes with you. You may be very close to some of these people. Some may be from your hometown or you may have attended high school together. Most college students have a number of favorable social relationships with persons they consider their "friends." Although you cannot make everyone your friend, you have an ability to invite many others into favorable relationships.

Regretfully, like Arnold and me, you may have some unfavorable relationships as well. These unfavorable relationships might be with former girl- or boyfriends, former roommates, people who have stolen from you, or others from down the hall who don't like you because of who you are or previous unfavorable interactions. If these relationships truly are irreconcilable, it is far better to jettison such relationships than to continually attempt to re-establish the relationships or ruminate about what you did wrong or did not do right to bring about the unfavorable relationship. Stated differently, continually dwelling on these unfavorable relationships wastes your limited energy and valuable time. Instead, strategically reinvest your time and energy. Support the favorable relationships you have and continually invite others to co-create new favorable relationships with you.

When I was directing a counseling center at one university, I was supervising a case where a student's girlfriend broke up with him. For confidentiality reasons, let's give him the fictitious name of Tom and his girlfriend the fictitious name of Laura. Tom and Laura had dated since high school. Tom was admitted to a number of prestigious universities. However, he decided to attend the university where Laura was going. Tom wanted to marry Laura. He feared Laura would break up with him once she met others at college. Laura was very attractive. Within hours of arriving on campus and moving into her dorm, she had the attention of many of the dorm's young men. This infuriated Tom. He became very jealous and domineering. As one might anticipate, Laura ended the relationship. She refused to put up with Tom's jealous behaviors. Tom was devastated. He felt his life was over unless he "won" Laura back.

At first, Tom continued attending classes. However, he did not invest time studying. Tom reported he could not study, because he constantly pined his time away thinking about Laura and their ended relationship. Soon, he found his only relief was to drink to the point of intoxication. On multiple occasions while under the influence, Tom went to Laura's dorm room and pleaded for her to date him again. When this did not work, he would threaten her. As well, Tom began threatening every male Laura dated. Tom began to ruminate on suicide. He believed he would be better dead than living without Laura. Tom devised a plan to kill himself. His thinking had become very myopic. Tom believed the only two options available to him were either to win Laura back or to commit suicide.

Can you understand how it might have been helpful for Tom to jettison his relationship with Laura rather than continually dwell on getting Laura back? Tom was highly intelligent. He was articulate and personable. This certainly was someone who had significant success potential and would undoubtedly have other relationship opportunities. I even recall Tom reporting other intelligent and attractive women from his dorm flirting with him. Nevertheless, Tom remained intensely focused on his ended relationship with Laura. Tom nearly took his life, because he was unwilling to relinquish the past and move forward. Regretfully, Tom is not the only college student who refused to jettison an ended relationship or dream instead of building new favorable relationships or creating new dreams.

Another case I supervised was Sally. She was a music major. Sally's two older sisters, mother, father, multiple cousins, and grandmother all majored in music and were accomplished musicians. All received their music degrees from the same university where Sally had enrolled. When I met Sally, she presented as extremely depressed and irritable. Sally reportedly came to the counseling center because she was failing three music courses. It did not take a genius to determine that Sally was unhappy. When Sally reported she "hated" music as a major, as well as the university she was attending, the counselor was puzzled. Further counselor queries provided clarity related to Sally's dilemma. She wanted to be a geophysicist not a music major. She liked being outdoors. She enjoyed complex mathematical reasoning and science. In addition, she disliked social interactions. As Sally put it, "I'm not a people person. I want to be by myself exploring the wilderness rather than cooped up in a music studio with people I don't know." Given what you now know about Sally, her dislike of being a music major, her dislike of the university she was attending, her desire to be a geophysicist rather than a music major, and her enjoyment of the outdoors and math and science, list three things you would have suggested to Sally:

1. _____

2. _____

3. _____

Here are the three things Sally's counselor suggested. See if your suggestions match the counselor's suggestions. First, if you do not like music as a major, switch to a major that is better for you. Second, if you do not like this university, identify two or three universities you would like to attend. Make applications to those universities and attend the best university for you. Finally, pursue a career that matches your love of the outdoors and mathematical skills and reasoning. Can you guess how Sally responded?

This is what happened. Sally burst into tears. Sally reported that she *must* attain her music degree. She *had* to graduate from the university she was attending despite her overwhelming desire to attend elsewhere. When the counselor asked why, Sally declared that her grandmother, parents, sisters, and cousins would be *disappointed* if Sally did what she really wanted. In other words, Sally's fear kept her from doing what she wanted. She feared her favorable relationships would be jeopardized if she did not do what she thought people important to her wanted. Doesn't that sound crazy? Yet, no matter how crazy Sally's behaviors seem, many of us—including me—sometimes do what we think others want rather than please ourselves. Let me tell you a story about what I did to please my mother.

During graduate school, my mother sent a Christmas present. It was a medium-sized sleeveless black shirt. The shirt was far too small for me. On a good day, I wear an extra-large shirt. Despite knowing the shirt was far too small for me, I forcibly put my head into the undersized neck opening. Although I shimmied and squirmed, and I frantically attempted to pull the shirt over my head, I could not. The shirt actually became stuck on my head. It was stuck above my chin, but under my nose and ears. Finally, with all my might, I yanked the shirt over my nose and ears. My eyeglasses flipped to the ground. My ears and nose burned from being yanked upward toward my scalp. However, I finally got the shirt over my head and slipped my arms into the sleeve holes. Regretfully, as I then stood in front of the mirror, I realized there was a large gap between the bottom of my undersized shirt and the top of my blue jeans. The shirt simply didn't have enough fabric to cover my stomach. I was uncomfortable, and I was embarrassed. More important, I was ashamed of how I looked. Yet, I felt I *had* to wear that shirt. Certainly, my mother some 200 miles away would be *disappointed* if I did not wear the shirt she gave me. Is that the epitome of crazy thinking or what?

My wife laughed as I walked into our apartment living room. She told me to take off the diminutive shirt and put on a shirt that fit. Despite not liking the puny shirt, I actually argued with my wife. I reported I *had* to wear the shirt. My wife reminded me that my mother lived 200 miles away and would never know whether I actually wore the shirt. My wife logically claimed my mother would gladly exchange the shirt. The only thing I needed to do was tell my mother I needed a different shirt. For a moment, I hesitated. Then, I realized the craziness. I was wearing a shirt I disliked, because I was trying to *make* someone happy.

Here are four little exercises designed to help you identify social relationship craziness in your life. Are you up to the challenge? First, on the lines below, indicate what things you are doing because you are trying to *make* others happy or behaviors others are demanding of you to make them happy (e.g., wearing a shirt you don't like because someone purchased it for you and you don't want to make him or her angry, etc.).

1. _____

2. _____

3. _____

Second, answer this question by circling either "yes" or "no" below, "Are you ready to eliminate these behaviors or will you simply continue the behaviors to make others happy?"

Yes   No

Third, on the lines below, succinctly indicate the costs associated with continuing these attempts to please others (e.g., feeling embarrassed wearing the Christmas present, etc.).

_____

_____

_____

_____

Finally, on the lines below, indicate the costs of eliminating these behaviors (e.g., having mother act frustrated if I ask to exchange the shirt for a larger size, etc.).

_____

_____

_____

_____

Returning to our social relationship overview, the final social relationship type is termed *indifferent relationships*. These are neither favorable nor unfavorable. Most often, indifferent relationships are uncultivated or un-nurtured. Time typically is the major factor influencing indifferent relationships. In other words, indifferent relationships frequently can become favorable relationships if given time and energy. However, there is a caveat. One only has limited time and energy to invest. Thus, you need to wisely determine which relationships receive adequate time and energy. Here is a hint to the wise. After being a Licensed Professional Counselor for more than 25 years and a professor for 22 years, as well as being a former college counseling clinic director, I have helped college students, their peers, their families, and college faculty address just about every kind of college student stressor, dysfunction, concern, and problem. From suicidal thoughts and roommate quarrels to substance abuse and failing courses, I have witnessed nearly everything. Based upon my experiences, I believe it is best to invest time and energy in relationships that nurture you, and in relationships where *all* activities are legal, moral, ethical, and healthy to you and others. Let me explain.

Some social relationships may at first appear favorable or indifferent. However, over time, it can become apparent that the social relationship is either lopsidedly in favor of the other person or covertly harmful. For example, if you find yourself constantly giving and helping another person and rarely, if ever, being supported or helped by that person, there is robust probability that you are being used. An example of this might be a so-called *friend* who constantly borrows but never repays money or someone who continually speaks poorly of you or lies to you. Glen was such a college friend. Glen would often accidentally forget his wallet when we went out to eat, and he never contributed gas money for trips. He frequently borrowed my car but never refilled the gas tank. Glen was a fun person. He always had funny stories, he had a high degree of spontaneity, and he had a sense of adventure. Life was never boring when you hung around Glen. However, after rooming with Glen for a semester, his pattern of using others became strikingly apparent. He was highly irresponsible, prone to great exaggeration, and often had angry outbursts when he didn't get his way. Glen and I parted as roommates when it became apparent that at least some of his behaviors were bordering on illegal. For example, Glen was known for authoring term papers and completing course projects for the charge of $22 per page. For a much higher price, Glen would even take others' quizzes and tests. When I asked Glen to consider the potential consequences of his behaviors, he rationalized his behaviors. Glen said he was just helping people stay in college. Then Glen told me, I was too "straight-laced" to understand how authoring others' term papers and projects or taking their quizzes and tests helped others attain the grades they deserved and the money he needed. According to Glen, it was a "win-win" situation. Less than six months after we parted ways, I learned Glen was suspended from the university. Apparently, the university was too straight-laced to understand the value of Glen's behaviors as well.

About a year later, I met Glen's previous roommate. When he told me about how Glen had stolen the roommate's high school ring and had stolen money from others, I suddenly realized

I was lucky. I had escaped many of Glen's harmful behaviors. The moral of the story is to stay away from users. This is the only way to insulate oneself from potential harm.

Social Capital

Now that we have discussed the three types of social relationships, let us discuss social capital. Most have heard the term *capital* used in business and industry. It broadly means assets corporations have available. Business executives utilize capital to ensure their corporations' successes. These assets provide some type of value to the corporation. Assets often include money, unfinished goods or raw products such as steel and concrete already purchased and available to the corporation, as well as factories and equipment used to manufacture or produce products and services. Human capital is similar. However, instead of assets used to bring value to a corporation, human capital refers to assets that bring additional value to the person. For instance, one's educational accomplishments and degrees increase a person's value.

Physicians, for example, spend years in their education and residency experiences. Thus, physicians typically earn far more money than physicians' assistants or nurses. All are important to appropriate medical care. However, physicians typically have the greatest amount of education and training. Thus, they receive the greatest amount of pay. In other words, physicians have greater human capital due to their education and residency experiences. This human capital is recognized and rewarded with greater pay.

Social relationships also create social capital. The people you know and interact provide social capital—opportunities that provide increased value and potential success. This is especially true in college. For example, when I was in college, another friend, Russ, introduced me to his father. Russ's father was a business executive. At the time, I was working in a restaurant to pay my college tuition. Prior to Christmas break of my sophomore year, I was charged with establishing the restaurant's catering services. Russ's father visited campus and took Russ and me out for dinner. During dinner, Russ told his father about the long hours I had worked on marketing the restaurant's catering business and my intent to make the catering venture successful. Russ's father was intrigued and asked many questions. He asked about my cooking and catering experiences. He wanted to know how I established prices for the catering events. He asked where I purchased my food, and how the food was prepared. He also queried me about my staff, and how I hired them.

At the end of our dinner, Russ's father asked to visit the restaurant where I worked. It was late and a long drive away, but I obliged. Once there, Russ's father inspected the newly purchased catering vans I had enthusiastically described to him. I showed him how I had outfitted the catering vans with large heating and cooling containers. The containers could be locked into place during the food transportation process. Once on location, they could be unlocked and rolled into the actual catering event. Russ's father seemed impressed with all the planning I had done and the thorough details of the catering business.

The next day, Russ's father called me. He thanked me for the tour of the restaurant's catering facilities and the vans. He also requested a list of events I had recently catered and contact information for those who had used our catering service. I provided him with everything he wanted but had little idea why he wanted all this information. I thought he was just being polite. However, I was hoping that he might mention my new catering service to people he knew. A few days later, Russ's father called me and asked if our catering service was able to provide food for 400 employees at his company's annual Christmas party. He offered far more money to cater the event than I ever imagined. I was ecstatic. The event was highly profitable, and helped me establish my first restaurant catering business. The experience never could have happened without the social capital resulting from my favorable relationship with this business executive's son.

Similarly, a couple of summers ago, Michelle, one of the baristas at my favorite coffee shop, was puzzled about her career path. Michelle had an undergraduate psychology degree and wanted a career helping people. She felt underutilized as a barista and did not know what career to pursue. During the previous year, I had watched Michelle eloquently respond to irate customers, graciously interact with peers and supervisors, effectively train incoming baristas, and work her interpersonal magic with at least 100 satisfied customers. Frankly, she had the social intelligence and interpersonal savvy that very few others possess. I suggested she consider counseling as a professional career option. The next time I visited the coffee shop, she was very enthused about the counseling profession and wanted to apply to the master's counseling program at a local university. As a faculty member in that department and as someone who had directly observed this wonderful person demonstrate her superior social intelligence, I offered to author a recommendation letter. Although the letter I authored by itself certainly did not provide justification for acceptance into the program, it helped. Thus, our favorable social relationship provided helpful social capital. In both of the situations just described, social capital was derived from favorable relationships. These relationships provided interpersonal connections with opportunities that could not have otherwise occurred.

In addition to social capital providing interpersonal connections, social capital can be attained from the reputations of those one interacts with. For example, one's social capital increases or decreases based upon the combined reputations of those with whom we are seen. Recently, three of my outstanding senior master's students introduced me to an incoming master's student. Although I had never met the incoming student before and did not know of her counseling skills or background, I knew the other three students were dedicated, intelligent, ethical, and capable overachievers. As the five of us enjoyed our Starbucks coffee and conversations, the incoming student indicated her desire to someday present at a professional conference. Given her affiliation with the others, I invited her to co-present with us at an upcoming program. I made this offer based upon my previous positive experiences with her friends and my immediate impressions of her. The outcome was excellent. As I anticipated, based upon my knowledge of her peers and their favorable reputations, the previously unknown student greatly invested herself in the presentation and helped make the experience a success for all who attended. Her visible relationship with these peers provided social capital.

Conversely, reputations can hinder. Do you remember my previous story concerning Barbara? My reputation with Barbara, her friends, and her parents was likely tarnished due to my relationship with Arnold. How do you think Barbara's father would have responded if I had approached him about catering a holiday dinner for his corporation? He likely would have judged me incompetent based upon my friendship with Arnold and my reported immature behaviors. In the same way, I am often surprised by the lack of care students sometimes use when establishing social relationships. It is important to establish social relationships that help one move toward one's professional goals and objectives rather than hinder or oppress. Again, it is easy to understand how choosing social relationships can help or hinder.

Students also gain social capital via peer tutoring and sharing important information. If you have never taken college algebra, but a peer has, your peer can help supplement course lectures with some minor tutoring and advice. Stated differently, peers can utilize their previous experiences to help you better achieve your goals. Additionally, if peers have had superior professors, they can tell you which professors to take. If they have had poor experiences, they can tell you which professors to avoid. Also, peers can provide new information regarding majors or programs of study that might be helpful.

For example, I knew of a student who wanted to attain his graduate degree in physical therapy. Despite his dedicated efforts, he was unable to gain entrance into a physical therapy program. A peer who earlier was unable to gain acceptance into a graduate physical therapy program was accepted into a graduate occupational therapy program. Thus, the peer provided helpful information and advice about his experiences. Specifically, he told the younger student how he found an alternative to his initially desired physical therapy program. What was the result? The student I knew pursued his degree in occupational vis-à-vis physical therapy and graduated with honors. Such information from knowledgeable peers is helpful in attaining professional and career goals and is another example of social capital resulting from favorable social relationships.

Concomitantly, favorable social relationships with those who are more successful and have greater social intelligence also help temper and refine perceptions and behaviors. This can lead to additional social capital. Here Sullivan's interpersonal theory (Evans, 2005) has significant parallel implications. Sullivan believed that interpersonal relationships aided one's development and helped extinguish rouge behaviors and increased acceptable behaviors. Thus, if someone struggles with social relationships, surrounding him daily with three or four peers who demonstrate superior social relationships provides opportunities for new social relationship skills to develop and extinguishes behaviors that diminish social skills. This is similar to the construct of mentoring. However, the construct suggests that people mimic the behaviors of others. Thus, as one observes valued peers affectively interacting with others, one learns how to successfully model behaviors and be successful too. Let me provide an example.

My father was a chef. As a youngster, he trained me how to wash pots and pans, operate the dish machine, and clean the walk-in refrigerators and freezers. When the day finally arrived for me to begin training as a chef, he asked that I observe the line cooks and him as they prepared the foods. For six days, I watched and I learned without doing a thing. When he finally gave me the opportunity to prepare food with the cooks, I mimicked the food preparation behaviors I had observed the previous six days. I did not yet know the reason why the cooks placed their index fingers over the backs of their French knife blades, why they added small scoops of sour cream to their beef bouillon, or why they always started their sauces with a butter and flour roux; I just did exactly what I saw them do. My observations resulted in fundamental learning.

In the same way, if we have favorable social relationships with a number of persons who have greater degrees of social sophistication, we likely will mimic those behaviors. Our degree of social sophistication and our human capital will rise. By observing our favorable social relationship partners use the dessert spoon at a formal dinner, we ultimately learn which spoon to use for the main course and which spoon to use for dessert. By observing our favorable social relationship partners shake the hands of others when they complete a business transaction, we replicate shaking hands once we complete a business deal. Thus, observing and having good social relationships will increase the repertoire of behaviors and actions that help make us successful. Our favorable social relationships with persons having greater social sophistication levels inevitably increase human capital and advance opportunities.

Conversely, the opposite is true. What would happen if one's favorable social relationships all publicly picked their noses? Over a period of time, if one were mostly surrounded by nose pickers, one would likely experience the behavior as typical and normal. The behavior within that small milieu would be acceptable. One would anticipate that if nose-picking behaviors were acceptable by friends we valued and esteemed, nose-picking behaviors would be accepted by others too. Can you imagine what would have happened if I had picked my nose during dinner with Russ and his father? Do you anticipate that these behaviors would have enhanced or reduced the probability of me catering a holiday party for his corporation? My guess is that Russ's father never would have considered me as a potential caterer if I had picked my nose during our dinner. In other words, my favorable social relationships refined my behaviors. I never picked my nose in front of Russ's father. Additionally, behaviors such as the affective use of direct eye contact, appropriate storytelling, and speaking with confidence, learned and amplified from my favorable social relationships, transferred into my meeting with Russ's father. Thus, it is easy to understand how favorable social relationships temper and refine our behaviors, and increase our human capital.

Human capital is also increased via synergy experienced within social relationships. I have a very close personal and professional friend named Pablo. He is a renowned suicide expert, a recognized researcher, and a prominent professional author. Together, Pablo and I have authored a number of refereed journal articles and books, and we have co-presented at professional meetings. Typically, Pablo or I will have an idea for an article or book and describe the idea to the other. This often energizes the other person, and within moments the excitement of co-authoring together generates increased enthusiasm for the project. As the enthusiasm builds, both of us begin developing the original topic and adding important aspects or features that had previously been overlooked. The result is a superior project with greater levels of complexity. Such complexity levels could not be accomplished by the first author alone. Both Pablo and I benefit from the synergy created as we work together. Additionally, that synergy ensures project completion. Authoring books and articles is hard work. It can become exhausting. Many times when Pablo or I feel drained or lose the initial enthusiasm for authoring a book, the other will call and enthusiastically describe his progress or a new idea specific to the book. This synergy invigorates both writers, enhances the writing process, and keeps the project moving forward until completion. Favorable social relationships incite synergistic energy, whether you are authoring articles or doing yard work. Therefore, working with others has the potential to help lessen your workload and increase the superiority of assigned projects for your courses.

Toxic Social Relationships

No discussion of social relationships is complete without describing toxic relationships. Although Barbara, Tom, and Glen, were quickly discussed previously, it is imperative that you understand how to recognize toxic relationships and how to avoid and escape them. In my professional experiences, toxic relationships cause more harm than all other unfavorable social relationships combined. Jacobson and Gottman (1998) researched the topics of domestic violence and relationships. They coined the terms "pit bulls" and "Cobras" to describe two types of batterers. This analogy has served my clients, my counseling supervisees, and me well in my understanding of toxic relationships on campus. According to Jacobson and Gottman, pit bulls bark, snarl, and growl. There is no missing them. From their snapping teeth and laid-back ears to their loud, intimidating growls and menacing barks, pit bulls make it known that they are aggressive and intend to harm anyone they perceive as a threat. The problem is that pit bulls perceive nearly everyone as a threat. Furthermore, if they do not perceive others as a threat, it is because they perceive the nonthreatening persons as weak and unable to defend themselves. There are few things pit bulls like more than taking advantage of the defenseless. Either way, pit bulls do not make favorable social relationships. Whenever one befriends a pit bull, the relationship becomes toxic.

Luke was such a person. The first time I met Luke, he was mandated into counseling for pouring lighter fluid on a fellow student's door and igniting the door. Earlier that same week, he had carved a swastika into the same door and threatened to kill the students living behind the door. When asked, Luke indicated he lit the door on fire because he did not like the symbols or quotes the room occupants had taped to the door. Like a true pit bull, Luke saw these students as defenseless and easy victims. Luke had a long history of police encounters commencing in middle school, and clearly had a difficult time complying with common societal rules and regulations. He had no remorse or compunction for scaring the persons whom he threatened, or feelings of regret for his intimidating or aggressive behaviors.

One would think most college students would stay clear of persons like Luke. However, in general, college students are an incredibly accepting group who attempt to be inclusive of most others. Concomitantly, those who encountered Luke perceived him as a counterculture oddity. His antisocial rantings about college administrators, politicians, faculty, and jocks were perceived more like a Robin Williams or James Belushi comedy skit or a N.W.A. or DMX rap song. This gave Luke near celebrity status among the predominately middle-class students who, for the most part, had never experienced someone with antisocial personality disorder. In other words, Luke was not perceived as the danger he truly was. Instead, most, except those whom Luke threatened to kill or physically assaulted, perceived him as a harmless person simply acting as if he were tough. Little could have been further from the truth.

Persons who act like pit bulls are fairly easy to identify. Should you ever question if someone is a pit bull, the mere fact that you are asking the question typically provides an affirmative answer. However, if you remain unconvinced or unable to make precise assessment, merely ask whether you would feel comfortable leaving this person to care for your elderly grandmother or baby sister without supervision. These questions should provide assessment clarity. If your assessment suggests someone has the potential of being a pit bull, do yourself a favor. Stay clear of anyone who you believe seems like a pit bull. Your avoiding actions will greatly benefit you.

Conversely, cobras are far more difficult to identify. Unlike the snarling and barking pit bull that makes its intent and location distinctly evident, the cobra's malicious intent is indiscernible. Often they will initially present as socially engaging. Many times, they are witty and charming. Unlike pit bulls, cobras are exactly the type of person you initially would feel comfortable to have supervising your elderly grandmother or baby sister. Regretfully, by the time you recognize their harmful intent, they have already struck. Surprise is a key element to their toxic relationships style.

Like the more common pit bull, cobras typically display characteristics of antisocial personality disorder. However, they are far more dangerous. Sasha was a cobra. She was strikingly attractive, had impeccable manners and superior social skills, and was utterly charming. It seemed everyone loved Sasha. She was elected to the highest post in her sorority, was an honors student, and volunteered at the most visible social events. Despite her petite size, sweet southern charm, and impeccable etiquette, Sasha had a dark side that few could imagine. For example, when Sasha perceived her boyfriend as paying greater attention to a fellow sorority female than to Sasha, someone added industrial-strength muriatic acid to the other female's shampoo. The result was a severe chemical burn to the other student's eyes and face. Sasha was the last to be suspected. However, over time, the list of people who encountered Sasha's more sinister intimidation behaviors exploded, and it was evident that the only person in common with all of the victims was Sasha.

Most often, cobras befriend others to gain advantage. Once they learn others' weaknesses, fears, and vulnerabilities, cobras begin to become more aggressive and abusive. This typically begins with verbal and emotional abuse and then escalates to physical abuse. This was the case with Ed. He had a way of latching on to younger female college students and making their worlds revolve around him. Within days, he would change from the verbally praising and romancing, Rudolph Valentino–type person to someone who would make his victims' lives hellish. Intimidated and fearful, these young victims often did not know how to respond or who to tell. Most often, these young victims believed they had caused Ed's anger and deserved Ed's verbal, emotional, and physical abuse.

Two rules reign should you ever find yourself entangled in toxic relationships with either pit bulls or cobras. Rule 1 is *immediately tell others*. Pit bulls and cobras isolate victims. They diligently work to separate victims from friends and family. Pit bulls and cobras realize that if others become involved, they become vulnerable and risk losing control of their victims. Should you ever find yourself being verbally, emotionally, or physically abused, immediately contact campus or local police. The police can provide immediate protection if you are injured or have been threatened. Additionally, they can transport you to either the university counseling center or campus health services or direct an ambulance to your location. Contacting the police also ensures that necessary documentation and potential care services are initiated. Therefore, if you were physically injured, the police will ensure your physical injuries are addressed. If you were verbally or emotionally abused, police officers typically have training to help ensure your immediate safety and can refer you to available counseling and support services. These help services may include campus or local groups that provide support, mentoring, or even emergency finances to students who have experienced toxic relationships with pit bulls or cobras.

Some may mistakenly overlook the police as a first resource. Instead, they may advocate first going to the university counseling center or simply telling friends. Depending upon the situation, I disagree. Based upon my experiences, contacting the police is the best first option. It allows the police to gather important factual information, respond to the student victim's immediate needs, and determine the student victim's best course of action. Experience has taught me that pit bulls and cobras create such toxic relationships that victims rarely understand the severity of the threats levied by their perpetrators. Therefore, victims often question whether they *really* experienced physical, emotional, or verbal abuse or threats.

The police are familiar with the subtle and overt manner in which pit bulls and cobras manipulate. Thus, they can help victims understand whether their experiences were dangerous and if the student victims are in harm's way. In other words, the police can make an immediate determination of what is in the student victim's best interests and respond. If the student victim is merely over-responding to an unpleasant situation, the police will make a referral, file their report, and appropriately detach from the situation. If this is the situation, minimally, a report will be filed. Thus, should the pit bull or cobra retaliate against the victim or should the pit bull or cobra repeat the toxic relationship behaviors with others, there exists a history that can be used in the future against the perpetrator.

Telling others in addition to the police is also important. Over the years, I have found that survivors of toxic relationships influenced by pit bulls and cobras often find it helpful to tell their parents, loved ones, and friends about their toxic relationship experiences. As previously mentioned, pit bulls and cobras are experts at separating student victims from loved ones and friends. Typically, they do so by creating dissention among and distrust of others. Informing important others of what happened and allowing them to provide support can be a major help to student victims. Furthermore, toxic relationships caused by pit bulls and cobras are like bad colds. They stay around. Student victims need the support of important others to ensure their continued emotional and physical safety, and provide the necessary support for the student victim to fully disengage from the toxic relationship.

Lashanda and Brian met at college orientation. They became inseparable. Within weeks, Brian had isolated Lashanda from family and friends, and he had become abusive. When Lashanda's stepfather realized what was happening, he stepped into the situation. At first, Lashanda resented her stepfather's involvement. She was so enamored with Brian that she failed to perceive the severity of the emotional and physical abuse she had become accustomed to. She also argued that the abuse was her fault. Once Lashanda finally realized she was in a toxic relationship, she feared ending the relationship. Her family was highly religious. Brian threatened to tell divulge Lashanda's sexual exploits, drug use, and shoplifting if Lashanda left him. However, with her family's help, Lashanda broke all communications and ties with Brian. Regretfully for Lashanda, Brian continued to call and frequent Lashanda's dorm room. Lashanda's stepfather finally helped Lashanda attain a restraining order against Brian. They also changed Lashanda's cell phone number and email addresses. Lashanda even had to change universities to finally break free of Brian's continued threats and manipulation. The entire process of escaping Brian took more than one year, and Lashanda told me there were times when she felt she would never escape Brian's threats and abusive behaviors. Separating from pit bulls and cobras takes a great deal of time and energy. The process would nearly be impossible if one did not have the support of loved ones. Therefore, it is imperative to tell loved ones what happened and to seek their support.

Rule 2 is *never give up*. Pit bulls and cobras create toxic relationships based upon fear and intimidation. They also are experts at manipulation. Pit bulls and cobras want you to believe that you never can live without them and that living without them will be far more painful than living with them. This is a lie. Do not believe them. When they perceive that you intend to escape, they will fight to eternally trap you in their toxic relationships. Too many student victims simply give up. They believe the manipulative lies. They believe escaping the pit bull or cobra is too hard. Thus, they stay trapped in the toxic relationship. Never give up. Focus on getting out of the toxic relationship and use family, friends, and professionals to your advantage. Never giving up means you will do what is best for you. It means focusing on creating new favorable social relationships and jettisoning unfavorable, toxic relationships. It means breaking free from pit bulls and cobras and their blanketing turmoil and pain.

Have you ever heard of a mulligan or a do-over? Both terms are used to allow a player a second chance. For example, I am a very poor golfer. When I golf with my friends and hook a drive into the Texas rough, my friends do not demand that I search the cactus-filled area teeming with rattlesnakes. This is because they like me. I further suspect they do not want to ruin their day listening to my high-pitched screams while I extract thorny cactus quills from my scrawny legs or racing me to the emergency room because of multiple rattlesnake bites. If my friends allow me a mulligan or do-over when playing an inconsequential game, I know they will give me a second chance to improve my life. The only thing that stops my mulligan or do-over is giving up. Therefore, Rule 2, never give up, is critical to your happiness and success. If you give up on escaping a toxic relationship or give up on living your life to the fullest, you will never find peace or happiness.

KEYS TO ESTABLISHING SOCIAL RELATIONSHIPS

This chapter started with a quote from the Gold Beach Oregon Volunteer Fire Department t-shirts (Putnam, 2000, p. 21) *"Come to our breakfast, we'll come to your fire."* As I understand it, the volunteer fire department was selling t-shirts that advertised the department's upcoming pancake breakfast. The fire department was using the pancake breakfast as a means to generate income and ultimately provide the money needed for the fire department to respond to emergencies within the community. The quote is especially relevant to this chapter. It demonstrates the reciprocity of favorable social relationships and succinctly demonstrates how favorable social relationships generate social capital. In the same way, this volunteer fire department invited community members to attend the pancake breakfast and financially support the department; it humorously suggested the resulting benefit. This benefit is that the fire department will be able to help those who attend the breakfast, because they have financially supported the volunteer fire department's money-generating endeavor.

Pay particular attention to three important points contained within this quote. The first underlying point is serving others. When our intent is to serve others, we frequently benefit. Serving others increases opportunities for favorable social relationships and increases our social capital. Social capital provides us greater opportunities for success.

Second, the quote serves as an invitation, not a demand. Only pit bulls and cobras demand. Healthy persons invite others into social relationships. Everyone will not welcome or engage in our invitations. This is perfectly fine. It does not suggest or imply that others do not want to participate because we are meaningless or flawed. Instead, their participation or nonparticipation in our invitation only reflects their limited time and resources. We make the decision of in which relationships and with whom we invest our time and energy. If someone prefers to invest his or her energy and time with others, it simply means those who engage with us are more committed to our relationship than to others. Cherish those important relationships and be the kind of friend you wish they would be to you.

Finally, these firefighters demonstrate their humor and ability to have fun. Who wants to spend time with people who are disagreeable, argumentative, and boring? Thus, the quote reminds us that the easiest way to make friends is to enjoy ourselves. When we enjoy ourselves, others are attracted to us. Conversely, if we whine, complain, and moan about the many injustices that we perceive, others will simply stay away.

CONCLUSION

This chapter has provided an overview of social relationships. It has described three types of social relationships—favorable, unfavorable, and indifferent. It has further provided self-response opportunities specific to areas in your life that you may wish to change as well as opportunities to describe the potential costs and benefits of making changes. The chapter describes social capital and how social capital benefits you. Toxic relationships are also mentioned, as well as the means to assess and escape toxic relationships. The chapter then addresses three keys to establishing relationships, and concludes with Reflection Activities.

REFLECTION ACTIVITIES

Below please find three reflection activities. These activities were created to help you personalize your reading experience and make this chapter helpful to you. Please complete the activities as fully as possible.

1. Please describe your most enjoyable social relationships and the resulting social capital you experience via these enjoyable relationships.

   _____

   _____

   _____

   _____

2. In your own words, describe pit bulls and cobras. Also, describe any past or current toxic relationships you have had or currently have, and what you have learned as a result of pit bulls, cobras, or toxic relationships.

_____

_____

_____

_____

3. The author identifies three keys to establishing social relationships. Identify which two are most important to you and tell why these are most important to you.

_____

_____

_____

_____

References

Beilmann, M., & Realo, A. (2012), Individualism-collectivism and social capital at the individual level. *TRAMES: A Journal of the Humanities & Social Sciences, 16*(3), 205–217.

Carolan, B. V. (2012). An examination of the relationship among high school size, social capital, and adolescents' mathematics achievement. *Journal of Research on Adolescence, 22*(3), 583–595.

Coleman, J. S. (1988). Social capital in the creation of human capital. *The American Journal of Sociology, 94*(4), 95–120.

Evans, F. B. III. (2005). *Harry Stack Sullivan: Interpersonal theory and psychotherapy.* New York: Routledge.

Ghamari, M. (2012). The relationship of social capital and happiness among high school students of Karaj City. *International Journal of Academic Research in Business and Social Sciences, 2*(1), 353–363.

Jacobson, N. S., & Gottman, J. M. (1998). Anatomy of a violent relationship. *Psychology Today, 31*(2), 60–68.

Kim, D. H., & Schneider, B. L. (2005). Social capital in action: Alignment of parental support in adolescents' transition to postsecondary education. *Social Forces, 84,* 1181–1206.

Putnam, R. D. (2000). *Bowling alone: The collapse and revival of American community.* New York: Simon & Schuster.

Raza, S. A., Hashmi, M. A., Zeeshan, A., & Shaikh, F. M. (2011). Human and social capital development for self-efficacy of university graduates: Bases for development of society. *Asian Social Science, 7*(9), 245–254. doi: 10.5539/ass.v7n9p244

Wells, R. S., Seifert, T. A., Padgett, R. D., Park, S., & Umbach, P. D. (2011). Why do more women than men want to earn a four-year degree? Exploring the effects of gender, social origin, and social capital on educational expectations. *Journal of Higher Education, 82*(1), 1–32.

13 CREATIVITY: SPARK OF WELLNESS

Samuel T. Gladding & Karen Michelle Hunnicutt-Hollenbaugh

Y ou may be wondering why there is a chapter on creativity in a course on wellness. Although they seem unrelated, creativity can play a major part in our overall physical and mental health (Gladding, 2004). Creativity can be defined as the ability to create something new within predetermined limitations (Sternberg & Lubart, 1999). As a phenomenon, "creativity is universally recognized as a basic human attribute" (Cohen, 2000, p. 13). Everyone has creativity, regardless of ethnicity, culture, gender, or age (Lubart, 1999; Maslow, 1971). Sometimes creativity is associated with mental health disorders; however, most creative people are well adjusted and motivated. Through creativity, individuals are able to express their originality, inventiveness, and problem-solving ability.

The importance of creativity in life is summed up in Mihaly Csikszentmihalyi's (1996) statement that: "Creativity is a central source of meaning in our lives . . . most of the things that are interesting, important, and human are the results of creativity" (p. 1). Basically, anything new, different, or exciting is the product of creativity. Creativity can give us purpose and meaning where there was none before.

Creativity is highly related with one's overall sense of well-being and wellness (Goff, 1993; Myers & Sweeney, 2005; Myers, Sweeney, & Witmer, 2000). Through creativity, individuals are able to navigate through difficult times and find direction, significance, and purpose in life. At its best, creativity helps us explore new ideas and views that we may not have thought about before.

Being creative isn't easy. To be creative one must be smart, knowledgeable, and motivated. Further, one must have a strong personality and be willing to take risks, have a thinking style that focuses on strengths, and be supported by the people and resources available (Sternberg & Lubart, 1995). Creative people as a group are independent, accept themselves and others, are confident, and can tolerate ambiguity (Carson, 1999). No one of these factors by itself guarantees creativity. However, in combination, these ingredients are powerful in the creative process. For example, Rovio, the company that created the wildly popular mobile game *Angry Birds*, was on the brink of bankruptcy and had created 51 unsuccessful games previously before finally finding success with *Angry Birds*. Since then, the game has reached over 1 billion downloads, and made over $106 million in 2011 (Klein, 2012). The game creators learned from their triumphs and failures, and used their motivation, independence, intelligence, and tolerance of ambiguity to finally come up with their end product.

THE BENEFITS OF CREATIVITY IN WELLNESS

Anyone can use creativity to be healthy and stay well. Every day, creativity plays a vital part in people's well-being and outlook on humanity. There are several reasons for this; however, the following seven stand out:

1. *Creativity opens up new worldviews.* People become limited in their outlooks and behaviors because they have narrow perspectives. They observe from a specific point of view, and act accordingly. However, creativity helps expand people's horizons. It gives them a new way of experiencing the world. For instance, having seen Picasso's *Guernica*, people can never envision war the same again (Weisberg, 2006). The destructiveness, horror, and pain of human conflict and suffering are captured graphically in the artist's painting. The glory sometimes associated with war is replaced with scenes of gore and carnage.

Likewise, having seen the movie *Crash* (Haggis et al., 2004), a movie on race and ethnicity and the consequences when individuals of different cultures and social classes collide, viewers may view racism and classism differently than they had before, as the movie realistically portrays individuals as they struggle with and act upon their prejudices and biases.

2. *Creativity allows for innovation both in starting and continuing productive hobbies and activities.* For example, Maud Lewis, a Canadian folk artist, best known as Grandma Moses, started her career simply. She began her work in the world of art by painting after the early onset of juvenile rheumatoid arthritis. While she began modestly by making greeting cards, her talent continued to develop into a unique style that many found pleasing. More important, her work gave her great joy and satisfaction (Bogart & Lang, 2002).

In contrast, Bethany Hamilton was a 13-year-old girl who lost her arm in a shark attack while surfing. Despite the fact that Bethany almost died in this attack, and faced learning to live everyday life without her arm, she was determined to surf again. Bethany used her creativity to teach herself to surf with only the use of her right arm. Not only was she able to surf again, but she was able to enter and compete in surfing competitions. Despite her hardship, she pushed through and used surfing and creativity as an outlet (Hamilton, Bundschuh, & Berk, 2012).

3. *Creativity helps others create new things.* People respond to creative activities from life experiences and thus gain insight into their own dreams, images, and memories. For instance, plays such as those by Sophocles and Shakespeare, or musicals like *Rent* (Larson, 1996) or *Les Miserables* (Hugo, 2008), that show suffering or trauma may spark within members of an audience an emotional release and a resolve in regard to what they can do or should do with the remainder of their lives (Winn, 2005).

This "co-creation" process can result in people discovering ways to be different and change personal situations. In this way, people feel energized and have the vision to focus on what they're capable of doing as opposed to what they're not capable of doing.

4. *Creativity strengthens resilience.* Individuals who are well do not succumb readily to the unfairness or capriciousness of life events. Rather, they strive toward goals and rebound when down (Benard, 2004). One example is Stefani Germanotta, the popular musician better known as Lady Gaga. Despite often feeling outcast during childhood, she channeled her energy and creativity into her music. This created a way for her to strengthen her ability to cope and led to her enormous success today (Callahan, 2011).

5. *Creativity helps the psychological and physical dimensions of people's lives, too.* Research by James Pennebaker (1997) provides an excellent example of this. He had individuals write

for 20 minutes a day about matters stressful to them, and found that not only did their scores on mental health assessments improve, but their immune systems became stronger and their visits to physicians decreased. He compared them to a group who did not do any writing, and found that writing can save people from emotional and even physical pain. In short, writing and the creative expression that goes with it can increase wellness.

6. *Creativity helps us remember and respect those who have come before us* (Whitfield, 1988). This type of connection links the past to the present in a healthy way, as people realize others have had similar thoughts, feelings, and behaviors before them. People identify more with past human events as well as what it means to be a person today. From paintings of Madonnas and other religious figures to 9/11 drawings and poems by children and relatives of those lost in the tragedy of terrorism, creativity promotes understanding for yesterday and today (Morrow, 2006).

7. *Creativity enables people to take control of their lives and keep events in perspective.* For example, the poem "Still I Rise" by Maya Angelou (1994) reminds those who read its lines that many situations in life can be better dealt with when they are seen from the angle of persons who take charge of their lives. Such individuals keep their heads when those about them are losing theirs. They make the most of their time, and stay focused.

WAYS OF PROMOTING WELLNESS THROUGH CREATIVITY

In reference to creative people, Mihaly Csikszentmihalyi (1996) once said: "The ability to discover what one can do well, and enjoy doing it, is the hallmark of all creative people" (p. 314). Creative people, whether in science, business, government, or elsewhere, are successful when they use their personal strengths and build upon them. In the process, they increase their own wellness and the wellness of others.

Creative activities that increase wellness can be expressed in many ways. One of the best ways to raise wellness through creativity is through the arts (e.g., acting, painting, and writing). These activities require action, concentration, and movement. The healthiest and most lasting ways of promoting wellness through the arts are discussed in the following sections.

Recitation

People can deal with negative emotions, such as anger or sadness, and move toward healthier emotions by voicing their feelings. In such situations, getting out what people want to say can be therapeutic and healing. One form of such speech is called "line savers." People can remember and recite useful sayings they were given or gave themselves. This process can be used to decrease bad feelings and increase positive ones (e.g., "Take your time," "Don't go to bed angry," or "When upset, a good rule is to keep your cool").

In addition to recalling and reciting line savers, learning and sharing meaningful words can be helpful. Wise sayings are found all over in literature, from ancient scripts to popular lyrics. One way to use these words is to share them with others. For example, if you found lines in a poem, book, or song that you believed described how you felt about someone in your life you were having conflict with, you could share them with that person. You could follow by expressing your feelings in relation to the words, and letting that person know that you are open to hearing his or her feelings as well. If you are both willing to have this discussion, through the use of words, negative or hostile thoughts and feelings can be replaced with renewed friendship or at least neutrality, and a sense of well-being is restored. Then you both will be able to focus on the positive aspects of life.

Writing

Regularly expressing thoughts through writing them down is another way to increase wellness creatively. Anne Frank put it this way: "I can shake off everything if I write; my sorrows disappear, my courage is reborn" (Frank, 1958, p. 177).

As mentioned earlier, keeping a diary or journal focused on the stressors of life is a great way to increase wellness. Further, college students who engage in a systematic writing program about topics that really matter to them find that their efforts pay off in higher grade point averages as well (Pennebaker, 1997).

An abbreviated version of this technique has been developed by Kay Adams (1998)—the Five Minute Writing Sprint. This activity is done daily, with the use of a timer, a pencil and a pad of paper or electronic notepad, and a comfortable place. Writers find a relaxing and familiar spot in which to write and begin by letting their pencils keep moving or fingers keep typing until the timer signals that five minutes are up. This type of free writing can not only help you express your thoughts and feelings, but gain insight into what is really bothering you and why.

Photography

Taking pictures with a camera can also make a difference in increasing wellness. Shooting pictures of an object from different perspectives may give people multiple new perceptions and change their views on the object (Gladding, 2004). For instance, if you're having trouble seeing someone else's point of view, you may become more open after taking pictures of a familiar object from numerous angles, such as mailbox or a door. In the process, you will discover that there is more than one view in regard to what something looks like. In the case of the mailbox, you may realize that the mail carrier sees the mailbox in a different way from the neighborhood dog. You may also realize that your point of view in a given situation may not be the only one that is valid. Pictures can lead to words and thoughts, giving you a healthier outlook on the world.

Movement

Dance, exercise, and movement can be used as a way to wellness (Goodill, 2004). The power of activity has been shown to improve individuals' health on many levels. Specific dance and movement steps are used in some cases. In other situations, 30-minute walks three days a week are used as a way to stay fit and healthy. Even 10-minute exercises three times a day can be beneficial.

However, movement can also be used to increase wellness through moving toward or away from people or places that increase or decrease our physical and mental health. For instance, moving toward people who are encouraging and have healthy habits may lead to an increase in one's wellness. Likewise, moving away from negative people may be life enhancing, if not lifesaving.

Humor

Creativity can promote wellness also through fun and laughter (Salameh & Fry, 2002). People usually laugh because something surprises them or does not seem right, but humor also helps people physically and mentally. One of the most famous cases of humor and wellness is found in Norm Cousin's (1981) *Anatomy of an Illness,* where Cousins describes his use of humor as a way to relieve pain. He was diagnosed with a painful spine condition, and he found that watching comedies ranging from slapstick to contemporary sitcoms helped him feel better. He said that 10 minutes of laughter allowed him two hours of pain-free sleep. Overall, humor can ease tensions, promote positive communication, raise infection-fighting antibodies in the body, and boost the number of immune cells (Salameh & Fry, 2002).

Humor can help people who are very depressed to feel better, too. If they take their negative thoughts and exaggerate them, it may make them smile or laugh. Telling a nonoffensive joke or story that has a universal message may promote humor and the wellness that goes with it. Basically, to be creative with humor for the sake of wellness takes courage, timing, and good taste.

Storytelling

Another way to help promote wellness through creativity is through telling stories. Lives can be reshaped or changed through storytelling. Herminia Ibarra (2003) emphasizes that telling good stories is essential to making smooth transitions in life.

Change is difficult, in part because major transitions, such as job changes, can make people feel that they have lost their personal stories. At these times, it might be helpful for someone to tell a story about his or her life that is rooted in identity. A coherent life story is one that suggests what we all want to believe: that our lives are made up of a series of events that make sense. In other words, the past is related to the present, and from that, we can see our future. The process of constructing that story can help us make sense of our past.

So, Ibarra, along with narrative-focused individuals such as Larry Cochran (1997) and Mark Savickas (2005), points out that healthy career change involves creating or modifying stories. When people get off balance, they need to change their stories (and often their careers) in order to find new meaning in their lives.

Music

Finally, creativity facilitates wellness by reinventing and reenergizing people through music. For example, R&B musician Mary J. Blige often sings about empowerment and self-love for women (2007). People who engage in sports often use particular types of music to help them stay motivated and focused on their goals—for example, the theme song to the movie *Rocky* (Charthoff, Winkler, & Avildsen, 1976). Or, sometimes people can choose their own "theme song" that they feel describes themselves or their current life situation (Gladding, Binkley, Henderson, & Newsome, 2008).

Writing your own music can also be extremely helpful during difficult times, including coping with injury and illness. This form of expression can you help process thoughts and emotions surrounding life stressors and increase healthy adjustment (Baker, Kennelly, & Tamplin, 2005).

SUMMARY AND CONCLUSION

Creativity is associated with wellness in many ways. Becoming and staying well requires individuals to be active, as creativity is a changing and interactive process.

As this chapter has pointed out, creativity is related to many characteristics found in people who are healthy, well, and living life to the fullest. Creative individuals are flexible, intelligent, open, playful, determined, and motivated, and have a wide range of interests as well as considerable energy. They move toward environments that are supportive of their efforts or they find ways to positively use the surroundings in which they live.

In addition, creativity is related to wellness in that it helps people to become healthier through:

- creating new ways of seeing the world,
- being innovative,
- strengthening their resiliency,
- using others's creative activities to engage in creative activities of their own,
- improving mental and physical health,
- remembering and respecting the past, and
- taking control of their lives by keeping things in perspective.

Further, individuals can increase wellness through creative efforts such as those found in the arts. Different art forms that increase health and wellness include recitation, writing, photography, dance/movement, humor, stories, and music.

Overall, creativity and wellness belong together in the promotion of human health. They overlap. It is probably impossible to be fully alive and well without being creative, and wellness can be enhanced by finding creative outlets for our talents. Regardless, creativity in everyday life enriches everyone associated with it. Planning to stay well, grow, and live to the fullest includes creativity. Sometimes the process may be difficult, but the rewards associated with creativity include better outcomes and enhanced quality of life.

Reflection Activities

1. As described in the Recitation section of this chapter, think of two or three "line savers" that you currently use or could use in your daily life. Why did you choose these sayings? What about them is helpful for you when dealing with emotions such as sadness or anger?
2. Have you ever come across any lines in stories or songs that you felt you could use to express to someone else how you were feeling? How might it have been helpful to use those lines to engage in a discussion with that person?
3. What is one way you can increase your wellness using humor? How can you incorporate humor into your everyday life to increase your overall wellness and creativity?

References

Adams, K. (1998). *The way of the journal: A journal therapy workbook for healing* (2nd ed.). Baltimore: Sidran.

Angelou, M. (1994). *The complete collected poems of Maya Angelou.* New York: Random House.

Baker, F., Kennelly, J., & Tamplin, J. (2005). Adjusting to change through song: Themes in songs written by clients with Traumatic Brain Injury. *Brain Impairment,* 6(3), 205–211.

Benard, B. (2004). *Resiliency: What we have learned.* San Francisco: WestEd.

Blige, M. J. (2007). *Growing pains* [CD]. Santa Monica, CA: Geffen Records.

Bogart, J. E., & Lang, M. (2002). *Capturing joy: The story of Maud Lewis.* Toronto, Canada: Tundra Books.

Callahan, M. (2011). *Poker face: The rise and rise of Lady Gaga.* New York: Hyperion.

Carson, D. K. (1999). The importance of creativity in family therapy: A preliminary consideration. *The Family Journal: Counseling and Therapy for Couples and Families,* 7(4), 326–334.

Charthoff, R., Winkler, I. (Producers), & Avildsen, J. G. (1976). *Rocky* [Motion picture]. United States: United Artists.

Cochran, L. (1997). *Career counseling: A narrative approach.* Thousand Oaks, CA: Sage.

Cohen, G. D. (2000). *The creative age: Awakening human potential in the second half of life.* New York: Avon.

Cousins, N. (1981). *Anatomy of an illness.* New York: Bantam.

Csikszentmihalyi, M. (1996). *Creativity.* New York: HarperCollins.

Frank, A. (1958). *Diary of a young girl.* New York: Globe.

Gladding, S. T. (2004). *Counseling as an art: The creative arts in counseling* (3rd ed.). Alexandria, VA: American Counseling Association.

Gladding, S. T., Binkley, E., Henderson, D. A., & Newsome, D. W. (2008). *The lyrics of hurting and healing: Finding words that are revealing.* Honolulu, HI: American Counseling Association Convention.

Goff, K. (1993). Creativity and life satisfaction in older adults. *Educational Gerontology, 19,* 241–250.

Goodill, S. W. (2004). *An introduction to medical dance/movement therapy: Health care in motion.* London: Jessica Kingsley Publisher.

Haggis, P., Harris, M. R., Moresco, R., Cheadle, D., Yari, B., Schulman, C. (Producers), & Haggis, P. (Director). (2004). *Crash* [Motion picture]. United States: Lionsgate.

Hamilton, B., Bundschuh, R., & Berk, S. (2012). *Soul surfer: A true story of faith, family, and fighting to get back on the board.* New York: Pocket Books.

Hugo, V. (2008). *Les misérables* (J. Rose, Trans.). New York: Modern Library. (Original work published 1862)

Ibarra, H. (2003). *Working identity.* Boston: Harvard Business School Press.

Klein, A. (2012). Will Bad Piggies knock out Angry Birds? *Newsweek Magazine.* Retrieved from http://www.thedailybeast.com/newsweek/2012/09/23/angry-birds-can-rovio-repeat-their-success-with-bad-piggies.html

Larson, J. (1996). *Rent* [Musical theatre production]. New York: Nederlander Theatre.

Lubart, T. I. (1999). Creativity across cultures. In R. J. Sternberg (Ed.), *Handbook of creativity* (pp. 339–350). New York: Cambridge University Press.

Maslow, A. H. (1971). *The farther reaches of human nature.* New York: Viking Press.

Morrow, A. (2006, September 11). Ways of creatively remembering those lost on September 11, 2001. Retrieved from http://dying.about.com/b/2006/09/11/ways-of-creatively-remembering-those-lost-on-september-11-2001.htm

Myers, J. E., & Sweeney, T. J. (Eds.). (2005). *Counseling for wellness: Theory, research, practice.* Alexandria, VA: American Counseling Association.

Myers, J. E., Sweeney, T. J., & Whitmer, J. M. (2000). The Wheel of Wellness counseling for wellness: A holistic model for treatment planning. *Journal of Counseling & Development, 78.*

Pennebaker, J. W. (1997). *Opening up: the healing power of expressing emotions.* New York: Guilford.

Salameh, W. A., & Fry, W. F. (Eds.). (2002). *Humor and wellness in clinical intervention.* New York: Praeger.

Savickas, M. (2005). The theory and practice of career construction. In S. D. Brown & R. W. Lent (Eds.), *Career development and counseling* (pp. 42–70). Hoboken, NJ: Wiley.

Sternberg, R. J., & Lubart, T. I (1995). *Defying the crowd: Cultivating creativity in a culture of conformity.* New York: Free Press.

Sternberg, R. J., & Lubart, T. I. (1999). The concept of creativity: Prospects and paradigms. In R.J. Sternberg (Ed.), *Handbook of creativity* (pp. 3–15). New York: Cambridge University Press.

Weisberg, R. W. (2006). *Creativity.* Hoboken, NJ: Wiley.

Whitfield, S. J. (1988). *A death in the delta.* Baltimore: Johns Hopkins University Press.

Winn, S. (2005, January 1). Endings are a catharsis. They give meaning to what comes before and change us from the way we were. *San Francisco Chronicle*, E-1.

INDEX

A

Academic research on wellness, 15–24
Achievability of goals, 39–40
Acrophobia, 62
Acupuncture, 21
Adams, Kay, 169
Addictive behaviors, emotion regulation in, 65–66
Adler, Alfred, 15–16
Advice, financial, 98
Affect
  definition of, 75
  exercise and, 75, 79–80, 82–83
African Americans, masculinity among, 145–146
Aging, and cognition, 57
Alcohol use
  emotion regulation and, 65–66
  in preventative self-care, 107–108
Alzheimer's disease, 57
American Medical Association (AMA), 6
American Medical Association Journal, 2
American Psychological Association (APA), 16, 18
American Psychologist (journal), 18
Amygdala, 61–62
Anatomy of an Illness (Cousin), 169
Angelou, Maya, 168
Anger, in motivation, 45
Angry Birds (game), 166
Antidepressants, vs. exercise, for depression, 76–77
Antisocial personality disorder, 161
Antonovsky, A., 123
Anxiety
  definition of, 78
  exercise and, 75, 78–79
  prevalence of, 73, 78
APA. *See* American Psychological Association
Ardell, Don, 23
Aristotle, 11–12, 15
Asclepius, 12
Astin, A. W., 119, 122
Astin, H. S., 119, 122
Attention deployment, 63
Attribution theory, 53–54
Awareness, in motivation, 45

B

Bankruptcies, 5
Basil, Saint, 13
Behavior. *See also specific types*
  theory of planned, 82
Behavioral interventions, 68
Behavioral medicine, 16–17
Behavior-related diseases, as cause of death, 2, 101–102
Behavior therapy, dialectical, 68
Belief(s)
  in cognition, 53, 57
  definition of, 53
  in hardiness, 124
  in placebo effect, 22
Believability of goals, 40–41
Belloc, N. B., 18
Belonging, in meaning of life, 125
Benson, H., 20, 22
Binge eating, 65
Biofeedback, 21
Biogenetic principles of cognition, 52–55
Biological conceptualization of health, 130–131
Biomedical model of healthcare, 1–7
Bipolar disorder, 64
Black Americans, masculinity among, 145–146
Blazina, C., 144
Blige, Mary J., 170
Body–mind connection. *See* Mind–body connection
Borderline personality disorder, 64
Boy turn, 143
Brain. *See also* Cognition
  communication channels of, 52
  emotions in, 61–62
  in health maintenance, 11
  imaging of, 51
Brainstem, 11
Breslow, L., 18
Bronfenbrenner, Urie, 132, 136
Buddha, 50
Buddhism, 50, 116, 117
Budgeting, 88–92
  definition of, 88
  keys to, 88–89
  steps in process of, 89–92
Buechner, F., 126

C

Campbell, Angus, 18
Cancer
  prevention of, 104
  wellness model for, 30
Capital
  definition of, 157
  human, 157
  social, 157–160
Career(s)
  emotion regulation in, 66
  as environmental factor in wellness, 134
  finding your vocation, 126–127
Caring, ethic of, 113, 114, 122
Carroll, Lewis, 36
Cashwell, C. S., 121
Centers for Disease Control and Prevention (CDC), 2
Challenge, in hardiness, 124
Change
  cognitive, 63
  five stages of, 45
Charitable donations, 91
Charitable involvement, 113, 114, 122
Chinese medicine, 14
Christianity, 13, 117, 118
Chronic diseases
  as cause of death, 2, 102
  in existing healthcare system, 2–3
Chronosystems, 136
Clinical and educational model of wellness, 33–34
Cochran, Larry, 170
Cognition, 50–58
  aging and, 57
  biogenetic principles of, 52–55
  definition of, 50
  genetics of, 51
  health impacts of, 51
  metacognition, 53–54, 58, 116
  in mind–body connection, 50–51
  social and cultural influences on, 56
  strategies for development of wellness through, 56–58
Cognitive appraisal of stressors, 17, 52–53
Cognitive-behavioral interventions, in emotion regulation, 68
Cognitive change, 63
Cognitive dissonance, 54–55

Cognitive modules, 50
Cognitive therapy, mindfulness-
    based, 116
Coherence
  meaning and purpose of life in,
    122–123
  sense of, 123
College campuses, spirituality
    and religion on, 113–114,
    119–120, 122
Commitment
  in hardiness, 124
  religious, 113, 114
Comprehensibility, in sense of
    coherence, 123
Compulsive behaviors, emotion
    regulation in, 65–66
Conditional goal setting, 40
Conduct disorder, 64
Conservatism
  religious/social, 113, 114
  rule of, in budgeting, 91
Context, as theme of wellness, 28
Control
  in hardiness, 124
  locus of, 67
Controllability of goals, 39–40
Cool pose, 146
Copernicus, 15
Coping resources, 17
Coping response, 17
Coping strategies and techniques, 17,
    123–124
Cortex, 11
Counseling, vs. exercise, for
    depression, 76
Counseling models of wellness,
    30–34
Cousin, Norm, 169
Crash (movie), 167
Creativity, 166–171
  benefits of, 166–168
  definition of, 166
  in goal attainment, 39
  health effects of, 167–168
  how to promote wellness through,
    168–170
Credit, 87, 92–96
Credit cards, 87, 92–94
Credit score, 93–94
Csikszentmihalyi, M., 47, 166, 168
Cultural aspects of wellness. *See*
    Ecological approach to wellness
Cultural influences
  on cognition, 56
  on emotion regulation, 62–63

D
Dance, 169
Death, historical changes in causes of,
    1–2, 101–102, 103
Debt
  credit card, 87, 92–94
  student, 95–96
Dementia, 57
Depression
  definition of, 76
  exercise and, 75–78
  prevalence of, 73, 76
  treatment of, 76–78
Desirability of goals, 42–43
Dialectical behavior therapy, 68
Diet
  and emotion regulation, 65
  and longevity, 19, 21–22
Disease prevention
  in existing healthcare system, 2–7
  future of, 7–8
Distraction hypothesis, 80–81
Doing, in meaning of life, 125
Domestic violence, 160–163
Dualism, in Western medicine, 15
Dual mode model, 79
Dunn, A. L., 77
Dunn, Halbert, 23
Dupey, P., 115

E
Eastern medicine
  in energy psychology, 20–21
  history of, 14
Ecological approach to wellness,
    130–148
  vs. biological understanding of
    health, 130–131
  definition of, 132, 133
  gender in, 143–147
  in high-level wellness, 131
  history of concept of, 130–131
  Maslow's hierarchy of needs and,
    137–139
  poverty in, 140–143
  power in, 139–140
  systems perspective on, 135–137
  types of influences in, 134–135
Ecological model of human
    development, 132
Ecology, use of term, 132, 133
Ecumenical worldview, 113, 114, 122
Educational and clinical model of
    wellness, 33–34
Education level, 141
Ehlinger, E., 87

EI. *See* Emotional intelligence
Ekkekakis, P., 79
Electromagnetic energy, 21
Emergency funds, 91
Emmons, R. A., 57
Emotion(s)
  definition of, 61, 75
  in motivation, 45–47
  negative, 66, 123
  positive, 20, 66, 123
Emotional intelligence (EI)
  definition of, 69
  in emotion regulation, 69
  impacts on wellness, 66
Emotion regulation, 61–69
  categories of, 63
  impacts on wellness, 63–67
  importance of, 62
  in men vs. women, 62–63
  steps in process of, 46–47
  strategies for improving, 67–69
Endorphin hypothesis, 81
Energy, in Eastern medicine, 14,
    20–21
Energy psychology, 20–21
Engagement, religious, 113, 114
Enjoyment hypothesis, 81
Environment
  definition of, 133, 134
  natural, 131, 147
Environmental aspects of wellness.
    See Ecological approach to
    wellness
Environmental identity
    development, 147
Environmental influences, on
    cognition, 56
Epidaurus, 12
Equanimity, 113, 119–120, 122
Ethic of caring, 113, 114, 122
Ethnicity, as environmental factor in
    wellness, 135
Evidence-based community
    prevention programs, 7
Evolutionary psychology, 56
Exercise. *See also* Physical activity
  challenge of promoting, 82–83
  definition of, 74
  health benefits of, 73–74, 169
  motivation to, 82–83
  vs. physical activity, 74
  psychological benefits of,
    73–83, 169
  socioeconomic status and, 140–141
Existentialism, 124
Exosystems, 136

Expenses, in budgeting, 91
Explanatory styles, 54, 55
Extrinsic motivation, 45
Extrinsic religion, 112. *See also*
    Religion

F

FAFSA. *See* Free Application for
    Federal Student Aid
Fair Credit Reporting Act, 92
Faith. *See* Religion
Family(ies)
    emotion regulation in, 65
    as environmental factor in
        wellness, 135
    as systems, 136
Favorable social relationships,
    150–152, 153, 159–160
Fear, in motivation, 46
Federal student loans, 95
Feedback, from role models, 48
Feelings, definition of, 75
Fight-or-flight response, 52–53
Financial Literacy 101
    program, 98
Financial Peace University, 98
Financial wellness, 87–99
    assessment of, 97–98
    budgeting in, 88–92
    credit in, 87, 92–96
    definition of, 88
    financial recovery in, 97–98
    importance of, 87
    resources and advice on, 98
Five-Factor Wellness Inventory
    (5-F WEL), 31–32
Five Minute Writing Sprint, 169
Flanagan, J., 18
Flexibility, in budgeting, 88–89
Flow, 42–43
fMRI. *See* Functional magnetic
    resonance imaging
Focht, B. C., 82–83
Focused meditation, 115–116
Folkman, S., 17, 123
Food. *See* Diet
Francis, L. J., 119
Frank, Anne, 169
Frankl, Victor, 122, 125
Fraud
    credit card, 94
    student loan, 96
Free Application for Federal Student
    Aid (FAFSA), 95, 96
Fuller, R. C., 110
Fully functioning person, 16

Functional magnetic resonance
    imaging (fMRI), 51
Fundamentalism, 113

G

Gardner, H., 69
Gause, C. P., 146
GDP. *See* Gross domestic product
Gender
    in ecological approach to wellness,
        143–147
    in emotion regulation, 62–63
    vs. sex, 144
Gender socialization, 143–147
Genetics, of cognition, 51
Geography, as environmental factor in
    wellness, 134
Germanotta, Stefani, 167
Goals, 36–48
    characteristics of good, 39–44
    cognition and, 53, 57
    financial, 89–90
    importance of, 37–38
    in motivation, 36–37, 42–43, 48
    performance vs. mastery, 45
    short-term vs. long-term, 89
    spiritual, 121
    strategies for attaining, 38–39
Golden mean, 11
Good, G. E., 145
Good life, 11
Gottman, J. M., 160
Grade point average (GPA), 119–120
Granello, P. F., 122
Gratton, L. C., 138–139
Greek medicine, 11–12, 130
Gross, J. J., 63
Gross domestic product (GDP), 5
Group living, 56
Growth facilitating goals, 43
Grzywacz, J. G., 140, 141
Guernica (Picasso), 167
Guite, H. F., 131

H

Hamilton, Bethany, 167
Happiness, 11–12
Hardiness, 124
Health
    biological conceptualization of,
        130–131
    definitions of, 1, 7, 15, 22, 131
    origins of term, 10
    striving for, 10–11
Healthcare
    cost of, 3–7

history of, 11–15, 101–102
    managed, 6–7
    placebo effect in, 22
    quality of, 3–4
    universal, 5, 6
Healthcare crisis, 1, 5
Healthcare system, U.S.
    fundamental problems with existing,
        1–7
    future of, 7–8
Health expectancy, 19
Health insurance, cost of, 4–7
Health psychology, 16
Healthy People 2000, 5
Healthy People 2010, 106–108
Heart disease, 102–104
Hedonistic theories of motivation, 82
Hettler, Bill, 23, 30–31
Hettler hexagonal model of wellness,
    30–31
Hexagonal model of wellness, 30–31
High-level wellness, 131
Hill, P. C., 121
Hinduism, 117
Hippocampus, 62
Hippocrates, 11
Holism
    in Eastern medicine, 14
    in Native American medicine,
        13–14
    in Western medicine, 15
Holistic Flow Model of Spiritual
    Wellness, 115
Hopelessness, in goal setting, 40
Horizontal relationships, 136
Howard, Clark, 98
Human capital, 157
Human development, ecological
    model of, 132
Human existence, unity of dimensions
    of, 27
Humanistic psychology, 16
Human potential, 8
Humor, 169–170
Hunt, Valerie, 21
Hygieia, 12, 15
Hypothalamus, 62

I

Ibarra, Herminia, 170
Identity development
    environmental, 147
    racial, 147
Identity theory, social, 145
Immunizations, 108
Incentivizing, in motivation, 48

Income
  in budgeting, 91
  as environmental factor in wellness, 134
Indifferent social relationships, 156
Individual traits, positive, 20
Indivisible-self model of wellness,
    31–32
Infectious diseases, as cause of death,
    1–2, 101
In-groups, 145
Innovation, creativity in, 167
Institutions, positive, 20
Insurance, health, cost of, 4–7
Intellectual self-esteem, 119–120
Intellectual stimulation, and
    cognition, 57
Intentionality, of prayer, 118
Intercessory prayers, 118–119
Interdisciplinary wellness, 15–22
Interest, credit card, 92
Interpersonal experience, definition
    of, 47
Interpersonal relationships. See
    Relationships
Interpersonal strategies, for sustaining
    motivation, 47–48
Intrapersonal experience, definition
    of, 44
Intrapersonal strategies, for sustaining
    motivation, 44–47
Intrinsic motivation, 42–43, 45
Intrinsic religion, 112. See also
    Spirituality
Introjected regulation, 119
Islam, 117

J
Jacobson, N. S., 160
James, William, 73
Japan, Okinawa lifestyle in, 19
Judaism, 12–13, 117
Judgment, in cognition, 53–54
Jung, C. G., 15
Jungian Path of Pretending, 112
Jyoti meditation, 116

K
Kabat-Zinn, Jon, 116
Kierski, W., 144
King, G. A., 125
Kirsten, T. G. J. C., 133
Koenig, Harold, 20
Kuo, F. E., 131

L
Ladd, K., 118
Lady Gaga, 167

Lazarus, R. S., 17, 52
Learning
  in motivation, 45, 47–48
  observational, 47
  from role models, 47–48
Lewis, Maud, 167
Life, meaning and purpose of,
    122–127
Lifespan. See Longevity
Lifespan model of wellness, 31, 33
Lifestyle-related diseases, as cause of
    death, 2, 101–102
Life tasks, in lifespan model of
    wellness, 31
Limbic system, 11, 61, 62
Lindholm, J. A., 119, 122
Linehan, M. M., 46
Line savers, 168
Loans, student, 95–96
Lobbying, healthcare, 6
Locus of control, 67
Longevity
  academic research on, 17–18, 21–22
  changes in, 1
  and quality of life, 17–18
  as theme of wellness, 28
Lust, K., 87

M
Macrosystems, 136
Magnusson, D., 133, 134
Manageability, in sense of
    coherence, 123
Managed healthcare systems, 6–7
Man's Search for Meaning
    (Frankl), 122
Mantra meditation, 115–116
MAOIs. See Monoamine oxidase
    inhibitors
Marcus Aurelius, 27
Marks, N. F., 140, 141
Masculinity, in ecological approach to
    wellness, 143–147
Maslow, A. H., 10, 11, 16, 137–138
Maslow's hierarchy of needs,
    137–139
Mastery goals, 45
Mastery hypothesis, 80
Mayer, J. D., 69
MBCT. See Mindfulness-based
    cognitive therapy
MBSR. See Mindfulness Based Stress
    Reduction
Meaningfulness, in sense of
    coherence, 123
Meaning of life, 122–127

Measurability of goals, 41
Medicine. See also Healthcare
  behavioral, 16–17
  history of, 11–15, 101–102
  placebo effect in, 22
Meditation
  in emotion regulation, 68
  impacts on wellness, 115–116
  mantra, 115–116
  mindfulness, 58, 115, 116
Memory, emotions and, 61–62
Men
  emotion regulation in, 62–63
  socialization of, 143–147
Mental health
  emotion regulation and, 64
  physical activity and, 73–83
  religion and, 20
Mesosystems, 136
Metacognition, 53–54, 58, 116
Metaphysical environment, 133, 134
Microsystems, 136
Mind–body connection. See also
    Cognition
  acceptance of reality of, 50–51
  in behavioral medicine, 16–17
  in Eastern medicine, 14
  in Native American medicine, 14
  in Western medicine, 15
Mindfulness, 68
Mindfulness-based cognitive therapy
    (MBCT), 116
Mindfulness Based Stress Reduction
    (MBSR) program, 116
Mindfulness meditation, 58,
    115, 116
Models of wellness, 23, 30–34
Money. See Financial wellness
Monoamine hypothesis, 81
Monoamine oxidase inhibitors
    (MAOIs), 81
Moods, definition of, 75
Moses, Grandma, 167
Moskowitz, T. J., 123
Motivation, 36–48
  definition of, 44
  difficulties of, 37
  emotion in, 45–47
  to exercise, 82–83
  extrinsic, 45
  forms of, 37
  goal setting in, 36–37, 42–43, 48
  interpersonal strategies for
    sustaining, 47–48
  intrapersonal strategies for
    sustaining, 44–47

intrinsic, 42–43, 45
  Maslow's theory of, 137–139
  for prayer, 119
Movement, promotion of wellness
  through, 169
Multidisciplinary wellness, 15–22,
  28–29
Music, 170
Myers, J. E., 5, 22, 131, 147

N

National Center for Complementary
  Medicine and Alternative
  Medicine, 24
National Institutes of Health, 24, 45
Native American medicine
  history of, 13–14
  prayer in, 117
Native Americans, emotion regulation
  by, 62
Natural selection, 52
Nature
  health impacts of contact with, 131
  in identity development, 147
Needs
  in budget, 90
  Maslow's hierarchy of, 137–139
Negative emotions, 66, 123
Negative reinforcers, 48
Negative self-talk, 40–41
Neighborhood effects, 140–143
Nelson, M. C., 87
Neocortex, 62
Networks
  social, as environmental factor in
    wellness, 135
  support, in motivation, 48
Noguera, P. A., 141–142
Nutrition. See Diet

O

OAM. See Office of Alternative
  Medicine
Obesity
  as cause of death, 2
  in preventative self-care, 107
Observational learning, 47
Occupation, as environmental factor
  in wellness, 134
Office of Alternative Medicine
  (OAM), 24
Okinawa (Japan), 19
Optimism, health impacts of, 66
Ornish, Dean, 100
Ouspensky, P. D., 61
Out-groups, 145
Overtraining, 77

P

Panacea, 12, 15
Pargament, K. I., 121
Partnership for Prevention, 104
Past experiences, as environmental
  factor in wellness, 134
Patience, in goal attainment, 39
Peck, M. Scott, 91
Peers, social capital of, 158–159
Pennebaker, James, 167–168
Performance goals, 45
Personal care, and longevity, 19
Personal characteristics, as
  environmental factor in
  wellness, 135
Personal growth
  goals facilitating, 43
  humanistic psychology on, 16
Personality disorders, 64
Personality traits, genetics of, 51
Personal responsibility, 23, 29
PET. See Positron emission tomography
Pharmaceutical industry, lobbying
  by, 6
Photography, 169
Physical activity, 73–83
  challenge of promoting, 82–83
  definition of, 74
  vs. exercise, 74
  health benefits of, 73–74, 169
  and longevity, 19, 21–22
  motivation in, 82–83
  in preventative self-care, 106–107
  psychological benefits of,
    73–83, 169
  socioeconomic status and, 140–141
Picasso, Pablo, 167
Pitts–McClure hypothesis, 78
Placebo effect, 22
Planned behavior, theory of, 82
Police, 162
Positive emotions, 20, 66, 123
Positive psychology, 18–20
Positive reinforcers, 48
Positron emission tomography (PET), 51
Poverty, in ecological approach to
  wellness, 140–143
Power, in ecological approach to
  wellness, 139–140
Prayer, 115–119
  and emotion regulation, 65, 68
  impacts on wellness, 115, 116–119
Preventative healthcare
  in existing healthcare system, lack
    of, 2–7
  future of, 7–8

Preventative self-care, 100–108
  definition of, 100
  history of, 100–102
  strategies for, 102–108
Prilleltensky, I., 135, 139–140
Private student loans, 95
Psychoanalysis, 16
Psychological well-being
  definition of, 75
  physical activity and, 73–83
Psychology
  energy, 20–21
  evolutionary, 56
  health, 16
  humanistic, 16
  positive, 18–20
  research on wellness in, 15–22
  social, 16
  sports, 22
Psychoneuroimmunology, 21
Psychospiritual outlook, and
  longevity, 19
Psychotherapy, vs. exercise, for
  depression, 76
Purdy, M., 115
Purpose of life, 122–124

Q

Qi gong, 14
Quality of healthcare, 3–4
Quality of life
  definition of, 100, 137
  and longevity, 17–18
  Maslow's hierarchy of needs and,
    137–139
  as theme of wellness, 28

R

Race, and masculinity, 145–146
Racial identity development, 147
Ramsey, Dave, 98
Randomness reduction, 54–55
Rappachannock tribe, 14
Reappraisal, 63, 67
Reciprocal inhibition, 42
Reciprocity, in social relationships,
  163–164
Recitation, 168
Reese, R. F., 131, 147
Reinforcers, in motivation, 48
Relationships. See also Family; Social
  relationships
  emotion regulation in, 64–65
Religion, 110–127
  academic research on, 20
  on college campuses, 113–114,
    119–120, 122

definition of, 111–112
and health, 12–13, 20
impacts on wellness, 115–122
measures of, 113–114
meditation in, 115, 116
prayer in, 116–118
and science, separation of, 15
and spirituality, relationship
    between, 111–113
Religious commitment, 113, 114
Religious conservatism, 113, 114
Religious engagement, 113, 114
Religious skepticism, 113, 114
Religious struggle, 113, 114, 121
Remembered wellness, 22
Reputations, social capital and, 158
Research, on wellness, 15–24
Resilience, creativity and, 167
Response modulation, 63
Responsibility, personal, 23, 29
Robbins, M., 119
Rogers, C. R., 16
Role models, in motivation, 47–48
Rovio, 166
Rumination, 67
Rutter, M., 134
Ryan, R. S., 23

S
Salovey, P., 69
Salutogen, 123
Savickas, Mark, 170
Savings, 91
Savolaine, J., 122
Schemas, 54–55
Science, and religion, separation
    of, 15
Screenings, preventative, 104–106
Selective serotonin reuptake inhibitors
    (SSRIs), 81
Self, drive toward wholeness and, 15
Self-care
    cognitive, 58
    definition of, 100
    preventative, 100–108
    as theme of wellness, 29
Self-criticism, meditation and, 116
Self-efficacy
    definition of, 80
    in exercise, 80, 82, 83
    in goal setting, 40–41
Self-esteem
    intellectual, 119–120
    meaning and purpose of life in, 122
Self-image, in cognition, 54
Self-realization, 16
Self-responsibility, 23

Self-talk, negative, 40–41
Seligman, Martin, 12, 18
Selye, Hans, 17
Sense of coherence (SOC), 123
SES. See Socioeconomic status
Set-points, 51
Sex, vs. gender, 144
Shame, in motivation, 45, 46
Simplicity, in budgeting, 88
SIT. See Social identity theory
Situation modification, 63
Situation selection, 63, 66
Six-dimension hexagonal model of
    wellness, 30–31
Skepticism, religious, 113, 114
Skin cancer, 104
S.M.A.R.T. goals, 43–44
Smoking
    emotion regulation and, 65
    in preventative self-care, 107
SOC. See Sense of coherence
Social capital
    in neighborhood effects, 141
    in social relationships, 157–160
Social cognitive theory, 82
Social connectivity, as theme of
    wellness, 29–30
Social conservatism, 113, 114
Social identity theory (SIT), 145
Social influences, on cognition, 56
Social integration, and longevity, 19
Social interaction hypothesis, 81
Socialization, gender, 143–147
Social network, as environmental
    factor in wellness, 135
Social psychology, 16
Social relationships, 150–164
    definition of, 150
    favorable, 150–152, 153, 159–160
    indifferent, 156
    keys to establishing, 163–164
    social capital in, 157–160
    toxic, 160–163
    unfavorable, 152–157
Social systems, 136
Socioeconomic status (SES),
    138–139, 140–143
Spending, tracking, 90
Spilka, B., 118
Spiritual bypass, 121
Spirituality, 110–127
    on college campuses, 113–114,
        119–120, 122
    definition of, 111–112
    as dimension of wellness, 114–115
    in emotion regulation, 65, 68
    how to develop, 121–122

impacts on wellness, 115–122
meaning and purpose of life in,
    124–127
measures of, 113–114
in Native American medicine, 14
problematic, 121
and religion, relationship between,
    111–113
vocation and, 126–127
Spiritual quest, 113, 114, 120, 122
Sports psychology, 22
Spurgeon, L. S., 147
SSRIs. See Selective serotonin
    reuptake inhibitors
Staleness, 77
"Still I Rise" (Angelou), 168
Story, M., 87
Storytelling, 170
Stress
    coping with, 17, 123–124
    definitions of, 17
    health effects of, 17, 52–53
    meaning and purpose of life and,
        123–124
    research on, 17
Stress response, 52–53
Student loans, 95–96
Substance use, in preventative self-
    care, 107–108
Subsystems, 136
Sullivan, Harry Stack, 159
Sullivan, Louis, 5
Sullivan, W. C., 131
Support networks, in motivation, 48
Suppression, emotional, 64, 65, 66, 67
Suprasystems, 136
Sweeney, T. J., 5, 22, 31
Synergy, in social relationships, 160
Systems
    definition of, 135–136
    in ecological approach to wellness,
        135–137

T
T'ai chi, 14
Tapping, 21
10-10-80 rule, 91
Thalamus, 62
Theravadin Buddhism, 116, 117
Tibetan Buddhism, 117
TM. See Transcendental meditation
Tobacco use
    emotion regulation and, 65
    in preventative self-care, 107
Toxic social relationships, 160–163
Transcendence, 115

Transcendental meditation (TM), 115–116
Transtheoretical Model of Change, 45
Travis, J. W., 23
Trust for America, 7

U

Understanding, in meaning of life, 125
Unfavorable social relationships, 152–157
Unfocused meditation, 115–116
Universal healthcare, 5, 6
Ureda, J., 135

V

Values, in goals, 43
Vertical relationships, 136
Violence
  domestic, 160–163
  masculinity and, 144–145
Virtue ethics, 11
Vocation
  definition of, 126
  finding your, 126–127

W

Wants, in budget, 90
Weaver-Hightower, M., 143
Weil, Andrew, 3, 22
WEL. *See* Wellness Evaluation of Life
Well-being
  psychological, 73–83
  striving for, 27
Wellness. *See also specific types*
  academic research on, 15–24
  definitions of, 23
  future of, as healthcare paradigm, 7–8
  history of, 10–24
  meaning of, 7–8, 10
  models of, 23, 30–34
  origins of term, 22
  striving for, 10–11, 27
  themes of, 27–30
Wellness centers, 23
Wellness challenge, 8
Wellness Evaluation of Life (WEL), 31–32
Wellness Index, 23

Western medicine, history of, 15. *See also* Healthcare
WHO. *See* World Health Organization
Wholeness, drive toward, 15
Wisman, J. D., 147
Witmer, J. M., 23, 31
Women
  emotion regulation in, 62–63
  socialization of, 143–147
World Health Organization (WHO), 1, 5, 7, 22, 131
Worldview
  creativity and, 167
  ecumenical, 113, 114, 122
Writing, benefits of, 168, 169

Y

Yalom, I. D., 124
Yates, S., 135
YMCA, 22–23
Yoga, 14
Young, M. E., 43

Z

Ziglar, Zig, 87
Zimpher wellness model, 30